C000220086

THE LC
PROJECT

Hackney, Haringey and our Neighbours

Edited by
DAMIEN MOSLEY & KIKA HENDRY

Foreword by
J. R. MCMENEMIE

i
n
Indie Novella

The Local Voices Project
AN ANTHOLOGY BY HACKNEY, HARINGEY AND OUR NEIGHBOURS

This anthology is a collection of stories, essays, poems and novel extracts from 34 Hackney and Haringey writers, with guest contributions from our neighbours.

It began life as a project to promote writing and writers at a grassroots level. To promote local voices by bringing up-and-coming and established writers together and allowing them to tell the stories that mattered most to them — stories of home, community, and what being part of Hackney and Haringey means to us.

First published in Great Britain in 2023 by Indie Novella Ltd.

INDIE NOVELLA www.indienovella.co.uk

Copyright © the authors, 2023

The moral rights of the authors have been asserted.

Editor: Damien Mosley; Kika Hendry; Cover Design: Callum Hood

A CIP catalogue record for this title is available from the British Library

Paperback ISBN 978 1 739 95999 9

Printed and bound by TJ Books in the United Kingdom.

Indie Novella is committed to a sustainable future for our readers and the world in which we live. All paper used are natural, renewable and sustainable products.

Indie Novella is grateful that our work is supported using public funding by Arts Council England.

Contents

Hackney, Haringey and our Neighbours

Foreword

My relationship with Indie Novella began in the summer of 2021. I'd just finished writing my novel *Full Wire*, and was a few weeks into what some writers call *"the trenches,"* which is a process of submitting one's work to agents and publishers in the hope of striking a deal.

In the trenches, the work we have struggled with and cried over, and come to view as a sort of child which we cherish and love with all its quirks and foibles and flaws, will doubtless be rejected by almost everybody we submit to. It's frustrating and demoralising, but as Winston Churchill famously said: "If you're going through hell, keep going." So we have to be stoical when it comes to this kind of rejection because, despite it all, if you've put the right amount of work in — and you have a little luck — eventually you may find a home for your writing.

Home. That's the overriding theme here, and it can mean many things. It can mean where you live, where you're from, who you're with, how you feel. Whatever it is, in general, home is the place where we define ourselves. "He's at home on the stage;" "She's at home when she's painting." For many writers, we're at home when we write, which in itself is strange, because writing is so hard. It's hard work.

We may write because we feel compelled to write. We may write to consolidate our thoughts, and to reinforce our ideas. We may write because we want to share those ideas, because we care about them. Ultimately though, we write because on some level it's worth it. It's worth all the frustration and heartache. It's worth doing two weeks of research just for one line of dialogue that you end up cutting. It's worth seeing a blank page turn into something meaningful. It's worth having just one person read your work and be moved by it.

Back in the trenches, I'd actually had a bit of luck. Two full manuscript requests from two publishers. I was feeling pretty good about this, and told my friend Alex, who runs my writing group. He replied saying he'd been approached by someone who was setting up an indie press and was looking for new writers. They seemed to be offering another way of doing things, without the need for the agency representation I'd been struggling to secure. I sent the requisite first three chapters and waited. A couple of weeks later they requested the whole novel, which was fantastic news!

Not long after, I received one rejection and one conditional offer for Full Wire. The offer was from a small but respected press who liked my novel but wanted to alter it to the point of it effectively becoming someone else's work. I didn't know what I should do, and I was probably awful to be around for the remainder of the day.

The very next day, however, I received an email that simply said "Hi John, we love it! Can we arrange a phone call?" It was from Damien at Indie Novella. We spoke on the phone, I signed the contract, and I met with him a few weeks later. I learned that they aren't specifically a publisher but also a social enterprise. They care about the stories and the people who write them. They're championing writers from diverse backgrounds, and producing beautiful books that readers will value. If we write because we care, they publish for the same reason.

It's the same for the group of wonderful writers presented here in this anthology. Each of them has a story to tell. Each has their own particular style. As writers, we aren't trying to be anything other than who we are. By reading our words, you're looking through the window into our hearts. You're seeing us at home.

John R. McMenemie. 2023.

Introduction

The Local Voices Anthology brings together writers from Hackney thinking about home. This is a heartfelt collection of stories, essays, and poetry from thirty-four writers talking about the subjects closest to them.

They think inwards, to the material brick, gravel, and flowers that make up their houses in Hackney, as in the case of Alice Chadwick's work. Alice writes of the planting jasmine in her small front garden, and the strangers who stop to talk to her as she tends to them. In Anu Kumar Lazarus's poems, he writes about the Colombia Road flower market, where 'midst poetry, scavengers, perpetual orchids and wine' life spills and overlaps between people, things, and nature.

In other cases, from the home these writers have made in Hackney, our contributors use writing to travel, in time and space, to other homelands, and to imagined histories. Denise EL Rawls found in the 1851 census that a fifty-year-old woman from Jamaica was the Bros family cook in Springfield House, Walthamstow, the starting point for her work. Also thinking across the Atlantic, Angela Kay Austin writes a powerful letter to her deceased parents in Memphis. Her words chart an emotive map of racism on both continents from the personal form of the letter.

Other work in the anthology is built on a sustained historical and political interaction with place. Nick Toner's piece 'On Placedreaming, Community Publishing and Arthur Machen' explores the history of N-Zine. Homes can be fraught. The zine provides a space for creators to see 'each other's yearnings and apprehensions warped into glossy little handbooks'. Sustained attention, or writing, makes place slippery, he argues, 'visible but encrypted' and full of 'our own little spectacles.'

Richard Abbot tries to hold onto the encrypted spectacles of place. Between Toronto and Tottenham, he is 'U-hauled by Love when she moved West.' The sea moves with him, as he calls us: 'listen, the rhythm deletes her own/her siren lace.'

City life ebbs and flows, too, in Caroline Anjali Ritchie's meditation on 'N-Zine, Centerprise, and Collective storytelling'. A collaborative poem of local voices, in her words, 'gives form and meaning to a lull in time, to the "hollow time" that punctuates the never-ending flux and flow of urban life.'

Other writers note incisively the feeling of our present moment, of rocketing rents and increasing gentrification. Kate Pasola's story 'The Yoke' paints a hilarious portrait of housesharing and hosting dinner parties on squeezed incomes. Pasola's writes of the 'red stripes carved into my palms, whipping marks for forgetting a tote', and the intimidating dinner party guest in 'her prairie dress and plaited lavender hair, a bottle with a wax-sealed cork cradled against her tattooed forearm', in this excruciatingly convincing comedy of manners.

Harry Penfold is also unimpressed at a party. This time, a contemporary art gallery, where: 'everything was in italics and everyone was unredeemed and you thought: did Christ die for these young professionals you were taught to admire, who are so grotesque at parties?'

Yet also, some of this work cannot be defined. Kooi Chock Glendinning provides an incendiary personal history bound up in Britain's colonial oppression in Malaya: 'I was born in a hot and sweaty coconut plantation [...] just in time to celebrate Queen Elizabeth the Second's coronation at this end of the world. This had somehow "connected" me to "her."'

Our writers range from their early twenties to late seventies, hailing from the Wirral, Sri Lanka, America, and more, echoing the way that Hackney, almost by accident, forms communities around us. The anthology finishes with an extract from Iqbal Hussain's forthcoming novel, *Northern Boy*; his story of moving his northern heart to London, and the vibrant community he found here.

These are works as diverse as Hackney itself, demanding our full attention. Farva Kaukab writes: 'I write stories about individuals who are underrepresented or have experiences that are alien to the types of people who exist in well-functioning democracies.' It was important to us to give space to voices from the community who might not call themselves writers, and we hope that you take the time to read each story and relish in the diverse reaches of our writers' imaginations.

Kika Hendry, 2023

The Story Behind the Anthology

I first moved to Hackney in 2005 but it wasn't until 2020, when I prepared to leave it for good, that I began calling it home. Lockdown was a strange and traumatic time for many but for me it was something of an awakening. Growing up not drastically far away, in a town near Heathrow airport, I was always confronted by the "other" box. "White/Caucasian", "Asian Indian", "Asian Chinese", "Asian Other" or sometimes just "Other". It is difficult to fully feel at home when every time you fill out a form it doesn't seem to have a category for who you are. I wasn't really even a Londoner as we lived in a Middlesex postcode.

So when I first moved to Hackney, I wasn't seeking a home, rather somewhere I simply did not feel "other". At first, at least.

My biggest abiding memory of lockdown was not just having the BBC News constantly on holding my breath at the rapidly accelerating numbers. It was also of these images initially coming out of America. Lockdowns of their own, police forcing people to stay home, but they weren't. People two decades younger than me – Black, White, Asian, middle-class, working-class, upper-middle class – had taken to streets, were showing open defiance, all in the name of something called Black Lives Matter.

I should make it clear that this anthology is not a radical piece of work trying to piggy-back on BLM. Personally, I wish I could do something that would have such an impact. Rather, while people were taking to the streets, I started thinking more about who I was and why I had made it my sole purpose in life only to fit in. To be anonymous in the London crowd when at the same time, I started to notice a lot of people who, when times were really tough especially for some more than others, weren't content to be quite so shy.

I popped into a bookshop called the All Good Bookshop in Turnpike Lane. I did my usual polite, 'how are you?' 'Knackered,' said this big man with a white beard. It turned out that this man was Tim West, the now retired bookseller, who had spent the whole of lockdown on his bicycle travelling around Haringey delivering books to those in need not just of books, but of a friendly face and a friendly chat. He was later awarded a Haringey Heroes award.

I'd been living just down the road from Green Lanes on and off for over a decade but it was my mate, Alex, who introduced me to the guys who ran Turkish supermarkets and my flatmate, Sophie, who told me how she used to live down the road from Yasar Halim in Haringey, showed me where she used to go for coffee and what breads to ask for from the bakery.

And then there was Newington Green Meeting House and Homerton and Dalston CLR James Library in Hackney. I had been asked to put on an in-person writing workshop and midway though the first a woman came up to ask my advice on some poems she had written. She had started writing in lockdown as she was caring for her husband and needed a way to process all she was experiencing. Someone else asked me how to go about writing a book about her diaspora community and what it was like for them forming a new home in Hackney.

This one-off workshop turned into six and each time I would meet a group of wonderful people all with their own incredible stories to tell. We had people who were born in Hackney, whose parents had settled here some time ago, people like me who were late arrivals, and people who had chosen Hackney because it was a place where they felt accepted. Hackney is a collection of communities.

I made the mistake during lockdown of leaving Hackney to live in somewhere with green fields and outdoor space. Soon I came to realise that outdoor space means very little if you don't have a community with which to breathe that clean, fresh air. So I move back to London, to Haringey. To Turnpike Lane and down the road from All Good Bookshop and Green Lanes and no sooner had I arrived than I suddenly felt at home.

This anthology is about capturing what it is like to be part of a community. That all our voices and stories are just as valid as they are unique and personal. To celebrate each of our identities and produce a book that reflects who we are and hence what Hackney, Haringey, and London is by celebrating our writers. *Our voices.* This anthology originally began life to celebrate Hackney and Haringey but these days community is even further reaching and we have contributions from far and wide, from some wonderful people. People like Tim on his bicycle, people who have found somewhere they have chosen to settle and call home.

Damien Mosley, 2023

Hackney

Kate Pasola

Leaving Hackney

The first time I held my girlfriend's hand in public without worrying about the consequences was in Clapton. We'd gone for dumplings, it was our third date, and it was freezing. All I remember was that her hand was warmer than mine.

You have an instinct for knowing when to let go of your partner's hand in public when you're queer. You develop an internal Richter scale, noticing the shudders around you if you're bold enough to be 'out' in the presence of others. You know when it's safer to be registered as 'friends'. You learn where to sit on the night bus, and not to put your head on your partner's shoulder, no matter how long your night's been. In the past I've chosen not to correct hospitality staff when they refer to my 'colleague', rather than my girlfriend. I've become a master of syntactic dodgeball; I can get through an entire conversation

3

about my home life without using the 'she' pronoun for my partner, if my gut tells me it's better that way.

I grew up near Newcastle, and nobody was openly, confidently LGBTQ+ in my high school – though a few boys were accused of it. One girl kissed another girl and was whispered about for the rest of her school life. Anyone struggling with their gender must have been doing it alone. In 2008, nobody had the vocabulary for that, not even bullies. Because of that, I have no doubt that I came to Hackney to allow myself to be queer, like people have done for decades.

But often, moving down to London feels like a bit of a pipedream. You see people 'fail' at it all the time. So many return; shattered by one thing or another. They didn't find The Job, or the rent went up again, they ran out of money, their friends all moved away (or they didn't find friends in the first place). You learn that you need good reason to choose London. As people give up and peel away, move back home, there's a silly pride in clinging to any footholes you can find, in staying another year.

I survived here by performing at first. I performed straightness, to fit in at my first job in journalism, at a glossy women's magazine. I also performed whatever social class the room required; if my accent needed diluting I'd dilute it. I was lucky; my magazine was the only title with any real working class presence, and the editor at the time was pretty devoted to social mobility. But the fashion titles around me on the same floor made it clear it wasn't worth sending along a prospective CV; the northernness was *dripping* from me, whether I dropped my 'ts or not.

Five years later, I'm still clinging to London. I've fallen out of journalism because I couldn't afford to stay here on the meager salaries; low enough to price out anyone who can't rely on inheritance or parental stipends. I had to choose between my dream job and living in Hackney. Maybe stupidly, I chose Hackney. I chose Donna Summer in Dalston Superstore and drag kings at The Glory and queer bookshops and the victorious feeling of kissing your girlfriend in the park without getting wolf whistled or hate-crimed.

But the parks are slowly shrinking under the shadow of new luxury high rises, the queue at Superstore is getting longer, the drag artists at The Glory are struggling. It's becoming clear that many of us can't cling to Hackney for much longer. Just this year, my landlord put our rent up by £600 per month.

Hackney taught me how to be queer, and showed me the future I might want; that it's possible – *normal*, even – to have a family in a same-sex relationship. If you can afford it, that is. There's where the bittersweet irony lies. I *can't*. I don't have the money for the life I've learned I want. I can't afford this community. I can't afford a home here. I can't afford a family. I can't even afford to buy some time by freezing my eggs.

So I'm writing *The Yoke* to reckon with this reality. The novel follows Whitney, a secretly bisexual east Londoner who happens to be infertile following cancer treatment as a teenager. Luckily she's got eleven eggs frozen in one of the best fertility clinics in Kensington. Unluckily, whether her eggs stay frozen seems to depend on the whims of everyone but Whitney herself. And when Whitney starts crushing on a woman, things find a way to get even trickier.

The Yoke is a comedy knotted with gnarly truths about how queerness, social class and fertility interact amid late-stage capitalism. It asks: who has the right to buy more choices? And why do some people get more chances?

The Yoke

one

You can't really nick a box of eggs. You definitely can't nick three dozen. I used to go to Marks and Spencer because they don't have cameras there. They trust their customers not to steal. But the M&S Foodhall just installed weighted checkouts, and I don't have it in me this afternoon for the security guards. I won't risk making this week any shitter than it's already lining up to be. I pass an Aldi, but wouldn't dare do it in Aldi; it doesn't feel right for some reason. So I head into Tesco. On my way to the dairy aisle, a sequence of WhatsApps ping my phone. Bethan's messages always feel like being machine-gunned with thoughtlessness these days.

> i'll be a bit late btw, more like 8

> also I went for lunch with Morgan and she wants to come tonight?

> new girl at the salon

> she's actually super chill don't stress

Bethan knows what she's doing here. Specifying 'no plus ones' on an invitation makes you look like an arsehole, but surely it's implied at a dinner for four? Especially under the circumstances. Plus, I haven't worked a single shift with Morgan since she started at Delilah Rooms, the salon where Bethan and I work. And Bethan's only ever had complaints about her. *'Kind of up herself, but maybe just like, in a cool lesbian way?'*

Anyway, the point is, tonight was supposed to be part of my grieving process. Bethan, of all people should give a shit about that. It's been in the diary for ten years, plus an extra two when the government extended the time limit because nobody could get to the fertility clinics through covid. I don't like talking about it, because it makes me sound perimenopausal, like a Real Housewife. I've still got a 26-30 Railcard for fuck's sake.

And Bethan should give a shit, because Bethan was there when this all began. She helped me google 'lymph nodes' when mine felt swollen. She came with me to the doctor's that first time. Once, she followed me out of a biology lesson and hugged my wet face to her school jumper, because we'd turned the page in a textbook and it was about cancerous cells. She was outside the room when they scraped my ovaries clean of eggs, she cradled me after they pointed the radiotherapy beams at my pelvis. We sat through chemo in ballgowns together – my treatment clashed with our sixth form leavers' do. She even took the photo of me ringing the pediatric ward's all-clear bell. Bethan helped me come to terms with the fact that, post-treatment, there were now a grand total of eleven eggs to my name, in a labeled chamber in a fertility clinic in Kensington. Eleven chances at being a mother. Soon to be zero, when 3 August rolls around and the clinic is legally required to, in their words, destroy them.

So these days when I drink, I get smashed, and when I get smashed, I cry. Or get the urge to cheat on Guy. Reliably so, actually, since the countdown became double – then single – figures. I don't want to drunk-cry in front of a cool lesbian called Morgan, especially not an aloof one. And certainly not one I'll be working with at the salon in the near future. I lock the screen and sling my phone into the basket.

Eggs are first on my shopping list. Were eggs once cheap? Happy Eggs definitely aren't cheap now. And neither are trimmings or sides or sauces for eight different egg dishes, it tran-

7

spires. Chives and mustard and stuff are all small enough to steal, provided you buy decoy items, like broccolini. My phone vibrates again, twice:

> I kind of assumed it was fine

> hope all ok!

I don't take the bus home. The plastic bags slice my hands as I walk, and by the time I've climbed the eight flights of stairs to my flat and dropped the shopping on the kitchen table, there are red stripes carved into my palms, whipping marks for forgetting a tote. As I'm unpacking the shopping, Guy appears in the kitchen. He refills his pint of water and I refuse to take a sip, busy finding our least shit pan and positioning it on the hob.

"Do you need any of these?" I prompt, a spatula angled toward the eggs. "For tonight?"

"*More* eggs?" He asks. I feel a scream rising.

"The whole point is to bring an egg dish. You're not exempt just because you live here." I drizzle oil into a pan and reach for the first box. "It's mournful, it's hilarious," I continue, "plus, it stops the day being, like -"

"-depressing?" he offers, a bit too quickly.

I slam the first egg against the rim of the pan. Its insides reluctantly slide into place, whites finding a grip against the hot metal.

"So, Bethan's bringing the one from work nobody likes," I start.

"No, no, why are you starting with fried eggs?" He interrupts, flinging his arm sideways over me and my frying pan, like I'm his daughter and he's just braked suddenly. "Whitney, they'll go cold. It's only five thirty."

I wordlessly slide the frying pan away from him with a sidestep to the next hob along, and there's an insolent metallic screech. He yelps (his arm was *nowhere* near the flame), swears, and marches into his room.

To elicit a reply from me, I guess, Bethan tags me in a TikTok made by someone called @ChildFreeChloe. In it, Child Free Chloe lists reasons why she's childfree by choice, as she eats rotisserie chicken in a jacuzzi. I prop Child Free Chloe up by the hob and the TikTok plays on loop over and over through my bluetooth speaker, booming "Reason number two - and this one's probably the most important of all... Reason three, and stay with me here..." I've fried three eggs by the time I notice she's still talking.

Guy's listening to old Arctic Monkeys in the shower and I feel a fury build, though I can't place exactly why. It would feel good to kick open the door and rip the shower curtain down. I open Headspace. Nobody would pick a meditation with a title like 'on the brink of an absolute fucking meltdown' so they're all called stuff like *Permission to Rest* and *Wait, what's going well?* I connect my phone to the bluetooth speaker and play a Martha Wainwright song instead. I crack another egg into the now smoking pan. *I wish, I wish, I wish I was born a man*, Martha croaks from the speaker.

I don't know how I do it, but by the end of the morning I've managed to make eggy bread, at least. And scrambled eggs on tiny toast ovals, plinths for my thrifted chives. There's a quiche, which definitely counts. And some compromised pavlova nests I found in the reduced section, smashed with bruised strawberries into a poor man's Eaton mess. The crown jewel is a bowl of poached eggs, wobbling humbly together on a bed of spinach, and a ramekin of hollandaise sauce. All of this Guy seems infu-

9

riatingly surprised by, when he re-emerges huffily. I can smell his shower through the bathroom door left ajar; synthetic mango, spearmint, and the ghost of a shit he must have taken while the door was locked. Trying to live with a man makes trying to love one even harder. I put out mismatched cutlery, tealights in recycled Gü dessert ramekins, and pastel paper napkins from some Easter party we must have had once. There's a small cactus in the middle of the table where there should be flowers.

Guy compromises, finally, and orders a bottle of Veuve Clicquot and a shakshuka on Uber Eats, making a holy fucking show of tipping the delivery driver in cash. It's a cop-out, but at least, I figure, the Champagne will wind up Bethan. My joints clench at the thrill of predicting her face when she sees it. I bet she thinks she'll be the only one to bring something without a screw top. To be fair, it's always been screw tops in the past. But this party's different. It's not like we're not toasting to the new year, or my birthday, or Bethan reaching 50k followers. Plus, we need as much distraction as possible from the bleakness of it all. Guy's Champagne adds a nice element of irony to the whole thing.

Iris arrives at 7pm on the dot. She's nailed the brief, a silver tray, balanced on her hip. Exquisitely ironic paprika devilled eggs, piped with all the nostalgic splendor of a weeping housewife. A loaf of rosemary sourdough she definitely couldn't afford. And a little card in a purple envelope. A tacit understanding that the whole egg thing is a big joke, and sentimentality is out of the question – in fact, it's rude and thoughtless. It's my fertility, I'll cry if I want to.

The Champagne label is saturated with condensation by the time Bethan actually arrives.

She lingers by the door, giving us all time to see her prairie dress and plaited lavender hair, a bottle with a wax-sealed cork cradled against her tattooed forearm. It looks like it's a prosecco, which is weird, because Bethan constantly tells us she only likes skin contact wine, as if any of us give a fucking shit. Bethan ceremoniously places her own bottle on the table, and it's not a prosecco, apparently, *it's a Crémant*. Guy once told me Crémant is what you bring when you want to disassociate yourself from M&S gin in tin drinkers, but also don't think the recipient deserves Champagne. I probably called him classist.

"And, look!" Bethan instructs, with a wave of a feathered, purple bell sleeve. "Tea-stained eggs." Six violet-veined eggs roll around in a glass cylindrical tupperware. She fixes her eyes on mine. "I watched a YouTube tutorial from this amazing Asian content creator. They're good luck in... Japan I think?". I don't ask what the fuck that's supposed to mean, and how luck is going to help me at this point. But that's Bethan – always overstating the relevance of luck. Always the lucky girl. She tells her followers that luck is spreadable, deliciously, like butter. But it isn't spreadable, is it, Bethan? Not like money. Or misery.

"Tea-eggs are originally Chinese though, right?" a voice says from the hallway, behind Bethan. My mind cartwheels, trying to place the Scottish accent. The disarming raspiness. The nerve to call Bethan out on her pretension. She's just a silhouette. But then she reaches a hand under the lampshade she's standing next to, and switches it on, first go. All of a sudden she's backlit, a hallway Debbie Harry, gold lamplight spilling over her shoulder, through her inky hair, down her white ribbed tank top; reflecting off a tiny gold septum hoop hugging the middle of her nose.

"Oh, yeah." Bethan chimes. "Everyone, this is Morgan."

Angela Kay Austin

Angela Kay Austin has always loved expressing herself creatively. An infatuation with music led to years playing several instruments, some better than others. A love for acting put her in front of a camera or two for her thirty seconds of fame before giving way to a degree and career in marketing and communications. After completing masters in marketing and creative writing, Angela combined her love for all things creative and worked in promotions and events for many years. Although today much of her marcomm work mainly supports amplifying voices of many who are vulnerable and not always able to be heard, she continues to write and publish--sometimes her stories include a look into the world of marginalized communities.

Today, Angela lives in London, which is her home-base from which to explore the world.Read More from Angela Kay Austin:

www.angelakayaustin.com

Hey Mom and Pop, from Clissold Park

Hey Mom and Pop,

I know. I know. It's been a minute. But y'all will forgive me, right? It's been harder than I thought it would be to sit down and make myself write this, for so many reasons—right now, my tears and the freaking sunshine. Before that, mainly just tears.

As I write this, I'm sitting in a park – Clissold Park. It reminds me of the park near the Zoo back home in Memphis. It even has a few deer, but it doesn't have the stench of the goats at the farm animals' exhibit. Thank God. Instead, I'm surrounded by bikes, dogs, and joggers, not terribly far from my new flat! Yep, I did it, Mom. You know I always wanted to travel, and was so so disappointed when I couldn't go on my senior trip for Spanish class—Spain. Now, Spain is just next door. In short, Mom and Dad, your little puffy ponytail wearing Tennessee baby, walked away from it all and started over in a whole new country!

I tried Mom. Dad can back me up on this because he was with me longer, I gave it my best damn shot. It's just that the whole city became a big sad memory for me. Driving down the streets that we once walked for the Susan G. Komen Race for the Cure, laughed as we window shopped, shouted about the racist actions of restaurant managers who refused to seat our too Black family in their high-end steak restaurant became too much. Today, I'm not so worried about some good ole boy in an unnecessarily big truck driving past me shouting "nigger," as my friends and I mind our own damn (sorry for cursing, Mom) business. Now, don't get me wrong, they have their own problems here—the family of Stephen Lawrence feels pain every day because no matter where you go Black people still have to fight, Pop.

Instead, as I sit in the sun on an old bench with a little plaque that tells me it was dedicated to someone by their loved ones, I feel a sense of calm that I haven't felt in quite some while. Is it the new country. The new city. Or the bench, maybe I should've placed a bench in a park somewhere in Memphis so that that city remembers how amazing you both were, but for now that city will have to remember you through the scholarship I set up at the university. Mom, I know you love that. The thought of you smiling and nodding your head in approval brings me tears and makes me smile. Too many emotions, but not as many as there once were. Pop, I did it for you because I hate the idea of another father or mother having to drop out of school for any reason. Our little scholarship has helped so many! There are people who will say thanks to both of you in their prayers each night because you bought them books that allowed them to do what they needed for their education. I won't let that city forget that you both walked its streets! I PROMISE!

Mom, I know you're probably worried about me being over here by myself, but you know you took me to church enough times for me to know that I'm never alone. I have everything I need and more. What does it say in Philippians 4: 6-7 – don't worry about anything. Each day, I wake up with an expectation of joy. That doesn't always happen. Sometimes, I do get a little low, Mom. When that happens, I know where to go. It took me a little while to find a church because there wasn't one near my flat that worked for me, but I found one on Tottenham Court Road. It's inside of a theatre! I mean, come on—two things I love in one place. The music feels me up from the inside. Sometimes, it reminds me of your homegoing celebration, Mom. Pure light and love.

The faith I found myself losing years ago, is growing; but it's not the only reason I've learned to smile again. Mom, I've met someone. He's kind-hearted, makes me laugh, doesn't take himself seriously at all—completely opposite to me! I think I was born taking everything seriously. It's only taken how many years, eight, for me to find myself in a place where I have found it easier to laugh and feel the sunshine on my skin. Only problem with feeling the sun is that it makes me remember the times we would go out to Collierville to shop. That open-air shopping mall was one of our favorites. Firebirds. Bath and Body Shop. H&M. I haven't found an open-air shopping mall like it in London, yet. But I love the high street here in Stoke Newington, it reminds me of downtown Memphis. Mom, you would love it. I can easily see us walking the high street picking up things for my new flat. Ugh, I hate this so much sometimes. I wish you were here with me, instead of me writing in my journal. Why are things in life so unfair?

There I go again, getting all sad. I swore I wouldn't do that today.

So, anyway, back to my guy because thinking of him makes me smile. He and his family have lived in this area forever, when I look at this community through his love for this little part of London, I love it more. It makes me think of the love you both had for Memphis. Maybe that's one of the reasons I love him—because he feels so familiar to me. He feels like home. Stoke Newington feels like I might have found *my place* in the world, tucked away in a tiny little part of London.

When I left Memphis, I only wanted to find a way to manage the heartache that had begun to cripple me—you both being ripped from my life so suddenly, left a hole. One that hasn't been filled, but that is mending slowly through love and patience and maybe this weird milk and tea situation that I'm drinking at the moment. (I take that tea bit back, Mom. Nothing beats the tea you cooked on the stove top with lemon and sugar! Wish I had a glass or two of it now. I think it would heal everything.)

I love you both, and I promise, I won't take so long to write the next time.

Bye for now. Love you much!

Newington Green Meeting House

Our Friends at Newington Green Meeting House – N-Zine

There is a lot that can be said about Meeting House on Newington Green and I would wholeheartedly recommend anyone unfamiliar with it to go along between 12 and 6 on a Thursday or Friday, or to look for their next tour on their website. To sum it up in one sentence, it is everything a community should be.

It's called Meeting House because that's what it was. It was a meeting place for radical thinkers and dissenters who wanted to stand up to the government on social causes. It then became a Unionist Church. It's now become the site of a non-religious church that is available for everyone, which champions identity and runs outreach and heritage projects on its radical history. Caroline and Nick both work with Meeting House and are key contributors to the projects being run including the wonderful N-Zine.

N-Zine, Centerprise, and Collective Storytelling
By Caroline Anjali Ritchie

In the early '70s, a group of local writers gathered on Wednesday evenings to work on a project they called "A People's Autobiography of Hackney." The project was based at Centerprise, the legendary bookshop and community centre in Dalston (1971-2012). According to Ken Worpole, the group's first convenor, the project sought to "make history an engaged mass activity." The memories recorded in this writing group were later published under the Centerprise imprint, making for an incredibly rich, diverse, and moving record of lives lived and paths travelled across Hackney's ever-changing landscapes.

Some fifty years later, as a relative newcomer to Hackney, I was moved by Centerprise's example to set up, with Nick Toner and Amy Todd, a local writing and publishing initiative called N-Zine (the "N" stands for the North London postcode prefix). N-Zine was launched in 2021 and is now approaching its fifth issue. The zine and our writing workshops are hosted at Newington Green Meeting House, which has long been a hub for sharing ideas and creating change at a community level, ever since its beginnings as a nonconformist place of worship frequented by radical thinkers. We wanted to revive the Meeting House's spirit of dissent as well as the radically inclusive, communitarian spirit of groups like Centerprise and the feminist bookshop Sisterwrite, formerly based nearby in Islington. And we wanted to continue, in a creative sense, the project of collective autobiography, of "making history an engaged mass activity."

This would be a democratised history – and storytelling more broadly – and it would be actively and imaginatively produced by local communities as much through poetry and fiction as through anecdote, memoir, and photographic documentation.

We literalised this idea of creative, collective authorship in a 2022 poetry workshop organised for the local women's migrant group Xenia, in the lead-up to the second issue of N-Zine. We used the issue's theme of "Arrivals and Departures" as a prompt for a collaborative poem, written line-by-line by alternating members of the group. The resulting poem was later published in the zine, and it is quoted in full below. In the poem, playfully mundane details jostle with a deeper sense of anticipation and suspense. For better or for worse, Hackney is always on the cusp of change, its residents always kept on their toes. The local voices in this poem collectively give form and meaning to a lull in time, to the "hollow time" that punctuates the never-ending flux and flow of urban life.

Here Now

By Xenia

Still now, waiting for the rush
Hollow time
Walk in the sunshine
Makes me happy
I'm waiting for holiday
I want to go somewhere to relax

*I'm waiting for my grand-daughter's birthday
    party*
I'm waiting for my divorce
I'm waiting in line for coffee
I'm waiting for my driving lesson
Waiting for my life to change
Waiting so long, so long waiting.

Originally published in N-Zine Issue 2: Arrivals and Departures, 2022. Follow us on Instagram: @nzine_london.

On Placedreaming, Community Publishing and Arthur Machen
By Nick Toner

The N of N-Zine was, as Caroline writes, chosen because of the Newington Green Meeting House's postcode letter. But it also paid psychic homage to a psychedelic novella by Welsh author Arthur Machen, a novella which was set in the Meeting House's ends and which bore for its title that same single glyph. *N*, published in the 1930s, is one of Machen's gems. It resonates perhaps because it takes such a lucid look at the power and consequences of placedreaming.

In *N*, the environment Machen creates is eerie, mythological. A trio of friends – Arnold, Perrott and Harliss – meet to wallow in recollections of Londons gone by, recalling lost figurines and demolished houses. There's a premonitory feeling that, while the descriptive realities of recounted memory lets them bond for now, it won't be enough. Soon, it seems, they will need to delve into a world of visions, oddities, peculiar coincidences. Sure enough: the trio can't agree on whether a sublime Stoke Newington park – containing "deep hollows with streams running from the rocks; lawns all purple and gold with flowers" – is real or the stuff of imagination. Later, Arnold flicks through a book of meditations written by a reverend, and finds within a chronicle of a series of encounters with a "very singular person", a local mystic named Glanville. Glanville tells of his belief that long ago there existed a "soft and ductile substance, which could be moulded by the imagination of uncorrupted man into whatever forms he chose it to assume". Glanville talks of a "prosperous city" that transforms into a lake, and of a carpet that "transports us in an instant of time, or rather without time, from one end of the earth to another".

Just before he leaves Stoke Newington, the reverend is summoned to Glanville's window. Glanville first invites the reverend to look out and see the "streets and crescents", the "familiar spectacle". But then Glanville lightly taps our dog-collared hero on the shoulder and invites him to look again. This time the reverend sees what might be the phantom park: a "panorama of unearthly, of astounding beauty". There were "roses whose hues outshone any that are to be seen in our gardens" and "architecture of fantastic and unaccustomed beauty"; the reverend finds his soul "ravished by the spectacle displayed" before him. But the dreaminess soon turns to a "swift revulsion of terror". He can't explain it, but it's perhaps terror at the enormity of the difference between what he expected and what he saw. Or perhaps it's terror at the difference between what he perceived and what he thought existed, or even at the way this metaphysical experience had alerted him to the potential within people for risky and hallucinatory imagination.

Later, Arnold is back in Stoke Newington. He reports that the land on which Glanville's house likely stood has been turned into seats of learning (institutions that are so often the settings of night terrors), with purpose and architecture that "curdled the blood". "They looked", Arthur reports, as if "Mr. H. G. Wells's bad dreams had come true".

* * *

N, and Machen's art of enchantment, is a useful jumping-off point for exploring how we imagine and re-imagine our own environments. N-Zine hopes to channel at least a morsel of the visioning that Machen so expertly showed placedreaming to be capable of bringing about. Free from the imperatives of commercial publishing, and buttressed by its democratic and peer-led framework, N-Zine makes it convenient and safe to go beyond what's right there, to express the fantasies and anxieties our environments generate. We can put words to our existential uncertainties, like in issue one of N-Zine when John Davies asked: "Who is ever truly present in a place?". We can wonder about the places of the hereafter with both trepidation and intrigue, like in issue three when David Walter imagined how "supercentenarians live beyond the year 2100" and how they survived "the trial of becoming ghosts, seeing the shadows of the future from the corner of their eyes". And we can render tangible our hopes for our environments to be more just and less hostile, like in issue two when Wendy Pettifer reminded us that "we can do better, reach into ourselves". "Welcome the children," she wrote. "Pull them from the waves."

* * *

Ravished by the spectacle displayed before me: except, in N-Zine's case, the spectacles are laid before us, together, each other's yearnings and apprehensions warped and wefted into glossy little handbooks that bear our proud bylines. Our individual desires and fears become a body that enables the asking of insurrectionary questions: why do we see what we see? Why do our places sometimes seem to us like things of *astounding beauty* but sometimes *curdle our blood*? What will be restorative?

* * *

N, the letter, is a code rune. Algebra, negative space, giving dimension to what isn't yet there. N is to be decoded. The first dialogue in N the novella is about both what's present and what's absent: "I know every inch of that neighbourhood, and I tell you there's no such place".

N-Zine's writers often know in detail the visible but encrypted versions of the places they write about or are inspired by. But then place becomes subject to decryption, and when we start decrypting environments we know the corporeal details of, they suddenly become so open to interpretation that they might as well be unreal. Like the reverend stood at Glanville's window, nothing's a single objective reality, a *familiar spectacle*, any more.

Done right, this can be so freeing it's therapeutic. But all this decoding also runs the risk of leaving us adrift, insecure, consumed by any anxieties we're trying to express. In the end, we just have to go with it, be carried together by the emotional paths that our zines and writing workshops take. In N, the reverend is left petrified by what Glanville decodes with him. And Arnold's odd tales seem to leave him ambivalent and displaced. It's at the end of the novella, a bantam thing that is easily read in one go, that he wonders aloud whether the trio of friends are in fact "now sitting among desolate rocks, by bitter streams". At N-Zine, writing in this monotonously temporal and sterile age under systemic insecurity and climate breakdown, we might well be sailing close to Arnold's desolate rocks. But we can also believe we're on Glanville's carpet, being transported between the ends of the borough or the earth, displaying before each other our own little spectacles.

Penny Walker

Penny has lived in Hackney since 1994. She bore and brought her children up here while also working first as an environmental campaigner and then as a self-employed facilitator. There have been a few changes over those three decades. Foxes used to be a rarity, now they are everywhere. In the early years frogs laid spawn in the shallow puddle formed on top of a discarded carrier bag, now the beautiful pond in her garden hasn't had tadpoles for five years. Secondhand kids' clothes shops and book shops have given way to vintage clothes shops. Penny's hair has gone grey, and she's seen one child get married in the same register office she got married in. She used to be the only one in the family to work from home, now there are four adults working from her home, and four bikes to organise into the right order so they can all leave the house smoothly. She used to run all her workshops in-person with flip charts and sticky notes. Now it's Zoom and virtual whiteboards. It's not all better but it's all good.

Pet Respect

1. Cat

Cat doesn't live here. She visits from time to time when her real people are away.

Cat has a black stripe down her spine, and a tail which can triple in size in a heartbeat. She hisses when challenged and will scratch you if necessary. On her first trip outdoors, she brought back a pigeon. There is wild in her.

Cat has soft, salted caramel ice cream belly fur, dotted with chocolate chip spots. She runs into the kitchen when her bell is rung, for the frozen treats which are her reward. She chirps and purrs. She has her own microchip key for the cat flap. She is a thoroughly modern princess.

2. Fox

Fox has lived here all its life. 'Here' is two-thirds of an acre of back gardens, enclosed by terraced houses and burglar-proof fences. Fox and its family live in dens under decking or below garden studios. They come out at night, and at dawn, and at high noon. Their parallel world has tunnels running behind thickets of rosemary and jasmine, holes through fences, places where wall and rosebush meet with just enough room to jump through. They nap on top of sheds and drink from ornamental ponds. They dig under compost heaps and forage in dustbins.

When the council planted street trees, the foxes scattered the soil to expose the roots. Neighbours carefully backfilled the holes, protecting their work with silvery chicken wire weighed down with half bricks. The street Facebook group was alive with spiky conversation.

During lockdown, our very elderly neighbour's essential shopping list included frozen chicken pieces from Iceland. "My foxes. They come at three o'clock every day. If I don't have it, they look so disappointed," she explained through her double mask. She is not on Facebook.

Fox's tail is thin. Its grey flank has a patch of shorter hair, as it if has been shaved for stitches. Perhaps this is what happened. There are people who take foxes to the vet.

Treasure fox has brought to our garden includes:

- plush Iggle Piggle, with its stuffing partly pulled out.
- poo bags (full).
- balls, both foot and tennis.
- bin liner containing poo bags (full).
- swatch of paint colours, Shackell, Edwards & Co Ltd (est. 1786).
- faux leather zipped pencil case (shredded).
- roll of food waste bags (unused).
- roll of traffic-cone-orange electrical tape.
- 165ml tube of Titanium White oil paint (RRP £17.35).
- toy bone.

One morning, drawn by the noise, we saw fox on the grass playing with a squeaky dog ball. Spotting us, fox retreated a few yards, then came back for its toy.

Some evenings, the helicopters drown out the fox noise, and sometimes the foxes outlast the helicopters.

3. Cat and Fox

When cat comes to stay, fox craps nearer the house, almost on the back door step. The turds are tight and dry. They smell of *liquorice and separation*. I don't know whether the dark nuggets are an offering, or a warning, to cat. She sniffs them delicately.

We used to chase the foxes out of the garden before letting cat out. She is not our cat. It is not our place to expose her to predators. Then cat joined in, rushing at fox across what passes for a lawn. Fox fled. Reassured, we now just watch as cat asserts herself and fox demurs.

Cat has been here for three weeks. She has found the tunnels and shady caves, used the hidden portals, climbed onto the roofs. No-mow-May turned to June and the pseudo meadow was cut. Green has become gold. Stubbly islands stand out above the soil. The bare earth between them collapses into dust.

It is hot and dry.

Fox lies curled up in the sun near the end of the grassy area, close to the cherry tree and rotary clothes airer where we have put a bucket of water. Cat approaches, stealthily, crouched low. On her spine is an elongated Mohican. Her tail is bushy. Fox's ears twitch and it lifts its head. Seeing cat, it settles back down but its ears are alert.

Cat lies low, tail extended, facing fox. She wriggles a little, as if she might strike. She changes her mind, and rolls on to her side. Fox looks up again, its whole head visible over the dusty orange curve of its back. Cat twists and stretches, belly fully exposed, a shade lighter than the bone-dry grass. She shimmies her spine into the dust, all the time facing fox.

Cat pulls herself closer to fox, who uncurls and begins to rise, yawning. It dips its head, extending its front legs, rump high, posing in a perfect downward facing dog. Fox yawns again, drops its hips, rises on its front legs and stretches its back for up dog. Then it walks a few paces and looks at us and at cat, who is now back in her pre-strike coiled position. Fox eats something. A cherry? A chunk of poo? Some paint?

Cat twists and rolls again, first dark side on top then a whole body flick to show her creamy underside wide open. Fox sits up, scratches its side with a back leg, and walks to the furthest part of the parched grass. It treads a tiny circle and settles down again in a neat curl, tucked in under lemon balm and teasels, facing cat. Cat lies still, then begins examining one paw.

Their slow-motion dance-off lasts two and a half minutes. They have taken turns to show their moves, checked each other out, and reached an accommodation. Mutual tolerance. Some kind of respect. They are experts in performative nonchalance.

Cat went home yesterday. Fox brought Nando's wrappers to the garden. We refilled the bucket before the rain came.

Kooi Chock Glendinning

I saved my thirteen colleagues, myself, and the rest of the world but was threatened, bribed, and bullied into becoming a suicidal mental health patient, losing my beloved job in the process. These three wicked and incompetent managers got away with trying to kill us and the rest of the world for almost four months. Meanwhile, PM Boris Johnson had to resign for just one night of partying at Number 10 Downing Street during the COVID lockdown.

Reluctantly paid to retire, I am now living the time of my life, pursuing all the hobbies I could only dream of before. My grandparents separately fled the Boxer Rebellion in China during the Qing Dynasty and settled in colonial Malaya. I was the third generation there and was born just in time to celebrate Queen Elizabeth II's coronation in 1953.

As a consequence of Article 153 of the constitution dictated by the British before granting us independence, which sidelined us Chinese, I was deprived of many human rights. In 1972, I, along with many other Chinese teenagers, came to the UK to help the NHS. Six years later, I retrained to become a Biomedical Scientist.

I met and married an English/Scottish man in the Sahara Desert, and we have four lovely children and a grandson. The wealth of my traumatic and eventful life provides me with colourful material, making me an interesting writer, person, and artist. Local theatres like Arcola, Immediate, and even Hackney social radio allow me to explore my dramatic talents.

I keep fit with new-age games of tennis, badminton, and cycling everywhere. My free time is also occupied with art, choirs, exhibitions, and cooking. Last month, I performed Verdi's Requiem with the Hackney Singers and an orchestra at the Royal Festival Hall.

My claims to fame include cooking for 400 people single-handedly for the Chelsea and Westminster Pathology Christmas party and, a year ago, serving as a security officer for Prince Charles and his consul Carmela.

I enjoy giving back to the community by volunteering my life experience at local libraries and serving as a tour guide in Chinatown.

My Palace

It was a sunny, hot afternoon in July 1985, with temperatures reaching up to 28 degrees Celsius. I was a stressed-out, sweaty passenger in a removal van advertising, "£5 for the day or £15 to hire for the weekend." We were cautiously approaching Hackney. The radio was blaring out Bon Jovi's *Living on a Prayer*. "got to hold on... doesn't make a difference... make it or not... We've got each other..." The driver, my husband James White, reached out his hot, damp hand for mine—a gentle, soft touch of love, as electricity travelled straight to our young, vulnerable, lovesick hearts.

Was I lucky to have met and married him? The forever-smiling Goddess of Mercy had fatefully played a part in James's and my union. She was the protector of all things, according to our Taoist religion. I had always prayed to her, no matter what. I felt that she would always protect me. With her divine intervention, somehow, at the beginning of my second year in the UK, she changed my homesick mind to be persuaded by Sheila Brennan, a fellow Irish nurse. She was a gentle giant full of fun, while I was a tiny and shy five-foot-nothing. "Come on, Chockie. Omar Sharif galloping on a camel through the Sahara Desert will drive any homesickness away. You can't run thousands of miles home each time you miss your Mama!"

Call it caution at first sight; on my part, I was scared of what might happen. We somehow felt a mental and physical attraction for each other. "But remember," I told myself, "Papa said, 'No Brit! Or I would disown you like your Fifth Sister.'" Mama cried for about a month non-stop on that orange plastic sofa! I couldn't take my eyes off his gorgeous green, blue, brown eyes and such fair, delicate skin, going redder as the scorching sun mercilessly shone on it. In contrast, my already tanned skin was getting darker and darker.

He was merely eighteen, green as the spring blossom across the oceans, and three years younger than me. I was officially his sugar mummy—a twenty-one-year-old migrant and trainee nurse from the Old Church Hospital, Romford. Sheila shook her head at me ogling James. I just winked back.

My Mama told me, when she eventually met James years later and after succumbing to having him in the family, "The Goddess of Mercy has found you the love of your life. Him, a crafty, mischievous monkey chasing you, the beautiful slippery snake, to eternity! A marriage made in heaven!" She ended with a hearty, hollow laugh, so pleased for herself—or was it for me?

What was Papa going to say? So, I didn't tell him. If I had heard Mama's comment earlier, I would have married James the very minute we met in the sweltering but romantic Sahara Desert. He, with his aristocratic nose and almost perfect features but trickled with droplets of perspiration, was completely opposite to my minute everything: flat little nose, above a small pouting mouth, and the most prominent mountainous cheekbones. When I laughed, which was often—probably because I was nervous trying to merge into this strange, exotic world—my cheeks would rise so high up that my almond-shaped, little slanting eyes got really squashed, and I could hardly see through them. Thank goodness my short eyelashes couldn't get in the way, or I would be totally blind when I laughed or smiled.

Freckles were the only visible common features that we had. His amazing hippy, shoulder-length, and shining blond hair softly caressed his wide, muscled shoulders as the hot wind rushed in from the window, pleasantly cooling us down. If it wasn't fate guided by the Goddess of Mercy, what was it? A coincidence that we had to travel 1,672 miles to meet in the hot, sandy desert while we were only living seven miles apart in London?

I looked around anxiously as if I were lost. Bon Jovi's song came back to us: "hold on... to what we've got..." For a few moments, tears dripped down my mountainous cheeks. He quickly wiped them off and then "dragged" his eyes back onto the busy road. My right hand gently went for his face and lovingly caressed it, forcing a thank-you smile at him and shyly whispering, "Love you." He whispered the same back but with an "I" in it.

I had only been in the UK just over a year when I met James, and so my command of the English language was extremely limited and grammatically imperfect. My excuse was that I would rather roam the Bukit Mertajam streets with my five other tomboy classmates or go scrambling for rambutans, nutmegs, and firewood in the dense overgrowth of the forest by my Berapit Village. So, no time to read.

Lack of reading is, to this day, my one big regret, and it has cost me jobs, led to some serious bullying, and caused embarrassments. It was not my priority in life then to read. No one had told me it would be my passport to respect, understanding, opportunities, acceptance, and even Bafta awards for the best screenwriting, the Booker Prize, or even the Nobel Prize for the little things that I did and still do as a Biomedical Scientist.

With hindsight, all the subsequent discriminations I experienced, and those yet to come, would be less painful if my command of English had been good. I never thought I would come here until the last resort, after years of being oppressed by my homeland. To be honest, I was born in a hot and sweaty coconut plantation a few days before, and just in time to celebrate, Queen Elizabeth the Second's coronation at this end of the world. This had somehow "connected" me to "her."

Of course, Her Majesty had no idea about little nobody me. We didn't live next door to each other and didn't have cream tea and scones together. It didn't do me any favours, as British Colonial rule then made me a second-class citizen because I was born the wrong race, at the wrong time, and in the wrong place. Life is like a lottery, based on luck. But hey, I am here now, and I needed to make something out of it. I couldn't and wouldn't repeat our family history of both my grandparents, who separately ran away from their war-torn homeland, China, in the early 1900s. I needed to try and settle here. Maybe marrying an

Imperial Brit wasn't such a bad idea after all, considering that I tried so hard not to because of parental and cultural preferences.

Our heavy van, jam-packed with our life's possessions accumulated over the last five years together, jolted, sunk, and rose again as it unknowingly went over a pothole. The heartbreaking crashing sounds seemed to go on forever, sinking our already anxious hearts and catapulting me out of my thoughts into a different mood: fear. We both looked at each other and held hands for a few moments. In despair, I uttered in my Malaysian Chinese slang, "Aiyoo. Our dinner set! Our blue China set... all broken... smashed together like our breakfast cornflakes. And... our champagne glasses! The champagne, our first-ever bottle!"

"Don't worry, darling, we still have a few quid in my pocket, and you said you have some coins in yours. So, plenty of money to get another bottle. I'm sure the offer is still on at the off-licence. That is if we can manage to find our new home," consoled James.

I, the dutiful but rather useless navigator, was sweating not only from the heat but from the stress of trying to get ahead of the game by frantically looking at the A-Z map of Hackney. I must admit I hated doing this as I got very car sick, bending down to scrutinise the tiny writing to search for our road. James was getting incredibly stressed too, trying to be patient but unsure whether to stop, turn right, or just carry on.

"Come on, darling. Tell me quickly. I thought you were in the scouts in... Bu... Bukit Mertajam?" I shook my head in disappointment and disgust, thinking that my lovely naive husband of five years had not been listening to me. It was probably my fault; I should have taken him home to meet my beloved family and friends and to eat all those durians, mangosteens, rambutans, and not forgetting those laksa, curry mee, and nasi lemak... yummy... and those Nonya delicious kuehs!

Before I got hungry, I reverted to my judgemental, spoilt, childish temper. Poor James... actually, looking back, I sympathise with him for putting up with me. Back then, I truly was unforgivingly harsh towards him.

M Delahunty-Light

In March 2020, at 23 years old, I moved to Hackney (Stoke Newington, specifically) after living in a small village in Kent for most of my life. It was a strange introduction to the community because just two weeks after I moved in, lockdown began. I think, though, that this helped me to feel part of the community more quickly and sincerely than I otherwise would have.

I am disabled. I am autistic, have ADHD and suffer from chronic migraines and severe depression, among other things. These can keep me housebound for long stretches, leaving me feeling detached from place and time. However, almost as soon as I arrived here in Hackney, 'Stokey mutual aid' leaflets were posted through my letterbox and somebody volunteered to bring my medications from the pharmacy. Looking out my window I could see pavements declaring 'PAY RISE FOR OUR NHS STAFF' and 'BLACK LIVES MATTER', carefully emblazoned in chalk by my next-door neighbours, and every Thursday at 7pm they delivered rousing speeches about the good the community was doing, thanking care workers and mentioning local NHS workers by name. New Unity, the nonreligious church in Newington Green, started hosting their Sunday gatherings on zoom, and I met, heard from and shared with kind, thoughtful people across the community. I have been a member ever since.

What I am struck by even now is that since things have opened back up, this community – *our* community – remains not only accessible to me, but actively inclusive. I feel not just accepted but welcomed. The church a few hundred yards up from me, at the top of Amhurst Road, flies the rainbow flag and even recently updated it to the Progress Pride flag right at the time I happened to be coming out as nonbinary. The staff at my pharmacy greet me by name if I manage to walk there and, if not, they recognise my voice on the phone. I try to walk to Newington Green when I can and when I cannot, I am welcomed to gatherings and craft clubs and caring circles on zoom, just the same in my little Hackney flat as I am in that historic Hackney building. I have learned, gardened, sewed and painted together with other Hackney residents at a local not-for-profit social enterprise, Core Arts. My mum and I both wear beautiful jewellery made by the silversmith two doors down from me. The chocolatier at the farmer's market even knows my mum by name because I buy his truffles for her so often.

Moreover, I am continually, delightedly discovering new pockets of community in Hackney. The spring before last, I tended to graves in Abney Park and learned both the place's history and the lived history of fellow volunteers, several of whom have been part of Hackney's community for longer than I have been alive. I visited the Garden Of Earthly Delights (a guerrilla garden on a formerly derelict site) for the first time last week and was taught woodworking. I'm now hoping to contribute and attend their weekly gardening get-together, health permitting. I learned about Indie Novella just this past month, through events they held in Newington Green Meeting House about this local anthology and now, having experienced writing as a mostly solitary activity, I am awakened to a fantastic literary community that has been right under my nose for over three years!

These communities within the community are amazing and always make me feel like I've stumbled across buried treasure. Each time I am thrilled not only by the community itself, but also that Hackney is full to the brim with so many wonderful people and places and projects. There are struggles in my life but time and time again, I am reminded that there is sunshine behind the clouds. There is always something and someone wonderful to meet. As someone driven by their heart and curiosity, I am proud and grateful to call Hackney my home.

Extract from M Delahunty-Light

Chapter 1

Kate is juggling green tea, her laptop and a glass of water when she lurches to a halt. The momentum keeps her dinosaur of a laptop going forward, the glass of water tumbling after it as Kate instinctively reaches to catch it and suddenly her tea is on the floor too, the café logo splintered over ceramic shards.

Someone is picking up her laptop – they're checking it for dents – and then they're speaking to Kate.

"Blimey, that – I mean, uh-"

"You're sitting in my seat-"

"-doesn't look that bad," the imposter is still going, "I think those scratches were- sorry, what?"

"You're-" Kate stops herself and huffs, "nobody ever sits here. Except for me."

The table in question is tucked behind a pillar, just out of sight of the café's till, and most importantly has the only chair within four feet of a plug socket.

"Oh!" The guy smiles and dimples appear. "Well, glad to be of service!"

"What?" Kate is too tired for this. She planned for three hours here and that time is ticking away, and there is green tea and broken porcelain on the floor and-

The stranger is dragging a second chair over.

"Here you go!" He beams.

Kate wonders if his jaw hurts from all that smiling.

"I'm Elliott! Double 'L', double 'T'."

Kate's brain finally catches on to Elliott's expectant grin. "I'm Kate. Just one of each letter."

"Nice to meet you! The, uh," Elliott hesitates, before adding encouragingly, "the toilets are just over there!"

"What?" Kate regrets ever walking into the café. Why didn't she just stay at the dorms?

She blanches at the thought, forcefully reminded that going back there is not an option right now. She clenches her fists, looking back over to Elliott impatiently.

Elliott gestures to her torso nervously.

Kate looks down and belatedly registers that most of the green tea is now seeping into her jumper. Her face flushes as she turns on her heel and marches towards the loos.

Five minutes later, Kate is walking back to the table. The surface is shiny and wet, but the dark stain is even across the light plywood now. Elliott – double L, double T – reaches the table at the same time as her, holding up some napkins and a mug.

"Here we go!" He announces, placing the mug in Kate's hands and the napkins on the table. He wipes the table dry with them, then puts Kate's laptop in front of the new chair and sits down opposite, pulling some stapled papers and a calculator towards him.

Kate finds herself sitting down.

"Um, I have a lot of work to get done, so-"

"Oh, don't mind me!"

Kate shakes her head, shrugs and fishes out her latest problem set.

They work in silence for a while, until Kate reaches out to her new mug and takes a gulp. "Hey, you got the green tea?"

"Yeah, that's what Paula said you ordered," he looks up anxiously, "that's okay, right?"

"Who's Paula?" Kate should be writing, should be concentrating, but her hands stay cupped around her mug, soaking up the warmth.

Elliott looks at her blankly. "Paula? The barista?"

"Oh," Kate says. She pauses, searching for the thread of conversation- when she should be searching for her *calculator*, she has *so much* work to do- "-you come here often then?"

"Only just started in the New Year." Elliott smiles.

"...It's January 8th."

"Yeah! So, like, I've been here maybe twice?" Elliott has perked up, his papers forgotten.

Kate nods. She reaches down into her rucksack, grabs her calculator and uncaps her pen once more. "Well," she says. "it's basically an office to me- and I do need to get some work done."

Elliott deflates a little. "Right. Well- good luck." He turns his gaze down, hunches his shoulders and starts writing.

Another forty minutes passes before Kate pulls back. Her brain is fried and she still has one more lecture today. She picks up her bag and hastily swipes her pens and papers into the rucksack.

"You off, then?" Elliott breaks into her train of thought- Kate had almost forgotten he was there, he'd been so quiet.

"Yeah, I've got a lecture to get to."

"You're at the uni?"

"Yep. Studying physics. You?"

"Oh," Elliott looks sheepish. "I'm on a gap year, actually, but I've got a deferred place doing maths. But no-one recommends a gap year for maths, so I've got to keep my brain in gear in the meantime."

"Huh. Shouldn't you be like, feeding orphans or building houses or something?"

To Kate, all of Elliott's previous smiles seemed like manic forgeries, but this one – stiff, almost pained – throws their sincerity into sharp relief. "Nope! Most I'm doing at the moment is saving people's dishes from getting cold at the White Hare. I'm a waiter there."

Kate stands up and fidgets. "Cool. Well, bye."

"Okay," he smiles up at her, "see you here tomorrow?"

"Sure, I guess?"

Kate turns hurriedly and walks away. That was so weird. He was so *nice*.

She stops, turns around quickly.

"Hey," Kate calls. Elliott looks up, already beaming expectantly. "What did you mean earlier? By 'being of service'?"

"Oh!" The beam grows even more intense than Kate thought possible. He's *preening*, she thinks. "Well, you said you never get any company?" Did she say that? "Because nobody ever sits behind this musty old pillar except you?" Ohh. "So, there I was- here I am," Elliott stretches his arms out wide, "company!"

46

Kate smiles despite herself. "See you tomorrow, Elliott."

Chapter 2

It only takes Elliott twenty minutes to lope home, even though he stops to pet both Mrs Baker's cat and Doctor Woodward's dog, as well as the tabby for whom Elliott has yet to find an owner. When he reaches number 43, Elliott's grin stretches even wider; both cars are parked in the driveway.

He hops up the front steps, narrowly avoiding knocking over the cement discs imprinted with doughy handprints and the words 'ABBY', 'HARRIET' and 'JANE'.

"Mum! Dad! I'm home!"

Two voices yell back indistinctly. Elliott wanders past the mantelpiece, Abby and Jane beaming out at him in their graduation caps and Harry waving in front of her second start-up's offices, until he finds his dad splayed out on the living room sofa.

"Tea?"

"That would be great," Geoff smiles, the dimples he gave Elliott appearing, "your mum's in the study."

Elliott trots down the hallway and pokes his head around the door. Ruth is sitting on the floor surrounded by binders and stacks of densely worded paper.

"Cup of tea, mum?"

"Hmm?" Ruth flicks several pages back and forth, frowning as she does so. She grimaces and adjusts her headwrap absentmindedly. Elliott tries again.

"Would you like a cup of tea? I'm making one for dad."

She looks up, meets Elliott's eye.

"Tea?" She asks. Elliott nods and her face breaks into a smile. "I'd love one, honey."

* * *

Elliott nudges Harry's hibiscus tea out of the way as he reaches for the Yorkshire Gold. There's only half a pint of skimmed milk left in the fridge – he'll go to the off-licence later, Elliott decides as he waits for the kettle to boil.

Five minutes later, Elliott is just barely balancing three mugs of tea in two hands while simultaneously trying to open the living room door with his elbow. It's not going well.

"Son," Geoff cranes his neck so he can meet Elliott's sheepish smile with a mild look and a raised eyebrow. "Put one of them down and see where that gets you."

Thirty seconds later, Elliott is inside the living room and holding just two mugs. He carefully hands one to his dad.

"Alright day?"

"The usual. You'd think kids could tell the difference between my scrubs and a police uniform, but then you'd be surprised," Geoff sighs and takes a gulp of tea. "That's the stuff. Best thing I ever did, showing you how to make a proper brew." He grins at Elliott.

It's an awkward segue, but he'll take it. "Yeah, uh- that's why I always choose fruit tea at the café! You set my standards high, dad," Geoff hums good-naturedly and Elliott ploughs on, "oh, the best thing actually happened at the café today – this girl went like, flying-"

"Was she okay?" Geoff looks alarmed.

"Yeah! Yeah, that wasn't the – um, the*good* thing that happened wasn't her dropping her tea, it's that I actually helped her clean up and we got chatting and-"

Geoff is wincing. "Eli, could you take it down by an 'L'?"

"Oh, sure," Elliott lowers his voice, the excitement still

thrumming, "so, we're chatting, and Paula is shaking her head at me from the other side of the café, and then-"

"Eli," Geoff interrupts. "I think your mum's tea might be getting cold."

Elliot's smile falters, but Geoff's tone is indulgent rather than impatient, so he pins it back in place. When he pushes the study door open, Ruth is still rifling through the same stack of sheets as before, glaring at them all the while. Elliott nabs a coaster from her desk and places it next to her, on the floor-boards, while holding out the mug.

"Tea, mum."

Ruth's eyes stay on the pages as she reaches out blindly, grips the mug and places it in front of herself. Crouching down, Elliott picks it up and slides the coaster underneath before replacing the mug. He hovers.

"So, you know how you mentioned about making some more friends?" He ventures, "Well, today, at the-"

Ruth has put her head in her hands.

"Mum?"

"They've screwed it up. It's just one thing, and they can't even- damn it."

Elliott kneels. "Mum, what's up?"

Ruth's head rises and she stares into space, resigned. "The clerks have messed up the page numbers. Again. After that last bundle, insisting it wouldn't be a problem with this one." She meets Elliott's eye at last and smiles dejectedly. "That's my night's sleep gone, with the cross-examination notes still to do. And when your dad's not working nights for once, too."

"What about if I repaginate?" Ruth opens her mouth, and Elliott scrambles to add, "I'll only need to look at the corners-just the page numbers, mum. No reading, promise."

Ruth's shoulders sag in relief as she gazes up at Elliott, who has straightened up in earnest.

"What would I do without you, eh, Elliott?" She heaves a deep sigh before dropping two big binders by Elliott's knees and dragging a few more towards herself. They both settle down onto crossed legs and get to work, the silence broken only by pens scribbling and Elliott's periodic reminders to "drink your tea, mum".

His tea is still sitting in the hallway, outside the living room. It goes cold.

Ken Jones

Hi, I'm Ken Jones, and am based on the Wirral. I have dabbled with writing since leaving school in 1971. Yes, I'm seventy years of age with plenty of life experience. Numerous unfinished manuscripts littered my study unwilling to co-operate with my intentions to cobble together a believable ending. However, since recently completing a BA (1st Class Honours, walking away with an award for Outstanding Contribution) and MA, in Creative Writing at LJMU, I have disciplined myself to force a narrative to completion. My genre invariably veers towards dark comedy in contemporary settings – placing ordinary characters into challenging situations and letting the story run.

I strive to write crime stories about everyday characters finding themselves out of their depth. In previous attempts, teachers, veterinary surgeons, and disabled army veterans all found themselves in unfamiliar worlds, placed in conflict with unsavoury underworld characters.

Employing humour to dilute darker issues, I use Merseyside as the backdrop for all my stories, to explore the interweaving of normal and criminal worlds; their union being only a mis-step away.

When not writing, I enjoy the great outdoors; hiking, biking, and looking for new characters to write about. I am not fazed by my Hawaiian shirt on an episode of The Chase causing more of a stir than any of my literary ramblings.

Rachel

Outside of honesty, this was her last shot. A roll of the dice which she imaged could solve all her problems. As she waited, only two facts dominated her racing mind. He was late, and she needed him. She hated admitting the second one. She checked through the window again, watching the chilling rain turn to light snow. Scanning passing traffic, she noticed a taxi, wipers working overtime, splashing through the surface slush. Not him. Snowflakes laced the double-glazing, distorting the action outside, giving the street an unnatural shimmer.

Just as she was going to risk ringing him, his car arrived out of the dusted gloom; a flash of red braking next to her Golf on the driveway. Rachel raced along the hallway, kicking junk mail clear to open the front door. She heard music as he opened his car door. He looked up and smiled through the windscreen. She waved and shouted.

'We need to talk.'

Harrison climbed out of the car, hunching his shoulders into the light snow. Soft flakes sparkled in his hair before melting into him, flattening his curls. He shook his head and raced for shelter under her porch.

'What's so important? I can't stay long, got a script to read through.'

'Can't it wait.'

'No, I'm not great at remembering lines.'

Rachel gave him a quizzical look. Late again, after another one of his disappearing acts. 'We can talk inside.' She led him into the lounge. He followed, closing the front door with his foot.

'What time's your mum home?' He held her waist with both hands. 'Can we go upstairs?'

'Not today.' She shrugged him away. 'Get out of that wet shirt and I'll get a towel.'

As she left, Rachel noticed him inspecting the wall-mounted portrait of her mum above the fireplace. She hoped he saw the family likeness, the McGuire lips and enquiring eyes which seemed to follow you around the room.

She returned from the kitchen and threw a towel over his shoulders. 'Still got that shirt on?' She looked into the mirror, checking her makeup for blemishes.

'Are we going upstairs, or what? You are confusing me now.'

Rachel shook her head. 'I said we need to talk.' She watched him peel the shirt from his damp body and hang it over the mantelpiece. 'Sex can wait.' She saw he was distracted by the prospect.

'What's so important?' He rubbed fingers across his abdomen. Her eyes focussed on the hairs clustered on his chest, watching their symmetrical movement as he breathed. He adjusted the towel on his shoulders and waited for her to speak.

'Can you keep a secret?' She asked.

'Haven't told anyone about us, have I?'

'I mean a big secret. Can I trust you?'

'You know you can.'

She moved away and sat on the settee, her body rocking gently as she searched for the right words. 'I've been stupid.

53

Really screwed up.' She covered her face with her hands, emitting a squeal like a wounded animal; a sound she hoped would bring out his protective nature.

'Did something happen at work?'

'No, everything is fine. Perfume's flying off the shelves.' She paused, thinking how she should continue. 'It's my dad.' Rachel watched him rub his hair with the towel. 'You know he's due home soon, right?'

'I can't wait to meet him.'

She detected an element of sarcasm in his voice but decided to ignore it. 'He still calls me his Little Princess, but they are just words. He can't expect to come home and play happy families after eight years. I'm older now. God, if he knew we had sex in his bed.' She felt her right eyelid twitch in a faint muscle flutter.

'Wasn't it you who stopped visiting him?' he asked, dropping the towel onto the floor. He kicked it, trying to send it into orbit to catch, but it wrapped itself around his ankle. He shook it free and walked to the mantelpiece.

She joined him, crouching nearer the gas fire, enjoying the warmth on her face. 'It was pointless in the end. We kept saying the same things.'

He remained silent. She stared trance-like into the fire. The mesmeric flames willing her to speak. But he broke the silence.

'You said you screwed up. How?'

She looked up as if startled from a dream. Her eyelid twitched again. 'You know Dad's inside for embezzlement, right?'

'You said it was insider trading.'

She paused for a moment, her eyes searching the fire for guidance. 'Yeah, that too. Well, the money was never recovered.'

Harrison nodded for her to continue.

'The thing is, I knew where he stashed the money.'

'I don't understand. Didn't the police search everywhere?'

'Yes. They turned our house upside down, but it was buried on Grandpa's allotment under his prize cabbages. Dad showed me in case he didn't survive prison. The information was like a curse hovering over me. Taunting me. Do you know how difficult it was not to check it was still there? After six years I moved the money. It's in the attic under my skis.' She noticed him shake his head and smile. 'This isn't funny.'

'I'm not laughing. I'm just relieved you're not pregnant.'

'Where did that come from?'

'When you said we needed to talk. That you'd screwed up, I thought—'

'I'm old enough to know what I'm doing. I'm not stupid.' She watched his shoulders shake, unable to control his nervous laugh. 'This is serious stuff.'

'I'm listening. Tell me everything.' Harrison led her to the settee by the hand. She sat and took a deep breath, looking at the carpet between her feet. She rubbed her thighs before entwining her fingers as if in prayer.

'I've taken some of Dad's money now and again since I put it in the attic. Just for essentials. Clothes, makeup, and stuff.'

'How much are we talking about?'

Rachel was reluctant to answer, rotating her thumbs around each other. 'I intended on replacing it, every time, but it got out of hand.'

'How much?'

'Ten thousand.' She looked at him for approval as he let out a whistle. 'There it is. I've never said it out loud before. The truth is I need some help. I've taken today off work to see you. I know you would know what to do.' She picked at the cuff of her sweatshirt, finding comfort from the unravelled stitching. He took her hand and smiled awkwardly. She could see sympathy and concern in his eyes, and an element of fear.

He seemed to choose his words carefully. 'What do you want? I haven't got ten grand. Don't know anyone who has.'

She rested her head on his shoulder, her breathing becoming irregular as she struggled to control her speech. She felt his body move in time with her gentle sobs, enjoyed him wiping her cheeks with his thumb. Feeling the tickle of moisture.

'Dad will kill me. He's not the forgiving type, especially over his hard-earned money. Not exactly earned, but you know what I mean.' She wiped her face on her sleeve. 'What am I going to do?'

'Can't your mum help?'

Rachel snorted a mixture of disgust and laughter. 'She is worse than Dad. Imagine her face if I told her. We need to think of something else.'

Harrison stood to inspect her mum's portrait again. Rachel sat waiting. This was the moment she had both anticipated and dreaded in equal measures. They hadn't been together for long, but she knew she could rely on Harrison to come up with something. He was smart. He could perform. She'd seen him invent crazy stuff during open mic improv nights. But most importantly, they were a couple. That was the clincher. She had seen it in his eyes the last time they had slept together.

He turned to face her, nodding again with a thoughtful expression. 'Maybe I've got something. How much money are we talking about?'

'Ten thousand, I told you.'

'I mean in total. Did you count it all?'

'Of course. It wasn't easy. No lights at the allotments. I had to use Grandpa's shed, but I counted it.'

'How much?'

'A hundred thousand, mainly in fifties.'

'And ten is missing. That leaves ninety.'

'I can do the maths, Harrison.'

He ignored her comment. A strange smile appeared on his face as he paced the room, turning dramatically like a lecturing professor to make his point. It was working.

'I remember in drama class; we did a session on stress relief in psychology. Relief is a strange feeling. Is your dad a glass half full type of guy?'

'Where are you going with this?' Rachel asked from the settee.

'If money was stolen, most people would be happy to recover ninety percent. In a business model that is known as acceptable losses.'

'Enough of the school stuff. What are you trying to say?'

'Hypothetically, if all the money was stolen, then, if at some later date ninety grand was recovered, I think your dad would be happy with that.'

'Are you crazy? Do you know what he's capable of?'

'You're not seeing the bigger picture. The greater the lie, the more believable it becomes.'

'You don't get it, do you? This is Dad's money; he probably dreams of it every night on his prison bunk.' She stood to repeatedly punch a fist into her free hand. He held her hand to stop the pumping.

'He'll get it back. We'll just hide it for a while. He'll be delighted to lose only ten thousand. Trust me, I know how people think.'

'There must be another way.'

'Unless you can find ten thousand before he is home, this is your only option. After a week or two, we can give him an anonymous tip-off. Tell him where it is.'

Rachel freed her hands and met his eyes. 'I know my father. He will want to know who robbed him.'

Harrison thought for a moment. 'What if we faked a home robbery.'

His words triggered a light in Rachel's head, as if she was running a film trailer through her brain. 'It could work. I can just picture it. I disturb the thieves. I'm tied up and gagged on the bed, maybe roughed up a little, but I don't see faces. They have spooky latex celebrity masks. All I remember is Boris Johnson and Putin hitting me. One of them had hairy arms. It was terrifying.'

She closed her eyes and kissed him, arms around his shoulders, bodies pressed tightly together. As Harrison raised his arms to hold her, she pulled away. 'I knew you would think of something. I'll get the money.' She disappeared up the stairs.

Rachel sang while she rummaged through the attic; a light airy song which she played endlessly on Spotify. She ran through their plan again in her head, looking for pitfalls. It seemed like a practical solution, the best option at short notice, but wondered whether she was getting too excited by it. Sometimes she could get too wired.

As she came down the staircase, she saw him standing in front of the family photographs on the mantelpiece. She wondered if he had been examining them. She had to admit, her dad looked handsome in the picture. A tanned, younger Sonny McGuire looking out from the canvas. She hoped Harrison believed her story of financial irregularities, accepted her dad was merely unfortunate. She dropped a dusty rucksack onto the carpet at his feet.

'I expected it to be larger, bulkier,' he said. They both stared at it.

'I can trust you, can't I?'

'Absolutely.' He nudged the bag with a foot.

'Only the fifties left. They are harder to spend.' She smiled again. She often wondered if it was a blessing or a curse to have devious McGuire blood running through her body. She had told Harrison a small lie, but there was a significant difference between embezzlement and armed robbery. 'When you hide it keep your phone switched off. Don't use any credit cards. Avoid CCTV and wear a hoodie.'

'Aren't you taking this a bit too seriously?'

'If you want to stay invisible you have to blend in.'

'Spoken like a criminal's daughter. I think you may have inherited your father's character traits. Dishonesty, shiftiness, and attractiveness.'

'Shut up and take the rucksack.' She smiled. 'Now, all you need to do is take me to the bedroom. Tie me up. And hit me.'

Natalie Reiss

About Me — Natalie Reiss

Hackney has captured my heart (and council tax) for a good 12 years now. I fled Sydney, Australia intending to be in London for 2 years, and whaddya know, the alluring chaos of this city — and borough — has kept me here. By day (for the bills), I'm a Creative in a FinTech world and by night, I compose poems, lyrics, short and long stories. My writing on culture and travel has been published by Virgin.com, Sydney Opera House, Loud & Quiet, CLASH and Unyoked. I've self-published a poetry book and in 2021, I was a writer in residence at Villa Lena. I'm currently completing the six-month novel writing course at Curtis Brown Creative. This submission is a snapshot of my London Fields life circa 2014.

Everything's Fine by Natalie Reiss [excerpt]

Settled into a distressed corner of the couch, I watched the news on my laptop and melted into a dissociated state, as rolling coverage of a Malaysian Airlines carrier hit by a missile played out in front of me. Bang. The front door closed and I knew by the weight of the slam that it was Chris, all inherent lankiness and complete disregard for the impact his 6-foot 3-inch frame was about to have on our spiral staircase. Everyday without fail, the man would run up and down those rickety stairs like a 10-year-old boy on too much Ribena, rooting each step with such unnecessary vigour, while the rest of our flat shook and my nerves began to resemble shattered teeth. 'I have bought a fishing rod!' Chris purposefully announced, snapping me out of my malaise as he stood there, arms apart and rod in hand, like a strange East-London Moses, minus the red sea and Hebrew wisdom. 'I'm sick and tired of hybrid hot dog pop-ups and those bloody burlesque excuses for nights out. This rod right here, this new hobby, THIS is how I'm gonna reel in the ladies. Ha, get it?' He chortled with a red face, completely satisfied with his hideous joke and simultaneously failing to notice the expressions of disdain, clearly visible on the faces of Claire and Audrey – like me, they too were tired of his faddish attempts to 'hook one in' as he so frequently referred to his consistently ill-fated ventures in seduction. Following his announcement, Chris took himself out onto our balcony, which in reality is a street-facing, narrow door that opens onto a step; roomy enough for one to person stand upon. Casting the fishing line back and forth, Chris began to test out his questionable wrist-flicking skills with a wild-eyed, crazed tenacity that could be put down to the freakishly hot summer day, but was most likely stemming from his failure to ever secure a second date. I looked on quizzically, as though my screwed-up face would better help me understand this endlessly frustrating flatmate. Ultimately, I decided that these peculiar endeavours must please him on some level and I had to hand it to him, the man was persistent. The girls and I left Chris to his street-fishing practice as we sauntered out of the flat and down towards the park, silently raising our arms to the sky and smiling foolishly at nothing but the sun and London heat. Eventually we settled on a patch of grass and lay down, surrounded by other human lizards who were also desperately trying to turn a slightly different shade of ivory. We watched a man with an average-looking physique morph his body into capoeira-type shapes as he entertained his children. The girls and I marvelled at his athleticism and we continued to watch this fatherly performance in what was a heated haze of a day. The field was dotted with bicycles and bodies, the latter covered in an array of artfully ripped clothing, while the ubiquitous sound of balloons being pumped with nitrous oxide filled the air. We listened to Caribou and Flume and sipped on fluorescent cans of Rio until deciding that we required liquid with legs. Into the local, up on the stools and it felt like home. Well, more of a home than living with a heavy-footed doofus with a penchant for fishing rods and zero fish. 'This town has taught me how to drink properly', said Audrey, her Parisian accent coating the statement with a coquettish edge, only she could get away with. Dark-haired and doe-eyed, Audrey worked as a lawyer and was easily the most adversarial human I knew. Upon arriving at a friend's birthday in February, she promptly approached me once inside and said 'ok, point out your friends so I know which people not to offend'. I shouldn't have been surprised because confrontation was to her what coffee was to me – an enjoyable and daily-administered addiction – I guess I was just happy that I never found myself on the other side of an argument with her. Claire, Audrey and I sat in a row at the bar, as though judging an imaginary talent show, dripping in cliché as we sipped craft beer, the bubbles soothing our throats following the rough burn of complimentary whiskey shots - a standard welcome from the bar that felt like our own version of Cheers. The girls started jokingly swiping on tinder, while I kept trying to woo the bar cat, which was successfully ignoring me whilst languishing in the afternoon sun and taking up a seat of its own. I looked around and spotted Sol; grey-haired, turtle-neck wearing Sol. Sol, who 6-months ago poured his heart out to me about the passing of his wife, before quickly shifting conversational gears and asking me to come back to his place for a drink, without the bat of an eyelid. Recent romantic disasters propelled me to consider the 70-something year old man's request before I snapped out of it and made a joke, hoping not to offend the likeable Sol, who was quite clearly just after the company of a woman. Any woman. 'How are you darling?' he said, planting a bearded kiss on my cheek, his one hand resting on my waist, whilst acknowledging Claire and Audrey by lifting his beer with the other hand. 'I'm alright Sol. Still waiting for you to propose but other than that, I'm fine.' Since our initial meeting, Sol and I had developed a warm kind of affection for one another – it was a specific brand of chit-chat happiness that was perpetually linear in a way that only acquaintances can sustain – a curious mix of never quite letting them in and never going too long without seeing them. The faint hum of background music suddenly grew louder, and the Italian bartender slipped us three more shots of brown liquor before we sank into our second beer. I felt my body relax, loosen and grow warm as the alcohol ran through my bloodstream, shifting my focus from interior thoughts to watching the singer on stage. A beautiful bird of a soul, the porcelain-skinned lady with blonde, feather-like hair sang her heart out underneath the red lighting, dark wooden panels, and American highway signs. I smiled in the happiness until the glow of my phone stole my attention. It was a text from Mum: 'Joshua was on flight MH17; I have been in touch with his dad. I love you so much my dear, can I call you?'

Rae Bennett

About Me

At the turn of the 20th century, my great-grandparents left their homes in Eastern Europe and took the long journey across the continent, eventually landing in Leeds, Liverpool and the East End. They were among many hundreds of thousands of Jews fleeing the Russian pogroms, a large proportion of them finding tentative sanctuary in the densely packed streets of Whitechapel, Mile End and Hackney. They spoke Yiddish, ate unfamiliar foods, had foreign customs and rituals – like many other migrant groups before and since, they were labelled as 'aliens' by the British government, and were treated as such.

Three generations later, I was born in Haringey, as British as they come and wearing my Jewishness with ease. I was barely aware of having any kind of dual identity – I was so fortunate in the accepting North London bubble I grew up in, that I never thought to wonder what life was like for those that came before me.

As I got older, I began to understand that I was destined to become much more conscious of my identity than I had been as a child. Sadly, some of this was because of anti-Semitism, but much of it was simply the awareness of the fact that, in most other parts of the country, Judaism was a pretty foreign concept. I went to university in Scotland, where many people I encountered had never even met a Jew before, and knew next to nothing about our culture or history. Through trying to satisfy the good-hearted curiosity of my non-Jewish friends, I found a need in myself to further explore this rich and ancient culture that I was born into, and that I had always previously taken for granted.

When I moved to Hackney two years ago, I had been aware my family had roots in this area, but it wasn't until my aunt said to me, "Did you know your Buba grew up on Bethune Road?" that I realised I was living right on the doorstep of my own history. I've been intrigued ever since with what life looked like here for my family, and how their lives differed from mine.

I'm currently writing a novel that tells the story of a pair of Jewish siblings living in Hackney in the '20s and '30s. It's been a useful vehicle for me to honour and investigate my cultural history. Hackney has mutated into an entirely different beast in the last century, and yet it's an area where the layers of generations that were here before us are still observable in every brick, if we look closely enough. My research into the period so far has shown me that my characters' London was not so dissimilar to ours. Many of the daily issues people faced, as well as the broader political issues of the time, are reflected to an uncomfortable extent in our reality now. Without an understanding of that history, and a willingness to learn from the past, we'll never be able to move forward.

Stoke Newington – 1930

Flora's church, St Mary's, was just a short walk from the flat. It stood cramped between a printer's shop and a chemist on one of the high road's tributary streets. Alma had passed it countless times before today and had never registered its presence.

Her lack of notice was not unusual. Churches were everywhere in London, as common and as unremarkable as postboxes. They were among the roster of objects in the urban landscape that belonged wholly to the English and their way of life, and so were largely disregarded by the city's Jews, a community accustomed to living quietly in the gaps. Along with the ham-vending butchers' shops and the pubs serving late on Friday nights, churches in their ubiquitous and stony presence proclaimed, *This place was not built for you.*

Nevertheless, Alma now stood facing a pair of tall oak doors, which were wedged ajar with a wooden doorstop. A framed sign fixed to the doorframe declared:

'ST MARY'S, CHURCH OF ENGLAND, PARISH OF STOKE NEWINGTON. ALL ARE WELCOME.'

On her brief journey here, Alma had tried to imagine Flora at synagogue, amongst that noisy, heaving congregation. Flora, gossiping in the gallery from beneath the brim of her hat. Flora, jostled by children running zig-zag between the worshippers' legs. Flora, joining the droning chorus of the *shema*. These thoughts were so ludicrous they had made Alma laugh aloud to herself as she walked. But now, at the church's threshold, she no longer found them funny. She did not know how to behave in a church. She had no hat, no gloves, no offerings. Her hair was unpinned. There was a rip in the hem of her dress.

It was clear that agreeing to come here had been a stupid decision. Stupid and reckless. Sadie, alone at home and believing her sister to be visiting the Rosens, would be furious if she knew.

Then Alma remembered the previous night, and Flora's expectant smile. She pushed the oak door open and stepped through.

The church was much larger inside than it appeared from the street. The look of it was not unlike a synagogue – the rows of benches, the sombre light, the pillared passageways flanking the aisle – but the quality of the air was unfamiliar in a way that made Alma nervous. It was stale and contained, starkly separate from the high street's heavy blend of fumes and smells; the change had been palpable the instant she entered. She shivered and hugged herself. The rough material of her dress prickled against her arms.

A number of women – mothers, presumably – were arranged in scattered groups around the pews and were conversing demurely. At the far end of the hall, at the foot of a gilded platform, an assembly of teenage girls wearing shapeless white gowns chattered to each other. Their voices echoed formlessly around the lofty space. Alma could not pick out Flora from their uneven circle, but even if she had, nothing could have persuaded her to abandon her position under the shadow of the entranceway.

Her gaze was drawn above the heads of the girls, to a sculpture of a man Alma knew to be Jesus. He was hanging in perfect

71

alignment with the aisle, in between two high windows. Alma's stomach turned a little at the sight of him. Even from a fair distance away, she could see the painted trickles of blood leaking out of his hands and feet, from his forehead and onto the rib-bones protruding from his torso. His sharp pelvic bones jutted in an irregular V from the rag covering his waist, the only clothing the sculptor had thought to give him. Alma looked away quickly, with a sense of having glimpsed something indecent. She assumed the priest must have to cover him up when there were children in the church.

"Alma!"

Alma's eyes returned to ground level. Flora was skipping up the aisle towards her with her gown ballooning around her ankles.

"Alma, I'm just so delighted you came!" She took both of Alma's hands in hers and squeezed them. Alma flushed and muttered a greeting.

Flora was wearing an overlarge, slightly lopsided ribbon in her hair. Her gown, also too big, swamped her frame and made her look much younger than her sixteen years. She stood close to Alma, an edgeless pink glow from one of the coloured windows lining the hall cast across her left cheek. Alma felt a more familiar kind of nervousness flutter in her chest.

"I've told the girls you were coming to watch the rehearsal. They're all so intrigued by you. They had so many questions," Flora said, letting go of one hand but keeping firm hold of the other as she looked towards the white-gowned group. Some of their heads had now turned and were staring along the aisle at Alma. "Come on, you absolutely have to meet them."

Flora started in their direction, but was halted with a tug at their joined hands. Alma paused, then released herself from

Flora's grip and folded her arms across her stomach. "Sorry. I'm feeling shy."

Flora shifted a little on the spot. "Oh, of course. Perhaps after the rehearsal."

Alma nodded briskly. "Should I... where do I sit?" she asked.

"Wherever you like. You'll be able to hear us all the way through to the back anyhow."

A tall woman, dressed in a schoolteacher's rigid brown jacket and skirt, materialised seemingly from nowhere at the end of the hall, barking for quiet. She clapped her hands once, and the girls and their mothers alike fell silent.

"Oh, goodness, there's Miss Roberts," Flora whispered breathlessly. "Will you be all right, Alma?"

Before Alma could answer, Flora was already hurrying back along the aisle, stumbling over the corner of her gown as she went. She took her place in the neat semi-circle that the girls had formed around their teacher.

Alma slid into the closest pew. By now, some of the mothers had noticed her, and were throwing wary glances in her direction. She could tell by the curl of their lips that they knew who and what she was, and that they were unsettled. She shuffled along to the far end of the bench and fought the urge to bring her knees up to her chin and hide behind them, like she used to as a child. She felt a flash of yearning for Sadie.

Miss Roberts had begun to speak to her students, her exact words disguised in the hall's booming acoustics. Alma looked over her shoulder at the oak doors leading back to the street, calculating how quickly she could reach them without drawing attention. When she turned again, Flora was looking straight at her from among the obedient faces of her classmates. They held each others' eyes for a long moment. Flora smiled, then moved her focus back to Miss Roberts.

Abruptly, the talking stopped, and Miss Roberts lifted both her arms in the air. There was a collective hush as the girls' breath rose in unison. Her arms descended, and a gentle, shimmering chord brushed its away across the hall. Alma sat perfectly still, and as the music began to weave its way around her, everything blurred but Flora.

Sarah Ferner

To Hackney and Back Again

My mum was born in Whitechapel where her dad had a fishmongers in Hessel Street before illness made it impossible for him to go on working but my dad was raised in Hackney. First in Woolpack House, a block of council flats in Morning Lane and later on the Pembury estate, to where his family was relocated after they'd been burned out of their home in the Blitz.

My mum and dad met and married in 1962. I was born in 1966 in Gants Hill near Ilford, in Essex; my sister came along sixteen months later. Our family became part of what was at that time the biggest Jewish community in western Europe, a community at its zenith.

My parents knew only peril, war and poverty as children. My grandmothers were sole bread winners who worked relentlessly to make ends meet; to support their children and husbands who could not work, disabled as they both were by heart conditions for which there were no adequate treatments. Totally understandable then that mum and dad dreamed of a quiet life in the suburbs, of raising their children in the safety and comfort. Much to their disappointment, I imagine, because we never talked about these things, their dream turned out to be a nightmare of stultifying boredom for me once I'd left my childhood behind. Like Dick Wittington I was dazzled; if not by the prospect of golden pavements; by the thought of London in all its brutal but life-affirming glory. This was the dream *I* wanted to make a reality.

I didn't grow up in Hackney, but it turns out that Hackney is in my DNA. I walk down Ridley Road when I am sad; feel myself moving with the rest of humanity in a place where no one seems to care where you came from, just that you are here now. I pass Hackney town hall and remember our civil partnership, what a joyful day it was, even though Mike and I had already been together thirty years; even though our guests had to wear masks because it was still Covid times; even though our daughter had just been diagnosed with cancer at the age of nineteen. Two years on, she's flourishing, thanks to the world-beating care she had at the Macmillan Cancer Centre at UCLH; a relative stone's throw from our front door.

When we were caring for our daughter through the terrible, life-saving chemotherapy she had to have, I would find respite on London Fields. I would cry onto the gnarled old trunks of the plane trees finding comfort in their wide girths. Those stoical old trees have always been there for us. The children played under them when they were small or in playground for hours on summer evenings while I would sit there gossiping with the parents I knew from Gayhurst, the children's school

The countryside's nice for a holiday and I love the seaside, but my heart belongs to Hackney: noisy, dirty, car-free (if you're lucky), tree-lined (in places), diverse, eclectic, troubled, wonderful, gentrified, down and out. Irrepressible.

Snow

His business was oil. His work for the company took him everywhere because there was oil everywhere. The sticky, black, distilled remains of trees and bones were just as likely to gush from beneath a sea bed in the chilly northern climes of Europe as they were from the deserts of the middle east. So why, thought Grayson to himself as he paid the for the cab, yanked his suitcase from its boot and looked up at the off-the-peg hotel in which he would be staying for the next three days, did they always have to send him to burning hell holes where he'd be loosening his tie and mopping sweat from his puce brow within three seconds of stepping into the street.

If there was one thing Grayson had learned in his years of working for the company, it was that there were as many different ways of doing business, as there were countries that produced oil. There were rules and there were customs. You had to learn them and made mistakes at your peril. Millions could ride on a greeting made in the right or the wrong way. But at least one thing never varied and that was the businessman's hotel: blinds drawn, a/c on, TV on. If he'd been beamed into one of these hotels by some kind of science-fictional device instead of arriving here in the back of a cab whose rushing cold air had frozen his hands and feet for most of the hour he'd been in it, he'd have had no way of knowing if he was in Oslo or Azerbajan, Kuwait or Kentucky. For this Grayson was grateful.

Up in his neat, clean room on the tenth floor, Grayson parked his luggage at the end of his bed, spent a cursory minute or two looking out an at undistinguished view of rooftops before taking a shower as was his habit. After a while he turned off the taps, wrapped the standard issue white towel around his waist and re-entered the bedroom where he bent down to peer into the mini-bar. Grayson's laptop winked from the room's dressing table where he'd put it down among the laminated cards promising free wi-fi, all day breakfasts and an exit route should the hotel start burning to the ground. He'd have to prepare for tomorrow's meeting, but it could wait a while. After an eleven hour flight and an hour on the road even *he* had to push the pause button. If only they could beam you across the world in the blink of an eye he mused to himself not for the first time.

Grayson settled himself back against maid-plumped pillows, opened his beer and clicked on the TV. On a garish red and yellow set the host of a show; which appeared to be some kind of televised craft competition; was talking to an expert. They were discussing who had done well and who was in danger of elimination, as was the way with these things. Behind them, half-a-dozen nervous looking competitors stood with their creations, awaiting their fates. Grayson flicked from channel to channel and back again without much interest: a tennis match came on, some grisly true crime thing, 24 hour rolling news, then back to the tennis via a cooking programme and a shopping channel. Aside from the language it was broadcast in this shit; like the furniture in his room; was the same wherever he went. Grayson flicked back to the competition again which he gathered was all about people building insanely sophisticated models from Lego. This made him decide to watch for a bit longer, since those sweetie-coloured plastic bricks had been a childhood favourite of his. Grayson inferred that the competitors had been asked to build a model suitable to be set inside a snow globe. The host and the expert approached the first model that was going to be judged, which was of a fox sitting next to some bluebells. This already had a shiny glass dome in the shape of goldfish bowl lowered down over it. A button was pressed and fake snow began to swirl around the animal's body. A spotlight came on and the expert began to wax lyrical about how true-to-life the fox's features were, but Grayson wasn't really listening because for some reason fake snow swirling around a fox made of Lego bricks had taken him straight back to that day. A day he hadn't thought about for a long time.

She had two free tickets, she said. She'd won them in her firm's Christmas raffle and would he like to go with her? "Come on," Grayson had scoffed, "a pantomime? They're for kids. Why would I want to waste precious time on some stupid show for seven year olds." But she had remonstrated with him. "God Grayson, you're such a humbug. Where's your Christmas spirit? Besides which, this is not any old panto. The dame is Clive Rowe. He's the best in the business. You've got to remember him from Tracey Beaker." As usual, she'd forgotten that he hadn't been allowed to watch TV as a child. Too busy working for the straight 'A's that would get him into Oxford eventually and then this not-so glittering career. He dug his heels in, until her wide brown eyes made contact with his. Her hands closed in mock imprecation. "Pretty please," she'd said.

When the day came, she was like a kid herself in her glee. They'd walked to the theatre from her house which had been conveniently just up the road. They were both wrapped up against the cold, striding along under a glowering December sky threatening rain. The streets were dreary with winter and, in spite of the fact that she was nigh-on vibrating with anticipated pleasure at his side, Grayson was not feeling in the slightest bit festive. He found himself wondering how long pantomimes last, but dared not ask her for fear of bursting the bubble of happiness she was in. She was the one thing in his life that Grayson had feelings for; feelings that made simple things complicated, feelings that he sometimes wished he didn't have. He stayed silent, slipped his overcoated arm through hers. As they rounded the corner though, it was as if someone had switched on the lights in a cold, dark house.

Christmas lights were on all up and down the High Street twinkling dimly in the midwinter daylight. To reach the theatre, they'd had to walk through the town hall square past a tall fir festooned with tinsel. The theatre when they got there, shone with ceramic tiles and stained glass. Its porch was frilled with wrought iron curlicues and beneath it a crush of theatre goers buzzed urgently; parents clutched the hands of their children. There were little girls in sugared-almond tulle accessorised with rhinestone tiaras; boys wearing antennae topped with flashing lights or hats decorated with dinosaurs or superheroes. The double doors of the theatre sucked in this pulsating mass of humanity steaming with hot breath and thrumming with the beats of many hearts. She and Grayson had had little choice but to shuffle forward with it. It was so hot and crowded inside that with some difficulty she and Grayson had had to strip off to their shirtsleeves, carry their coats and jumpers over their arms. When they were nearly at the front of the chaotic queue for the auditorium, she couldn't remember where she'd stowed the tickets, frantically patted all her pockets and searched her bag until with a relieved, triumphant flourish she produced them for a sanguine usher who directed them to letters and numbers. The excited crush of bodies pressed up against them, birthed them from cramped lobby into the gold and deep ruby redness of the auditorium. The gallery, the boxes and the procenium arch were piped with gold, with cherubim and seraphim, fruit and flowers; Victorian heaven realised in plaster and gallons of gold and scarlet paint. Grayson sunk into red velvet. The curtains that would soon open onto the afternoon's action were lush red velvet too. Grayson was more impressed with all of this than he'd thought he would be, but then he looked up and his sceptical, phlegmatic Grayson-ness fell away and was replaced by sheer wonder for somehow he found himself looking up into a night sky twinkling with thousands of tiny stars. It didn't occur to him even for a second to speculate about how this special effect had been achieved. Transfixed, he gazed up into the shining vault until called back down to earth by a fruity tenor voice proclaiming that the show was about to begin!

And he was up for it, he was up for it all. He'd laughed and shouted Behind You! He had shouted and sung along until he was hoarse; clapped his hands until they were sore. Where had this wave of enthusiasm come from? Grayson did not know. Every now and then he would become aware of her checking him out. Briefly, they would make eye contact and he knew that his unexpected display of warmth and innocent enjoyment had surprised her. Grayson liked that he had caused her to react this way. He had entered her bubble of happiness and been welcomed by her.

It was a fizzing, bubbling contented gush of folk that exited the theatre. The bees had had their pollen. Voices were raised in review, people were going over the bits they'd liked best. Parents helped their children into coats and pushed tubes containing the scant remains of smarties and fruit pastilles down into bags already bulging with baby wipes, theatre programmes and folded umbrellas. And it had snowed.

While they were all inside, shouting their heads off, absorbed in the spectacle on stage, outside it had been snowing. It was if somehow, the pantomime had burst its banks, had waved its fairy godmother's wand over the whole city. All who

81

came out through the theatre's ornate double doors were stopped in their tracks. There were gasps of speechless amazement. The square in front of the town hall was a white counterpain glittering under street lights; for night had fallen. After a while Grayson and she had begun to walk home, at first, arm in arm in happy, silent contemplation. But after a while she broke away dancing ahead of him in the crisp deep snow.

Wonder had turned to glee, then glee to mischief. Grayson scooped up snow and balling it inexpertly in his gloves (for this was something he had never done before) he hurled the snowball in her direction. Snow started to fall again in soft, fat flakes muffling her scream as she felt the snowball's icy impact on the back of her neck. Was she angry? Grayson panicked. Had he misjudged the moment? Got the etiquette wrong. Perhaps not, for it seemed that she was scooping up snow herself. He watched her moulding it in her hand prior to taking aim. Grayson ducked and the snowball whistled in a sparkling shower over his head. And all at once they were having his first and last snowball fight running screaming and laughing up the road until they reached her front door breathless with the thrill of it all and clutching their sides in agony.

Grayson had kissed her tenderly. He had knelt down in the snow and heard himself proposing to her. She'd hugged him. "A million times yes. Yes." she'd said. "You boring old humbug Scrooge." Of course I'll marry you.

A year later she was diagnosed. They had been married on the ward where she lay dying.

"This is not just Lego." the expert said, "This is art. You should be proud." Grayson had no doubt that the competitor who'd made the fox would go through to the next round. He clicked off the TV and dressed himself. He opened his laptop and put his earbuds in. Work never ended. Work was just something that had to be done wherever he was in the world and wherever he was in the world was of little consequence to Grayson. Grayson glanced down to the right hand corner of his laptop screen noting that it was 1am. His meeting wasn't until midday tomorrow, so he would be able to get in the eight hours sleep he needed to make sure that he was nice and fresh, that he got this country's business manners right. He prided himself on his ability to do so. Oil was everywhere, but this was a brand new field and with his help, it was going to make the company a fortune.

Sarah Lerner

I've lived in Hackney for almost 40 years moving here at first, to share a flat with two women friends on the Stoke Newington/Islington border, and gradually moving further east. I lived alone for several years before winding up, nearly thirty years ago, in the Clapton house I now share with my partner and our two grown up daughters.

Of course the area has changed a lot. When I first came to Clapton people thought of 'murder mile' when I told them I lived here. Now they're more likely to think of astronomical house prices.

I used to dream of leaving London to live in the countryside or by the sea, but work commitments, schools and the girls' social lives kept us here. Now I don't want to be uprooted.

I love cycling across Millfields past the new orchard and the areas of unmown grass, towards the Greenway and the Olympic Park, or to Walthamstow wetlands in the other direction.

With all the re-wilding that is going on around us, the boundary between city and countryside is becoming more blurred. Even though I haven't moved away from the city, it seems like the water and wildness is coming to me.

Departure

Rifke lies close to Avi her front against his back. She presses her cheek against his shoulder gently so as not to wake him. His shoulders are broad and, she feels the muscles through his skin. She tries to relax but that night she won't sleep. She just lies there, thinking and waiting.

Three year old Eli is stretched out fast asleep at the bottom of his parents' bed. Baby Sol is in a basket next to Rifke. When he needs feeding he'll wail and she must give him the breast quickly otherwise he'll wake all of them. Avi needs his sleep. Who know where he'll be tomorrow night? There'll be danger until he crosses the border. The guards will know he's trying to avoid the army and, if the money he offers isn't enough, they'll send him back.

Mame sleeps in a bed with Leah on the other side of the room. Once Avi has gone there won't be any menfolk left. Foter is dead and Reuben is in America. The women of the family, Rifka, Leah and Mame will have to manage somehow until Avi has raised enough money for their journey. The money in England is good. It won't take long.

Sol gives a little cry so Rifke turns away from Avi and picks Sol up. She opens her nightdress and takes him to her breast. He's only two weeks old, too young to be separated from his father. Avi had insisted on staying until after the birth, but he can't wait any longer.

Eli stirs in his sleep but thank God he doesn't wake. After a while Sol's mouth relaxes and she puts him down. Then she turns around to lie against Avi again, absorbing his warmth.

She must have fallen asleep without realising. There's a warm space in the bed where Avi slept. She feels cheated. She wants to hold him properly, put her arms around him one last time in bed. For a moment, she panics. What if he's already left? Perhaps he decided to go quickly to spare the pain of saying goodbye. Then she sees his shape moving around the room. He's being as quiet as possible, trying not to wake them.

The puch[1] he got from his parents lies on the floor. He's folded his tailor's scissors in rags to stop them cutting his clothes. He'll need the scissors in England when he starts looking for work. He checks everything, and folds up the puch.

His beard is prickly against her face. He kisses her quickly. She stands in the porch and watches him leave. The sky is getting paler but she can still see stars. No one else is awake. It will be a few days before the neighbours notice he's gone. He walks between the dark buildings, and disappears at the end of the street.

She dresses quickly. What can she do now but wait? Most of the family's savings have gone on paying for Avi's journey. Before long he'll send for them, and they'll all be safe in England, but for now they have to get by, here in Russia, with what they have.

The early September sun rises over the plot where they grow onions, cabbage, beetroot and potatoes. Their tree produces apples as well and then there are the eggs from the hens. She and Leah will have to look after their plot of land carefully and take care of the hens. Mame's hands and feet are twisted with arthritis, she can't dig and weed like before. It hurts her to bend down so she can't collect eggs. There's only Rifke and Leah left now who are young and strong. It's down to the two of them.

He's been gone eight weeks, and there's been no word. There could be a simple explanation. He'll contact her when he can. In the meantime she has to carry on and provide for the family. She packs her basket carefully with eggs and apples. She'll persuade the shopkeeper Chaim to buy them and start building up their savings again.

On the way down the lane to the main street she passes the Rabbi's house and the Schul. There's a group of people standing outside the dark wooden building. They're Jews, men mostly with skull-caps and beards, but she hasn't seen them before. There are a few women leaning against their puchs and sitting on the ground. Children sprawl next to them, their heads on their mother's laps. The men are carrying puchs on their backs. They've wrapped their possessions in their puchs, just like Avi. They look exhausted.

The boys from the Cheder[2] are gathered around these strange Jews. The Rabbi and his assistant teacher Isaac Mendel are speaking to the men. Rifke pauses, a little way off, and listens.

"Most of the families are already very cramped - you know how things are," the Rabbi says, "Still perhaps you can stay here in the Cheder. What do you think, Isaac?"

Isaac shrugs. "It isn't a palace, but since you have nowhere to stay..."

"Rifke feels sorry for the women. Their faces are sad. Even the children seem quiet, not running about. She wants to help them, but what can she do?

"Come on children, go to your homes. These people are

tired and need to rest," the Rabbi says, pushing a couple of the boys by the shoulders. One of them ducks away from the Rabbi's grips and turns to one of the strange men.

"Where are you going after you get to Hamburg?" he asks.

"Some to Palestine, others to England or America," the man replies.

These people are in a group not travelling alone. Avi should have travelled that way, it would have been safer, Rifke thinks, but when the call for the army came, they didn't have time to plan.

Rifke has the mad idea of asking those of them who are going to England to look for Avi and send word, but that's a ridiculous idea. How would they ever find him? If he is in England and wants to contact them he knows what to do. And if he's turned into one of those people who wants to leave his family behind, well what can she do? She pulls back before the people see her stare.

She walks on up the street, past the baths and the bakery. The blue-walled Church lies ahead at the end of the street. It dominates the town though Rifke has never been inside. She stops for a moment to admire the shimmering effect of the autumn sunshine on its golden dome, then turns to enter Chaim's shop.

The queue moves slowly towards the open door of the post office. Eli tugs at Rifke's hand.

"Stop it! What's the matter with you?" she says.

"How much longer?" Eli asks

It's boring for him when they come here. Then when they leave, she's always disappointed and sad. It's been four months and still no word. She tries not to take it out on Eli but some-times, she snaps.

She can see inside the door now. The post office is two

thirds the size of her family's room. The queue bulges and crams to get close to the counter. Rifke hauls Eli through the door. There's a smell of unwashed bodies, and onions. Eli tugs at her arm again. She reaches into her pocket.

"Here, have an apple," that will keep him busy for a while.

He takes the apple with both hands. Any minute now, he'll drop it on the floor. Rifke looks down. The floor is dirty. The people ahead of them have dung on their boots. There's a basket of chickens next to them on the floor.

Someone moves away from the counter and the straggling queue goes forward. More than half the people in the queue are Jews. Some she knows better than others. One thing she does know about them though, they're all waiting, like her, for news from abroad. Some will never get any news. Their sons or husbands will go to America or England and not have anything more to do with the families they've left at home.

She should have heard something. Even if Avi had walked the whole way without any lifts at all, he ought to have got there by now. What if he was arrested crossing the border. He might be in prison, here, in Russia and not be able to let her know. Perhaps he got ill, on the journey. Perhaps he was robbed. He might be wandering around some foreign town without money, hungry, and alone.

Hannah Mendel, wife of Isaac the teacher has finished at the counter. As she pushes past the queue she stares at the floor. Rifke knows what she's doing, she's trying to hide her tears. That means she still hasn't heard from her son. She looks up as she comes towards Rifke.

"Rifke-leh! How are you?"

"Well, thank you. And you? Have you any news?"

"Not today, but after all, it's only a few weeks. How about you? Have you heard?"

"Not yet, but perhaps I'll be lucky today."

"You'll hear soon, please God. I'm sure that he's safe. And how is little Eli?"

Hannah rubs Eli's hair and pinches his cheek, but he doesn't look up from his apple. Then she pats Rifke on the arm, and quickly walks away. Rifke knows that Hannah will go home now and cry. She hopes that Isaac Mendel will be kind, and comfort his wife.

Now it's Rifke's turn. She looks up at Grigor Micaelovich the post official. He seems greyer and more lined than usual today. That's what comes of a life spent indoors. He looks at her and raises his eyebrows.

"What name?"

He has only been at Gorodets for six months but surely he must know Rifke's name by now

"Rifke Epstein. Have you got a letter for me?"

He turns his back and Rifke knows there'll be nothing here. Why should today be any different? It's better not to hope. Then he turns around to face her with an envelope in his hand.

"Rifke Epstein?"

"Yes," how can he have forgotten so quickly?

"This letter's for you, it's got a British stamp."

She's shaking and her teeth are chattering. It must be the relief. She grabs the envelope and pulls Eli past the queue. Outside, the air is fresher. She leans against the wall. She tears open the envelope, and pulls the paper from inside. Her eyes go straight to the end, where Avi has written his name. She looks straight to the top, and makes out the address. She lifts Eli and kisses him, her tears are wet against her face.

"Daddy's safe, and in England," she says.

She takes the letter out carefully from the envelope and reads,

91

'My dear Rifke,'

'I have arrived safely in England and am with my cousins in Liverpool. I can never repay their kindness.

Your letter was here when I arrived. Thank G-d that you and the family are well. I know you'll take good care of the children until we meet again. For now you have to be both a mother and father, I pray to that it won't be for long.

I think about you and our children daily. My news is not so good. My cousins have helped me find work as a presser. They don't have their own workshop anymore so they couldn't give me work. They're working for other people themselves. The money side of things isn't as great as we thought. I'll save hard, to raise the money for you all to come but I don't know how long it will take. Perhaps a year if we're lucky.

Please try to be patient and don't even think about trying to come without train tickets. If it was only you and Leah that would be dangerous enough, but with two little ones and your mother that is out of the question. YOU MUST NOT TRY TO COME UNTIL I HAVE SAVED ENOUGH FOR THE TRAIN TICKETS. There are many perils on the road. I was robbed in Germany and only just had enough money left for the ship. The conditions on board were terribly cramped and I was ill when I got to Tilbury. I hope we'll have enough money for you to get a better ticket. Thank God there were Jewish people to help us when we disembarked. They took me to the Jew's Temporary shelter in London. They nursed me until I was well enough to travel to Liverpool.

I am in good health so please don't worry about me. In time I'll find a job with better pay. I've heard some people save enough money from their wages to set up their own workshops, and I want to do the same. At the moment it seems remote my dear... but who knows? If I am successful, our future will be bright.

Give my love to your mother and Leah. Write to me soon and often,

Your Loving Husband,

Avi'

She knows at once that a train ticket is a waste of money. If he can walk she could do the same. But how can she cross borders alone with the children? If she was with him in England, she could get a job and help him save. Then they'd have two wages, to put towards the cost of train tickets for Mame and Leah. But it's out of the question, she can't leave Leah and Mame alone. Then she remembers the group of people outside the Schul.

She can barely make out the lane beneath her feet but its rugged surface is too familiar to worry her. She holds the letter tightly. To either side of her the lane is hidden by tall trees. The next day, she and Leah will have to start looking for wood. They must make a good pile before the heavy snow comes. The loose wood around the stetl has already disappeared. If the men were here they'd go out and fell a tree. She and Leah can't do that alone. They'll have to go out to woods beyond Gorodets. There have been some high winds in the last few weeks, and if the fallen branches aren't too heavy, they can be dragged back across the fields.

If she goes who will help Mame and Leah? Perhaps something can be arranged-but no, it's impossible- she can't leave them-she doesn't even know why she's bothering to think about it.

She listens to the sound of her feet on the road. From

behind her she hears the call of an owl. She wants Avi, and yet she longs, already, for Mame and Leah as if she's already decided to leave them.

The Schul is dark when she arrives, but there's light behind the shutters of the Rabbi's house next door. She knocks, and the Rabbi answers.

The Rabbi has black eyes and heavy lids. He doesn't have any children, but lives alone with his wife. A long table and bench take up most of the room. In the middle of the table there's an iron samovar, a tea pot and some cups. The Rabbi's wife sits sewing at the far end of the bench. Rifke sits on one end of the bench near the door. The Rabbi sits opposite. His wife gets up to pour tea, hands mugs to her husband and Rifke, then and returns to her place.

Rifke stares at her steaming cup. She can't think how to begin.

"So, how are you Rifke?" The Rabbi asks clearing his throat.

Rifke sips her tea but it's too hot, and she nearly burns her tongue

"Please Rabbi, I need your help," she says.

The Rabbi raises his eyes, "Of course, but how?"

She pauses for a moment. She isn't sure how the Rabbi will react to what she has to say.

"Rabbi can you help us? Me and Avi. He's safe in England, but life is hard. The pay isn't as good as we thought. I am thinking maybe I should travel on foot, not wait for the train. Then when I get to England, Avi and I can both work, and send money for Mame and Leah."

She watches the Rabbi waiting for his reaction. The Rabbi takes off his glasses.

"Rifke, you have young children," he says staring at her.

She looks down as she answered. "Other people do it," she says.

"Not a woman alone, with two young babies, that would be foolish."

She knows he's right. Her stomach tenses, but she needs to ask.

"Can you help me Rabbi, find a group like the people who came here before? That way the boys and I will be safe. "

"But what about your mother? She isn't as young as she was. And you have no menfolk at home now. How can your sister manage alone?."

"But Rabbi, it won't be for long. When I get to England, I can work, and together Avi and I will have the money for their train tickets much more quickly than if I stay here like a lemon."

"Rifke - I don't think this is such a good idea. You don't decide something like this in a hurry anyway - think it over carefully. Maybe I can help you find travelling companions, but I can't promise."

"Rabbi could you make enquiries anyway, just so we know?"

The Rabbi tightens his lip into a thin line. "Rifke, let me be clear. In my opinion it would be much better to wait patiently for your husband to save enough money for the train. If you refuse to wait I will do what I can to make your journey safe, but still you'll be going against my advice."

She doesn't agree with him. Finding other Jews to travel with seems a perfectly good plan. "But -" she says.

The Rabbi holds up his hand. "It's no use arguing with me," he says, "We're not talking about this anymore tonight."

. . .

It's worse than she thought. Mame is crying, tears running down her face. Eli is clutching Mame's skirt, leaning his head against her. Sol has woken up and started to wail, softly at first and then louder, and louder.

"How am I going to live through this?" Mame asks, "Months of not knowing if you're alive or dead. And what about these two? What's going to happen to them? It isn't possible." Mame is sounding angry now, "this plan of yours just isn't possible!" she shouts through her tears.

Leah lifts Sol from his basket and holds him against her. She stands next to Mame so that the whole family is facing Rifke.

"You've always been selfish, Rifke," Leah says.

"What do you expect me to do Leah? Avi had to leave. If he'd gone to the army I might never have seen him again. Anyway there isn't a future for us here."

"So what does that mean for those of us who stay behind?" Leah's voice is cold.

"Leah you know, we want you to join us. We'll save the money and you'll come."

"And how will Mame cope with a journey like that?"

"She'll cope. Older people than Mame have gone to join their relatives abroad. We'll save enough money and you'll bring her by train."

"Are you prepared to wait till Avi's saved enough money to go by train? No, because you don't think it'll ever happen. That's why you plan to walk, even though that means putting the children at risk," Leah says tightening her arms around Eli. "You know, don't you that you'll never raise enough money for us all to come?"

"That isn't true," Rifke says quietly closing her eyes.

Mame blows her nose loudly. "How are you going to do this Rifke?" she asks. "By yourself it would be hard enough, but with these two it will be impossible. Eli's too heavy to carry, and he can't walk far. Sol's getting heavier by the day."

"Perhaps I can join others who will help. The Rabbi is seeing what he can find out."

Mame screws up her eyes, "The Rabbi? Is he helping you in this?"

Rifke looks away, "He doesn't want me to do it Mame, but if I am going then he wants me to travel as safely as possible."

"And what if you don't find any companions?" Mame asks.

"I'm sure I will," Rifke says.

Rifke sits by the stove, breast feeding Sol. If she has to have her clothes open, then she must keep warm. Two feet away from the stove the room is cold and it's impossible to sit at the far end by the bed without being under the quilt.

Outside the snow on the ground already comes to just above their ankles. The well is frozen and they have to break the ice to get to the water underneath. Later, the well will freeze solid. They'll have to fill saucepans and buckets before that happens so that they can get water. Even then, they might run out, and have to smash the ice with an axe then melt it in a saucepan on the stove. She thinks they'll have enough wood.

They can still go out though, and it's best to move to keep warm. In a few weeks the snow might come half way up the front door. They'll have to dig their way out, to go to the bakery to get bread.

They've stored food for the winter. Potatoes and onions will keep in the cold and they have eggs from the chickens. Some of the chickens might not live through the winter. If one dies they'll make soup. If they're snowed in completely, they can live for two or three weeks on what they've put by.

Rifke looks up, to see Mame watching her.

"There's a new baby at the big house," Mame says.

"Oh?" Rifke's never been inside the house but on the feast of Omer they've had picnics in the wooded part of its grounds close to the river. From there they glimpsed the house. It's larger than the Synagogue in Kobrin, as large almost as the town hall. It has tall windows, a terrace and a lawn leading down to the woods.

"Rich people don't like to breast feed," Mame says "You should go and see if they want your help."

Rifke frowns, she doesn't understand what Mame is saying. She remembers a time once, with Leah, when they went right up to the side of the house, but it was frightening.

"This could be a way of raising money for your journey-they'll pay you to breast feed their baby," Mame says.

Rifke is amazed that Mame is actually trying to help, but she's also shocked at the idea she might breast- feed another woman's child and get paid for it. She stares at Mame, who looks back without speaking.

"But, what if there isn't enough milk for Sol?" Rifke asks.

"Your body will produce what's needed, God will provide," Mame says.

She's too nervous to approach the house by the main entrance, and so goes down to the river instead, and then up through the wood. The house is at the top of a small incline and she gets warmer as she walks up the path that leads through the grounds to the side entrance. The snow crunches under her feet and the puddles are frozen. The leaves are trapped underneath. If she stands on the ice it won't crack, it's solid. She always tried to break the ice on puddles when she was a child.

What will they think when she knocks at the door? Is she clean enough? She looks down at her clothes. She can't see any dirt. Perhaps they'll turn her away when they hear her Yiddish accent. If they do she'll be disappointed. She's looking forward to earning this money.

The house is getting closer. She can see the tall windows at the back that overlook the grounds. Perhaps she'll be seen and treated as an intruder before being allowed to explain her purpose.

She goes round to the side door and knocks.

A large woman opens the door. She wears an apron, Her hair is streaked with grey. Behind her, Rifke sees the kitchen. A piece of meat is roasting on a spit over an open range. It looks like a pig. She catches a whiff of roasting flesh. She's never eaten pig. The smell makes her hungry but she tries to ignore it. There's a stove as well as the range. Lots of shining brass pots and pans hang from the walls. She wonders how many people live there. Her own family only has two saucepans.

She's been staring at the kitchen for too long, the woman looks impatient, "What do you want?" the woman asks.

"I heard there was a baby here."

"What about it?"

"I also have a baby, and plenty of milk. I've come to offer myself as a wet nurse."

It takes the woman a long time to answer. Rifke guesses the woman knows her mistress doesn't want to breast feed, but won't want to employ a Jew.

"Wait here," the woman says.

The woman doesn't ask Rifke to go inside, but leaves the kitchen door open. Rifke waits on the step. From where she stands she can see the globules of fat dripping off the pig. There's a hissing noise as they drop into the fire.

Another woman appears. She wears a black dress with a high neck. She seems to be in charge and Rifke guesses she's the housekeeper. "Follow me," she says.

Rifke walks through the kitchen. She feels shabby and poor. They go into a hallway which has a broad staircase. The woman leads Rifke to a door at the back of the hall. It opens out onto a narrow staircase that Rifke realises is for the servants.

They go up the stairs and the housekeeper takes her into a room with pale blue painted walls, and thick darker blue carpet on the floor. Rifke is worried that her wet boots will leave stains. In the middle of the room, there's a baby in a cradle. He's tiny, not more than a month old. In the corner there's a blue and white enamel sink with a large jug placed on the wooden surround. There's no bed for an adult in the room. Surely, Rifke thinks, these people don't leave the baby by himself in such a large room.

The baby opens his eyes and starts to cry. His features are screwed up and pink. He sounds hungry. Rifke recognises the cry.

A young woman comes into the room. Her fair hair is piled up at the back of her head. Her eyes are a piercing blue. She must be the baby's mother.

"How old is your baby?" the young woman asks.

"He's four months old," Rifke replies.

"And have you plenty of milk?"

"Oh yes, plenty."

"Let's see."

Rifke hasn't expected this. The housekeeper pushes a chair towards her. They want her to prove that she has milk. It's ridiculous, but what does it matter if there's money at the end? She undoes her blouse and pulls out her breast. It looks full and the nipple is swollen. The baby is light as she lifts him. She places him on her breast and feels him suck. She looks up at the women and wonders if they're satisfied.

So far money hasn't been mentioned.

"How much will you pay?" Rifke asks

"You'll get a rouble for each week, but you'll have to sleep here, he wakes in the night," the housekeeper says. "You can bring your own baby if you want to, and there'll be plenty of food."

"I also have a three year old son."

"You can't bring him here. You'll have to make other arrangements. You can visit him during the day," the house-keeper says.

A rouble a week is good money, but if Rifke has to leave Eli at night she's going to strike a hard bargain. She takes a deep breath.

"I'll do it for two roubles a week," she says.

The two women look at each other, then the housekeeper looks back at Rifke and nods. Rifke wonders if she could have got more out of them. Still if she works here until spring, that's at least twelve weeks. She'll give some money to Mame and Leah but most of it she'll save. There'll be just enough money for the land journey and the ship.

Notes

Sarah Lerner

1. A puch is Yiddish for a quilt, in which Jewish Emigrants used to carry their belongings on their journey to Europe and America.
2. Jewish School

Farva Kaukab

I moved to London seven years ago and, like many transplants to London, hopped around various neighbourhoods before adopting one. My now husband and I initially moved to Camden because of proximity to work. Although every area of London has something different to offer, this is where I've felt most at home with the lively and artsy vibe, the markets and great food, the eclectic group of people, and the easy access to parks and green spaces.

I'm a fairly multicultural person. A Swiss-Pakistani, I have lived/ worked in seven different countries and absorbed many different ways of being. I bring to my writing an interest in the human condition and a desire to move away from Western-centric perspectives and characters. I write stories about individuals who are underrepresented or have experiences that are alien to the type of people who exist in developed and well functioning democracies. It was a pleasure to attend the Stoke Newington Authors Panel in April and the Indie Novella publishing surgery in May. It brought a welcome sense of a local writer's community. My day job has currently swallowed up much of my time and mental space, but knowing there is a network and community I can tap into is very motivating. I hope to take advantage of the courses, surgeries, and writing groups over the course of the year*.

The piece I've submitted is about characters in the modern shipping industry. During the pandemic, for people working from home in the UK, food and groceries were still available at supermarkets, new phones or other devices could still be ordered. Yes there were delays, but the disruption to many people working from home was minimal. Shipping didn't stop during the pandemic and I have become interested in this world I did not have much exposure to. We hear about the bad factory working conditions when big retailers outsource their manufacturing to developing countries, but we don't know how those same retailers then get the products to us and what that means for the people transporting them. I hope you enjoy this piece of writing and that it brings salience to something unseen.

* Indie Novella are creating free workshops and writing groups in Hackney and North London and all are invited.

The MV Ingrid Ragnar, by **Farva Kaukab**

Aung skimmed through a tattered copy of Tintin's voyages at sea, trying to make sense of the story from the pictures. It had been left behind by Mishka, a large, shaved-head Russian he met the year before on board the MV Ingrid Ragnar. This time the ship was sailing from Yangon to Rotterdam and was currently moored in Karachi. Mishka hadn't returned, and instead Aung was bunking with two fresh-faced roommates.

Aung found the comic soothing and was hoping it would calm his nerves and the cramping in his stomach as he thought over the conversation he'd had earlier that day. "We are operating on a really tight budget," the captain had said, rubbing his temples when Aung interrupted him reviewing cargo logs. "We can't squeeze out bonuses for one person or we'd have to do that for everyone." Aung looked around the cabin, at the waxed leather shoes, the primly ironed sparkling white shirts (that he had pressed earlier), cufflinks on the dresser, a camera with a large flashgun attached, and then mumbled an apology and saw himself out. It had taken several months to muster the courage and he felt deflated. As the meeting replayed on loop in his head, it ondulated and morphed like wisps of smoke, and Aung began to have increasingly paranoid thoughts. Had he come off as too cocky? What if they thought he was going to abscond and decided to fire him first? The Second Officer poked his head around the sleeping cabin, jolting Aung out of his rumination. "Men, the ship's unloading now. Aung, Yorek, and Hamza, I need you three starboard to help unlock the reefer containers." He accompanied the command with hand gestures to make sure they had understood. "What? Where are the assigned men?" retorted Yorek at the officer, incensed at being disturbed in his solitary game of cards. The second officer scowled and left the room. Aung gave Hamza a knowing look; dealing with Yorek's temper was getting to them both, but their mandate had barely started. Minutes later the three men descended the staircase to the deck in file like schoolboys. Aung, more experienced with the equipment, helped guide the other two with unlocking the bars keeping the refrigerated containers, or reefers, in place. Familiar with American movies and slang, the term had initially elicited giggles from Hamza. Sadly, he soon learned that reefers were, in fact, the hardest containers to handle, and as the

Second Officer shouted commands, the three worked in unison to move the containers onto the unloading docks for the shore cranes to haul. The port was buzzing with activity and the routine rhapsody of sounds overwhelmed Aung. The strident shrill of the ship's horn, the voices yelling over each other in an alien language, the deep bass honks from trucks waiting to carry away the cargo to some unknown place. Aung's first job had also been to Karachi. As the ship had moored, he had climbed to the highest level of the superstructure to get a view of the sprawling port. What hit him was a world devoid of nature, containers packed together like mid-game Jenga towers with man, machines, and the sea as far as the eye could see. Later that evening when the ship was asleep, Hamza stumbled into the room from the mess hall, eyes bloodshot with fatigue and booze. "The night watch is enjoying themselves right now. They showed me the charting room." "Oh yeah, the charting room. Very important for not sinking." Aung replied. He'd never been in the charting room having not taken an interest in the wider mechanisms of the ship. In his several years of being a crewman, Aung did as he was told, kept his head down, and hoped every trip that he'd have enough money to return to Yangon and stay by his father's side. "They talked about a device that allows you to see in the darkness in the ocean. Something to do with sound." Hamza continued, sitting down next to Aung. "I think if I could learn how something like that works, I could also be an officer in a few years." He looked hopeful. "That is the stupidest thing I've heard." Yorek snarled from his bed. "Shut up and go to sleep." Aung shrugged at Hamza, privately agreeing with Yorek on this one, and switched off the lights. Unless Hamza was going to suddenly conjure up an expensive education, his dream seemed better left to non-waking hours. Aung tossed and turned that night. Unable to sleep, he got up to wander and, feeling competitive following Hamza's remarks, found himself in the charting room. The room was full of small beeping sounds and lit up displays. Clock-like panels with the hands quivering then rotating with no apparent pattern, red and white instruction-less buttons, and half a dozen maps displayed on screens showing their trajectory from various angles. Aung imagined how people far away were connected to this magical room, how his life and those of others on this ship depended on their competence. Walking back towards the cabins, he spotted two officers conversing on the bulwark. The ship was quiet at this hour, the water gently splashing against the hull a familiar lullaby. He drew closer in the shadows, and didn't have to strain to listen. Back under his covers moments later, his insides tied in knots like grapevines, Aung was unsettled by what he'd over-heard: Mishka hadn't disappeared, he'd been fired. He had asked for a two-month advance, and when the Captain refused, they'd gotten into a fight. Aung and Mishka were cut from the same cloth, dependent on these earnings, and subject to the whims of others. Consumed with anxiety over both their fates, Aung fell into a fitful sleep, a sharp, pulsating pain in the back of his head. The next morning after finishing his laundry shift, Aung received a call from his father. "Looks like you're in an area with a signal," he let out a chuckle which instantly broke into a fit of coughing. "How is this last ride going? Any lead with the Captain?" After lying through his teeth, Aung hung up. His father had been thrilled and Aung felt guilty but also relieved. He told himself the lie over and over again to imbue it with power. The more he told it, the more it felt it could have been true. He pretended he did have the money and started behaving like it. He dressed in nicer clothes for dinner, he stood a little bit taller, he went into long tales about his retirement plans when playing cards with the other men. Hamza pulled him aside one

107

day. "They could have you committed in an asylum for this nonsense," he hissed. Aung shrugged; his eyes glazed. He quieted down after that and went about his days keeping to himself. As his tour ended, his father came to get him. Aung rarely left his small room that winter and his father stopped probing after realising there was no payout. Come summer, he put on his suit and returned to the port ready to be at sea another year.

Haringey

Welcome to Haringey

In November, during the first year of the pandemic, I packed up my room in Stoke Newington and moved to a commuter town a forty-five-minute train ride from Marylebone. I had just started seeing someone a few short months before, during that surreal, sunny summer of meeting outside and drinking wine and take-away beers in parks until the sun fell in the night sky. I was excited. I was going to have the best of both worlds. Have the house, two bedrooms – two floors! – and a garden, and have a girlfriend who shared a flat near Lea Bridge. We'd spend our time between the city and the countryside, go to galleries, then escape for some fresh air. Life was going to be good. I think it took me a good nine months to eventually come home with my tail between my legs and admit it had all been a terrible mistake.

People from outside London sometimes like to comment how unfriendly London is. How noisy it is, how chaotic it is, how they can only handle it for a day. When I moved to the countryside what first appealed to me was the quiet. To go for walks where there was not a soul around. To nod politely and say hello to the people you did see. In that time when they closed down the offices and restaurants over the second lock-down, I would have spells where I would spend eight days in a row in the quiet of the countryside, going for walks with stretches where not a soul was around, then nodding politely at people who always nodded back, though it never went much deeper than that. Before I left Newington Green I had started to get to know all the café owners and wine shop proprietors, and the guys who ran my local shop. Somehow COVID seemed to bond us, get us talking. In Oxfordshire, in this small town I had moved to, everyone seemed friendly, polite, but there was something missing. I never once felt like I was making a home, or forming a community, or doing anything much more than going for a walk where not a soul was around and then coming back to a house that was double the size of the flats I've previously rented but twice as empty.

When I broke up with my girlfriend, I felt that emptiness tenfold. I had everything I thought I wanted, and I hated it.

With directions to the flat I had seen on Spareroom.com, I arrived at Turnpike Lane tube station. I was early and, as I had only previously been to Wood Green once, I decided to look for a bookshop I had seen online to ask if they would consider stocking some books I was peddling as a fledgling publisher. The only thing was, as a fledgling publisher, I was a useless salesperson. I walked past the shop twice before I eventually mustered the courage to go in. Instead of making my way to the counter to talk to the friendly-looking, big man with the white beard, I started to pretend browse, picked up a Martin Amis novel, which I still haven't got around to opening and spent ten quid at the till before I eventually opened my mouth.

"You're the publisher," said the bookseller. I said yes, and that I'd sent him a couple of emails about potentially doing a launch event at the shop.

"Can you do me a favour?" he said. "Are you free next month to sit on a publishing panel for us?"

I hate using the phrase 'taken aback', but I was at first. It felt like someone had hit a boost button on my back as I snapped to attention.

"Sure, no problem. That will be great."

"I'll be honest with you," the bookseller then said. "I'm asking you because everyone else I know in publishing is on holiday that day."

And that's how I met Tim West.

Tim retired from bookselling in June and I was really fortunate to go to his retirement talk at All Good Bookshop where he talked through his forty-year career in bookselling to an absolutely rammed shop full of people. There actually came a point, ten minutes after the scheduled end, where I fell out of the shop and had to go home because there was not enough space for me to get back in as we shuffled, opening the door trying to let in newcomers for the party that was going to kick off after. But over that hour, I had learned about Tim's four decades forming this wonderful community in a place called Haringey.

All Good Bookshop was the brainchild of Tim and his friends. They wanted to create a community-run bookshop that would sell good books and host events and be a space where the community of Green Lanes, Wood Green, and Turnpike Lane could gather over a mutual love of reading and storytelling. Tim had run the Wood Green Waterstones and during his talk, he told of his two conversations with the big cheeses at Waterstones – the first congratulating him on business booming and telling him that everyone in the shop was getting a bonus. The second, happening a month or so later when they called to tell him that the store was no longer a 'strategic priority' and that they were closing it.

Unperturbed, Tim went on to set up and run the Wood Green Bookshop, only for the fellow who put up the cash to take the shop to Hastings. As you do. Or as Tim says, Failed in London, Tried Hastings. Or FILTH for short.

So All Good became something different. A bookshop run by the community, for the community, where everyone was a shareholder with no need to depend on FILTH to put up the cash. Not saying things were now plain sailing. The doors to All Good Bookshop opened the same month something called 'lockdown' was announced, which admittedly was only going to last two weeks, but inconvenient none the less... I think we all know how that turned out. Tim and everyone associated with All Good Bookshop put a gargantuan effort into keeping the shop open in those early months, but even more so, they took it upon themselves to get out into Haringey and start bringing the community spirit of All Good to those who couldn't leave the house. Tim bought a bike and started cycling around the borough taking books to people far and wide. To many, he not only brought books but he brought stories and conversation, wonderfully colourful shirts, and most of all, joy. He got the Haringey Heroes award, but in a way that was beside the point. He made people's lives better, and just by the fact I literally found myself shuffled outside his shop onto the pavement unable to find the physical room to get back in, a huge amount of people turned up to his retirement party to tell him what he means to them.

Tim West was the first person I met when I moved to Haringey, at a time when I felt a tad bit of a failure. There are chance meetings which you could say changed your life, and corny as it might sound, Tim was mine – look, I've known the guy less than two years and I'm pretty sure that if I stop in at All Good on a Wednesday when he now volunteers he won't remember my name, but I remember his and how he taught me that there are communities in London, all working for each other, all getting on their bikes and bringing light relief when things are going a bit shit.

After meeting Tim, I met my flatmate, Sophie – Hackney born, a Haringey resident for the last decade, and without doubt the nicest human being I have ever met. Sophie actually taught me what true courage is – being shy but stepping out of that shyness to be kind to people. I then met the local Westbury Avenue community, feeling comfortable to drop in at The Westbury for a pint on a sunny evening and have a chat about everything and nothing. I even have my network of confidants and secret keepers, such as my friend at the kebab shop who despite me being an advocate for healthy living and non-processed foods, knows that at 11 o'clock on a Wednesday night he needs to flip a burger onto his grill and ask me just one question, "the usual?"

Damien Mosley 2023

Phoebe McIntosh

I am a writer and actor based on the Harringay ladder. I graduated from the MA Acting course at Arts Ed in 2008, but not content with the roles I was seeing, I began writing my own plays. I wrote, produced and performed in a sell-out run of my debut play, THE TEA DIARIES, at the Edinburgh Fringe Festival in 2013. In 2018, I co-produced my solo show DOMI-NOES with Black Theatre Live and the Lighthouse Arts Centre Poole as an associate artist, touring London, the South-east and Edinburgh. The show received 4-and 5-star reviews and calls for me to write a multi-character adaptation. So that's what I did! DOMINOES the novel is due to be published by Penguin (Chatto & Windus) in March 2024. It has been called 'a conversation starting love story' that explores questions of identity and the legacy of the slave trade in the 21st century.' My most recent play, THE SOON LIFE, has been long listed for the Alfred Fagon Award, the Theatre503 International Playwriting Prize and The Bruntwood Prize and came highly commended for the Tony Craze Award following my time on the Soho Theatre's Writers' Lab programme. I am currently writing my second novel which is set in my local stomping ground around Haringey. I am constantly being inspired by my local area. There are interesting characters at every turn and a story waiting to be told about each of them. I love heading out down Green Lanes ready to soak up the atmosphere – it is a melting pot of Black, White, Turkish, Mixed heritage and myriad languages, ages and class backgrounds. I feel lucky to live here and lucky to have discovered my writing voice as a resident.

The Surge by Phoebe McIntosh

You're tired. Your body aches with every attempt at movement. The throbbing in your head has been near constant for most of the night and you awoke at 4am convinced the day had begun, was going to begin, with or without your consent or involvement. You've been here before, of course. But it feels a little different this time. It's the definition of insanity, you note to yourself. Doing the same thing over again with the expectation that there will be different results. The first time you did this, it didn't go so well. You can admit that now, can't you? You're able to. It was many years ago. It went well in so far as you survived. And so did she. But everything else, the peripheries, the business - the stuff people don't understand to be just as important as survival, part of surviving – that stuff, not so good. It was never supposed to play out like that. But you glossed over the effects of it for months, years in fact, afraid to disappoint anyone. You left that place, went home, the two of you together - alive, bruised, shaken, wondering what had happened, if it had only happened to you or if others were going through the same thing but were simply too afraid to say so. You couldn't help but preoccupy yourself with what they thought of you and your failure to deliver - friends, family, strangers, other 'birthers' like you. What they would think of you when they heard and what they might already be saying out of earshot, behind your back, on WhatsApp. But you went home and got on with surviving and keeping her alive too. Your lower back feels like it's been carrying the weight of several worlds for several months. You're not swollen in any of the additional places expected of someone like you. But before you, physically in front of you, part of you, there is an omnipresent reminder. Always. It's positioned in a place that makes the ability to counterbalance difficult, makes precision in most given situations requiring physical movement more considered, trickier than it once was. Occasionally, there are movements within you as well, ones you have nothing to do with, no choice over whether they happen or not. Yet you will them to happen, every day, several times. It is your responsibility and yours alone to monitor them, to count them and to recognise if they are happening less frequently, report it, tell someone, knowing that if you fail to do so, the consequences could be grave. You fight the urge to lay down. There is so much to do. The dwindling list of life admin, the tasks that fill your days, never dwindles for long but continually re-germinates and grows like a newly planted seed. But there's nothing new about that. It has been steadily growing for many years, since you hit adulthood, since you found your own notepad and pen, took over the task of listing all the things there are to do in the world, in a day, from your own mother, allowing her to get back to her life in small, incremental ways not possible in the previous 18 years of life with you. You think about her more lately, about how she did this alone, walked herself to the hospital when she went through this very experience, carrying her hospital bag alongside her bump. You wonder how she stayed so calm, what it took for her not to panic that you were on your way, and she was so young, so alone. You drink that in now, that strength, you need it more than you did before as your mid-section tightens around the additional life it holds. You ask it not to cling too tightly, 'Please,' you think. 'Let go a little, body of mine, just enough' of your own musculature, your own skin holding onto the new skin that you've made from your own cells, but which doesn't belong to you. You call to mind words that bring about ease. Ease is all you want. For this to be easier this time round. Is it too much to hope? If anyone asks, no, no you're not scared. You throw them a bone: 'A little nervous, I guess.' That's all you admit to out loud. And on the inside too, within the secret folds of your mind that you never have to reveal to anyone else, there is no room to second guess that impulse either now, little room to reconsider or admit to truer feelings because you are occupied, full to the brim with fresh spring air, new bones, soft limbs, shoulders as yet unweighted by the reality of the world just beyond the confines of the short-term let of your body, housing her. Within you, there is a face that already knows how to smile. Fully formed eyes with fully formed tear ducts ready to be filled and emptied down the soft-ness of the barely-there peaks of skin which you have helped to mould into her appearance. You'll see it soon, no longer grainy and separated from you by glass and medical machines but real, looking back at you, asking of you all the things you would never ask of yourself because it would be too hard to envisage that you could do them. But you will. Because you've done it before. 'All I have to do is feed her and love her,' you tell yourself. And you can think of nothing truer. You are alone now, when for days you have been surrounded by people and anticipation. That's why it's happening now, the contractions, the shortness of breath, the knowledge that time, this kind of time, the kind you've grown so accustomed to recently, is short. A new time is dawning. And it starts now.

Ruth Valentine

My name is Ruth Valentine. I have lived in Haringey, near St Ann's Hospital in South Tottenham, since 2001. I worked for many years with refugees in London, and I volunteer at Caris Haringey, which supports families with no recourse to public funds. I'm also a member of Haringey Welcome, a campaign group that works to counter the government's hostile environment policies, which affect so many of our fellow residents. My novel *After Silence,* from which this is an extract, draws on all those experiences. I began writing it in 2014. I felt that my kind of neighbourhood, with all its richness and its problems, was never visible in the fiction I read. It obviously shows Haringey pre-pandemic, and the food fair described in this extract had vanished (for reasons I no longer remember) before I started.

I'm 77 years old, white British, and grew up in a very different environment, Bognor Regis, on the South Coast. I came to London at eighteen, to escape a conservative, monocultural town, and have stayed almost ever since. I've published several collections of poetry, and one previous novel, *The Jeweller's Skin.*

THE FOOD FAIR

It was Sunday lunchtime and she had almost no food in the fridge: a few cherry tomatoes, a piece of cheddar, a third of a dull pizza, and half a lettuce. It's the rent, of course. I've been avoiding shopping.

She could hear the noise as soon as she left the house: a bass-line blur of music, a muddle of voices. She walked towards Green Lanes and the sound increased. Late September but the sun was still warm; she had come out without a cardigan. A family passed her, a small man with a buggy, a little girl on a purple scooter, a woman following, the child's coat in her hand. A Turkish demonstration? Not with those speakers.

At the corner by the Salisbury she understood. Three policemen in hi-viz jackets were turning away the traffic into the side streets. To the left of them was a crowd right across the street, and market stalls. The festival: Joel had talked about it.

She threaded her way into the crowd, heading towards the Greek butcher's two blocks down. The music came from one of the streets on the right. Now she could tell it was something Middle Eastern, loud and plangent, a male voice pleading above lush strings. People passed her eating honey-balls. At a stall a man with thick glasses held out a petition: *Save Our Hospital*. There was cheap jewellery, and bright-coloured ceramics, and above all food. The cooking smells changed and blended as she walked: barbecued meat, spices, pancake batter, paella, piroghi. The crowd slowed her down from her usual pace, and she found herself acquiescing, wandering.

The butcher's was open, two of the men watching from the doorway. She bought mince and bacon, and since it was there, stacked on the glass cabinet, a box of Greek oregano. As she turned to leave, a group of young women appeared right outside, dancing, their skirts swinging, two boys with guitars following close behind. She stood in the doorway till they passed; but they chose to stop right there on the corner. At once other people began to gather round them.

'It *is* you. Hello.' A man's voice, just behind her. She turned abruptly. The man had been beside her in the shop, having a guinea-fowl jointed. Now she saw it was the English chess-player. 'Oh. Hello.'

She turned back to the street. The dancers were moving on. A small boy ran and caught up with them, turned triumphantly to a woman in African dress, heavily pregnant. She stepped down to the pavement; but the man was still behind her. 'Wonderful, isn't it?'

She ignored him, annoyed, and moved into the crowd. There were people she half-recognised from the shop, or just from the neighbourhood. The young woman from the chemist's, in embroidered gold shalwar-kameez, waved to her, a younger girl in green jigging next to her to the music. She wondered if Joel had brought along his children; if he had them this week-end. She stopped at a plant stall: thyme, marjoram, sage, small plants in pots tied with green ribbon. There were a few geraniums at the back: 'I had some white ones, but they've all gone,' the woman told her.

'I don't have a garden.'

'A window-box then? They're lovely in window-boxes. Ever so easy. A pound a piece. Or I can do you three for two, like in the bookshops.'

She shook her head. Still it would be good to be growing something. 'Maybe the herbs. What can I grow indoors?'

The woman fingered the little pots in turn. 'Trouble is, all these, they need full sun.' She considered. 'Basil though, you like basil? I've just got one left,' she bent and brought it up from

125

by her feet. 'I was going to keep it for someone, but you can have it. It's two quid though, you can see, it's well on.'

Ida bent over the plant. Two pounds; but the smell rose to her face, intoxicating. She took the coins from her purse.

'Have you got a bag? If I just pop it in a paper bag, it'll go in with your shopping, is that all right? Now you know you've got to keep watering it, eh? They dry out ever so quickly.' Then she turned away to another customer, a young man with blue spiked hair.

She wandered on towards the railway bridge. The music had changed down here, a Latin beat she felt through her body. A grey-haired couple danced on the spot for a moment, the crowd parting around them. The woman laughed and rested her hand on her partner's shoulder. A boy pushed past, calling out to someone, and the smell of basil rose again from her shopping.

On one of the side streets a queue had formed. She went closer. A woman in black turned away from the stall, licking a green ice-cream. I am spending too much, she thought; but the day was warm. She joined the queue, seeing what the people in front of her bought.

Pistachio ice-cream. The flavour on her tongue, a seaside resort, heat, she was a child. She allowed the memory for just a moment. Then it was her turn. 'What kind do you have?'

The man pointed to each plastic box in turn. 'Coffee, lemon sorbet, pistachio, raspberry, hazelnut. The chocolate's finished.'

'Hazelnut.' She must have tasted it, back home, but couldn't remember. Well, today I am experimenting. She paid and turned back to the main road.

And there again was the chess player, in the queue. He waved: 'What did you get? Is that hazelnut? Sounds good.'

She found a bench outside one of the jewellers. He would join her, no doubt. Well, I can talk to him for a few minutes. She licked the ice-cream slowly, and when it dripped onto her hand licked that away too.

'May I?' He tackled his own ice-cream – raspberry – with gusto. 'God, that's good. Just what I needed. How's yours, is it OK?'

'It's good,' she said, defeated. In fact it was, a delicate flavour, and the occasional softened sliver of hazelnut. He had capable hands, she saw, big and lean, with light-brown hair at the wrist. His physical presence on the bench beside her was strong, disturbing; she never did this, sitting next to a man, absorbed in the pleasure of eating. To distract them both, she asked, 'You said this is the second festival?'

He wiped his mouth, and looked round for a bin for the paper, then gave up and folded it neatly in his hand. 'Yeah, two years ago. It's every other year, at least as long as the Council lets it be. It took them ages to get permission the first time. Well, you must have seen, in the freebie paper?'

She shook her head.

'You know, the one they shove through your door every week. All school prizes and court reporting. Stabbing of the month, my daughter calls it.'

She flinched. 'No, I don't read it.'

'You're not missing much. Anyway, here we are, they gave in eventually and you can see what a success it's been. I reckon the shopkeepers can't believe their luck.'

She considered. 'But are people buying in the shops? The stalls, yes, but for the shops it's hard, so many people outside. The regulars, probably they won't come today.'

She had spoken with authority; he looked sharply across at her. Now he will ask how I know. 'Though I came out to do my shopping. I didn't know. I have to buy vegetables still.' She fingered the handles of her shopping bag.

'You'd been shopping the last time I met you.' He was smiling. 'Perhaps you're a famous cook, you come down here for the best ingredients.'

'I work,' she said flatly. 'Five, six days a week. Today I have Saturday off. I shop when I can.' She stood.

He looked up at her. 'What's your name?'

He said it casually; she paused – 'if you don't mind telling me.' So she told him. 'Ida. A lovely name.' He was trying to keep her. 'Did you know there is a Mount Ida in Crete? Did your parents tell you that?'

Her mother had told her, when she was quite small. Still for some reason she said, 'I didn't know.'

'Well, Ida, it's been delightful meeting you. I'm Bernard, by the way. Maybe we'll have a game of chess some time.'

She smiled. He stood up, and easily, shockingly, lifted her hand and kissed it. Then he strode away, into the side streets, at ease in his body, in jeans and a magenta tee-shirt that fitted close to a strong muscular back..

Anne G Dilley

I came to live in Haringey through personal contacts.

As I only came to the borough in 2020, there has not been a vast difference since I moved here.

Being in Haringey for me means being part of Green London, with a pleasing environment in which to live, that brings the country into the city.

It means access to a wide variety of artistic avenues where a person has the opportunity to network and share creativity with fellow artists.

Haringey also offers the opportunity for social networking, with organisations that are good at bringing communities and people from different backgrounds together.

The libraries offer the opportunity for people to learn about other cultures and languages.

The latter are particularly important as each language has its own music.

I also use the name Anne Gaelan.

Reclamation of a People – Women Creole Artists, Language and Legacy

Telling the story of how the Creole language became known and accepted in British culture and the diverse writers and performers who helped make this happen.

by Anne G Dilley

We can take anything that English education has to offer us, but ultimately, we must reject the domination of her influence because we are not English, nor should we ever want to be.

Norman Manley, first Prime Minister of Jamaica, 1939, quoted from p 1,

Miss Lou, Louise Bennett and Jamaican Culture by Mervyn Morris.

One topic that is relevant to the borough of Haringey is the achievement of Jamaican women who promoted their culture and aroused interest in it through performing poetry, stories or plays in their native Creole language, originally understood as dialect in the UK and termed 'patois'.

One of these women is unknown, the other, a celebrity in Jamaican culture during her lifetime, who deserves to be remembered and her legacy acknowledged today.

Before introducing them, it is worth sharing how the mother tongue of most Jamaicans is Creole and that 90% of Jamaicans are of African descent, forcibly taken to the New World as slaves.

The language is made up of words originating from other languages, mainly English, combined with language structures from Africa.

The literary heritage of this language is rich, consisting of songs, folk tales, proverbs, drum music and riddles.

The most famous examples of Creole literature are Anancy stories, about a cunning spider who, although no saint himself, reveals weaknesses in human nature.

One woman who made an impact on the English through use of Creole was the black nanny of a white American girl, who in adulthood studied at the Slade School of Art and became an occultist, poet and performer.

A highly intelligent girl, she became fluent in the native Jamaican language through her servant.

In adulthood, she fashioned a Jamaican identity for herself in early twentieth century London, claiming her father, who died when she was very young, was Jamaican.

Her name was Pamela Colman-Smith.

She captivated the world-famous *Swallows and Amazons* author Arthur Ransome, who wrote about this vibrant and ebullient young woman in his celebrated book *Bohemia in London*.

They met just before World War I and the first time he encountered her she treated him to the 'It' drink of the day, Opal hush, a mixture of claret and lemonade, before launching into a song,

'O the goo goo bird is a giddy bird,

No other is so gay.

O the goo goo bird is a merry bird,

Her zingeth all day...."

She went on to tell Anancy stories, another about a singing turtle, then the story of Chim Chim the little bird and also the Obeah Woman, whom we can find a reference to in a song by Nina Simone.

Ransome relates how she helped the English to understand Creole with the aid of wooden toys she made herself.

He writes,

P64 *Bohemia in London,*

To hear her was to be carried back to the primitive days of storytelling, and to understand a little, how it was that the stories of the old minstrels were handed on from man to man with so little change on the way.

Ransome was a great advocate of preserving dialect and languages of minority communities or language that is marginalised by any society, shown by his befriending the Gypsy community of Millom to the extent of learning their language.

Significantly, he refers to Pamela Colman-Smith as Gypsy in his account of her.

Another woman who was instrumental in promoting the Creole language in the twentieth and twenty-first century, up to her death in 2006 was Louise Bennett, popularly known as Miss Lou.

Born in Kingston in 1919, she learned Creole songs, legends, folk customs, proverbs and stories from her grandmother.

A poet, actor, researcher and teacher, she fought to gain international recognition and respect for the Creole language.

During her educational years in Jamaica, she became aware of opposition to use of Creole by the colonial authorities and sensed their attitude was that the songs, stories and verses she learned from her grandmother,

P26, Morris,

"ought to be despised and deplored as coming from the offspring of slaves who were illiterate, uncultured and downright stupid."

It was clear to her that the colonial authorities felt that the native Jamaicans of colour should cultivate only European art and she was aware of her African heritage, which deserved respect, being undermined.

Those who knew her said she faced prejudice with humour and humility.

She started reversing this as a teenager, when she wrote her first poem in Creole, identifying with the market women, who had to carry baskets and sit on the back of buses. These women resented it when other people tried to take the back seats and expressed this in her poem,

> *On a Tramcar*.
> 'Pread yuhself deh Liza
> Dress 'oman da look sey,
> She se' de li space side a we
> An want foace herself een deh.'

> *Translation*
> Spread yourself there, Liza
> A dressed up woman looks as though
> She sees the little space beside us
> and wants to force herself in there.

p8 *Miss Lou Louise Bennett and Jamaican Culture*, Mervyn Morris

During her lifetime, Louise Bennett gained a British Council scholarship to RADA, a scholarship to study folklore in West

Indian territories, had her own radio shows, acted in pantomimes, published and performed her own poetry in England, Jamaica and America, published Anancy stories, (like Pamela Colman-Smith), Jamaican songs, verses, recipes and folklore, gained an MBE for her services to Jamaican literature and theatre, became Ambassador and Special Envoy for Jamaica and took part in the film *Club Paradise* with Robin Williams and Peter O'Toole.

Her influence endures in Jamaica today.

Children in Jamaica like her, are bi-lingual, learning Creole in addition to Standard English, in which she was fluent.

Louise Bennett challenged opposition to Creole and won. Her desire to preserve Creole dialect had its roots in preserving the spirit and soul of another country and asserting what was essentially the foundation of her island race, preserving what came from African culture.

The English-speaking literary establishment admired her.

Miss Bennet did not reject Standard English, now Received Pronunciation, just also promoted her native tongue.

It is appropriate to end this essay with a quote from the admirable and eminently sensible Miss Bennett.

Perhaps the Jamaican nanny of Pamela Colman Smith would have echoed her sentiments exactly in Ms Bennet's statement,

"I think I speak for all Jamaica. I can't feel that I belong to any class or that I write for any class."

Richard Abbot

I am a long-term resident of Tottenham in Haringey. In fact, I was born here, though I grew up in Toronto. I found myself back here, in a sense in a search for my ancestors, and now realise I am rather closer to joining them than perhaps understanding them.

Sound and vision are motifs that enliven my practice, which has mostly been on the page though recently on stage. I am not a musician, but grow inspired by music, from 'ancient music', to ancient music origins in Mesopotamia, and recently Arabic Maqam. This interest also encompasses new and experimental music and I have recently connected with practitioners using visual musical scores, sharing an interest in the overlap of sound and colour. I have a background in psychology of language, interspersing my practice experimentally (in a soft sense introspectively) with the influence of 'wetware' on the way creativity conceals and reveals itself.

What I really meant, when I said, 'fine, no problem', from a letter never sent to ...

Stephen, people move on – the living and the
      dead.
They bring you, 'bitter news to hear, and bitter
      tears to shed'
And love, – doesn't die itself,
But it packs its things and relocates to a place in
      the past.
You are occupied, I guess, with tasks,
Maybe burdens, and other people,
And I understand, but I won't write you again.
I have a letter box in the door and it's open.
There won't be a little dog, haunching, waiting
For the daily drop of post,
Because that is Hope and Hope was crated
And U-Hauled by Love when she moved west.
But the hole in the door won't seal up either,
Not like that ear-piercing I got downtown
In the wig department at Eaton's.
Oh, who remembers us hardly grown?
So, if you're passing, or think of me again for any
      reason,
There's still an opening in my door,
And sometimes the gentle wind lilts through,
And I think of you as I would miss the colour
      yellow.

If you get asked for a recipe to cook rice.

To measure rice grains – per person:
You can't acquire this kind of cup for coin
ours was (bent and worn)
the pillar box-red plastic child's cup,
abandoned finally, maybe with scorn
(maybe mine?)

To pick over rice - (today):
is not required.
except to honour those who threshed the hand
    harvest in the sun,
on the frond-swept, stamped earth, the inden-
    tured ancestors
(maybe ours?).

To measure rice water – per pot:
This is not metric or imperial -
just a finger knuckle length above the rice line
(maybe my grandmother's)

To cook rice – directions:
These are the instructions to build a way of life,
from failing at the first attempt,
under the side eye of your mother-in-law,
and by process of elimination
day by month by year, repeating pot – hob –
    smell – sound -
and lastly feel.

To eat rice – by serving:
... your time at the long table of illiterate deep
     history,
by sensing, from hunger to belonging,
the comfort of sustenance
At Auntie's table:
Ole Year's Night,
fat, translucent and separate,
always a bit cool
(and abundant).
In Grannie's kitchen:
on the dot of noon,
hot and small grained, in clumps, Chinese style
(and abundant).
At home:
at the workday's conclusion, all of ours in shifts,
at mechanical speed,
opaque white and each grain end steamed open
     to an arabesque,
bland (and abundant).

These hands' signatures,
repose archaic now
(can you remember how cooking is relation?).
At checkout here, the sack of rice grains rattles
Like the click of lacquered chopsticks,
placing bones in silken cradles
at the feast of cremation.

An Un.even.tide Line

Listen, the rhythm deletes her own,
her siren lace
unfurled on shores to be withdrawn
again to silence.

Engines of ocean and moon
knot and untie
the marginal calligraphy
of weed, shell, bone.

By Dover the sea is calm tonight
where gill and lung
gasped in the Silurian,
and now small boats

of the Anthropocene wash up bands
of carrion.
Ocean is a mother of the first eons
who eats her own.

Three musical scores for three voices: *The performers are largely*
free to choose the auditory output from these simple rules, also the
instrumentation (with maybe ideally a triple harp and depending
on budget a Merce Cunningham-style dancer).

1.Imperative.
Begin the rhythm of green, being a thrumming.

But refuse Red. Banish that harsh foreboding,
kindling like flames licking up a kettle
drum.
Now have blue do a polyrhythmic follow
through. Enact this as a brief improvised
dance over the previous rhythmic ground.

2.Indicative.
A background timbre is desirable here of high
romantic purpose (but panic is uncalled for).
This is skilfully illustrated for example in
Penelope Fitzgerald's short historical novel,
'The Blue Flower'. The present however is a
variation where the lovers unite at the end,
instead of dying significantly.
Novalis' writing desk is situated by an open
window, overlooking an incongruous void,
perhaps some petrified body of water, and
this is perceived mostly by its absence of
sound, an anechoic auditory sign, a breath
held.
There is something like a hum of resentment in
the room, like a carpet stretched to a drum-
head over the floorboards, like a linen toile
tacked taut over wall battens and sound-
dampening.
Trivial chance at the podium raises the baton for
the downbeat. The writer is seated at the first
desk.
'Herzallerliebste' carries the tympany, maybe the
dustpan andante pensativa, and engages the
brush a la sonnambula.

*Now furiously at this motif the quill scratches
presto as Novalis transcribes from the palette
of ambient sound. This presently decom-
pounds into all the harshness and soft
longing whispering through his puzzled and
thwarted minds. By and by the poet almost
attains a peculiar and sublime achievement,
which is the aim of writing lucidly, but with
vivid obscurity. He deploys shyly on the
page. All those moot spaces and dark holes
weird feral thoughts stray through, where
unassimilated feelings seek a longed-for
shelter offer up for once a momentary respite
from wandering exile.*
This continuo *resounds* sostenuto *until the final
arpeggiated chord, eg.:*
A random freight cart rumble,
*A hoarse shriek from children at play, whose
home is in the street,*
A gap in the stream of time.
*Ah, and poetry still fails, diffidently, as it is
meant to do – wheezing and purple on the
white sheets.*

3.Subjunctive.
*You may imagine a chasm, apprehended just by
sound, as it might be 'seen' by blind bats. It
were easier perhaps to picture hearing in
your mind's ear the dumb reverberation of a
vast, still void – as different as that may be
from the muffled deafness you may imagine
in a close and solitary cell. May your hearing*

*encounter rather all the clear space latent
within the aerial blue. May this concordance
resound, may it hold open this sonic harbour,
diminuendo, till all variations of its interpretation be understood.*

Alana Beth Davies
FROM OUR NEIGHBOURS

I am Welsh. I will admit that I was not born in Wales, and that's because my parents were working in England for a few years. But as my mother used to say, 'Just because you're born in an allotment, it doesn't make you a cabbage.' I have lived in Wales since the age of three, and I am most definitely Welsh.

However, the fact that I was born in Walton-on-Thames has always been important to me, and something of which I am equally proud.

Every place I have lived has had a huge influence on me, whether a week living in a caravan when we would otherwise have been homeless, the 'back-to-nature' seven years in a run-down cottage on the side of a mountain in the Swansea Valley, or my twenty-years-plus in the little seaside town where I ended up running a B&B.

And now I'm living in Swansea, and I feel I have come home. Although only a resident here for under three years, I have strong family links, and I am welcomed and embraced in a Welsh cwtch, metaphorical or otherwise, by everyone I encounter.

In other news - I am now retired, having spent my working life in the world of education and politics, with a certain amount of entrepreneurship thrown in. I am a mother of five daughters, a grandmother and now a great-grandmother, and I recently achieved a Distinction for my MA in Creative Writing from the University of Wales Trinity St David, of which I am inordinately proud. I don't think I could have done this anywhere else!

Coming Home by Alana Beth Davies

The first morning in my new home. I'm not known here. I look around at the usual chaos that comes with moving house, at the labelled boxes where removal men left them. I hadn't intended to explore so soon, but black coffee has never appealed. So I close my front door behind me and check I have my keys and my phone, and enough cash to pay for a carton of milk, and I take in my surroundings. I'm a *Wedi Dod,* or so it would seem. But I don't feel like a newcomer, an in-comer.

Yesterday, ahead of the pantechnicon, my little car and I arrived in our new home, in a city, with its university, its leisure centre, with its familiar names - Mumbles, Cwmdonkin Park, The Brangwyn Hall. And I drove, with my last almost-forgotten bits and pieces, up Christina Street. My mother had pronounced it Chris-TYN-a Street, as do all Swansea people. Here, the first of the many hills en route to my new house. A good handbrake was essential, as I wait for the lights to turn green at the top of the hill, taking their time, allowing me to note the names of solicitors and funeral directors on the shop fronts, wondering which I'll need first.

When I decided to move out of my comfort zone, the place I'd lived for sixty years, I chose Swansea. For so many reasons. I spent childhood summers with my grandmother here, but this time it's no holiday. This time it's to make a new home. Now my chicks have flown the nest, all happily settled, some further away than others; and me, newly widowed, in search of new scenes, new hobbies, away from small-town familiarity. It's time.

Now, high on my six steps, I see the tops of grey boulders running the length of the street, each one washed and polished by the early sun. No longer a runway for tricky night-time visitors, their barks silenced now, their chasing and tail-swishing the finale of their evening performance, a show that surprised me as I'd lain in my newly-assembled bed. Others take over now, black and lean or striped and fat, pretending to be wild things, catching the echo of last night's party, but running to the call of food and sleep and stroking.

Over the wall, the Dyfatti flats dominate, vestiges of sixties slum clearances, vertical villages that didn't quite live up to the sixties' ideal or the dream of a newly-wed aunt. Pretty, coiffed, I picture her in her costume - always a costume, never a suit then - as she took me to the pictures in town. I was so in awe of her! I was eleven, she had married my uncle and she brought a lightness to my gran's staid terraced house when they both moved in. I wonder if all their changes had been popular with Gran? The inside, upstairs bathroom, no doubt! The sixties wallpaper, maybe not so much. The young couple had the front bedroom, a wide Ercol dressing table in the window, makeup and lotions and a toy soldier on top. My uncle would play 'Rose, Rose, I love you' on the old gramophone in the parlour. I remember the excitement when they heard they'd been offered one of those flats. They're safe in a bungalow now, other side of town, as close to the earth as they can get before they're consigned to it.

Tall and rigid though the flats are, these dated over-sized apartment blocks, with their ranks of blind eyes, can't hide the scene all around them, sheltering in the arms of the mountains and the bay. The city lays out its stall far below me, undiminished by impressive newbuilds, still a market place for new and old, bric-a-brac and shiny gadgets; soundless cranes and trains move in a well-rehearsed dance.

Mirages of puked fumes from Port Talbot lose their sulphur before they reach me. And further away, on the hills of St Thomas and Foxhole Road, rows of Lowry terraces, tier upon tier, slap me with a memory so vivid, of Peter Sellers in 'Only Two Can Play', a film that put Swansea on the world map. My grandson lives there, I remind myself, surprised again at the nearness of family.

And still I stand here, taking in the displays all around me. There's no rush. I jingle the new set of keys in my pocket. I have all the time in the world, and I want to get my bearings.

To my right, my daughter's house. The road rises, a little closer to the houses there, so she has only four steps to reach her door. Further along, I see the houses climb so high they're on a different road, dug into the mountain behind, like a cane sprouting from a rose bush - and somewhere up there was my mother's first home. Too far for me to see now, but I know it's there. A century of family, come together again by venture or by fate, drawn to this 'ugly lovely town', to this street where my grandmother walked, a young mother, with a baby wrapped Welsh-fashion, close and cwtched. All the times I visited her, climbed into her mountain of a bed, rearranged the crocheted doilies and the green glass jars, wondered at the mantle dogs and poked naughty fingers into the mangle rollers, I never thought to ask her – what was it like when you were young, Gran? Where did you live? What did you do?

A nod and a smile to the past, and I walk down my steps at last, turning left into unfamiliar territory. The pavement is a patchwork of tarmac, a criss-cross of layers, new upon old, a crazy hopscotch game without chalk, covering pipes and wires, lives and stories. The road drops down again, but the houses stay horizontal. Here there are twelve steps or more, front doors getting further away from me.

Now there's a bush straggling across the pavement so I have to walk into the road. Its soft spikes are pale, out of place in winter. A faint sweet scent of babies and night-time relaxation, but only if I put my head close. I can hear a laughing gurgle from inside the house, a low growling hoover, busy, busy.

The street comes to an end, at least for traffic, as neat bollards block the way. But first, I pass a street on my left, Baptist Well Place. What a story there must be to that name! Ancient immersions, sermons with *hwyl*, fights with the Methodists ... was that the real cause of the Mayhill riot? I smile at the irreverent thought, non-conformist guilt pecking at my shoulder. A handrail - grey, unpainted, icy to the touch - goes all the way to the top of this hill. I'm wary of steep walks, but I drag myself up, hand over hand. More bollards here, big ones this time, concrete. No car will get through these! But not placed there soon enough. Cars were set alight by rampaging crusaders, pushed to crash at the seat of the hill. A riot seen by millions; a revolt caused by misinformation exaggerated beyond logic - fake news delivered to our doorsteps.

This isn't how we want to see Swansea on the ten o'clock news. See? It happened before I arrived here, but I'm proprietorial already! I turn and look back, proud of the trek I've made. I feel like a mountain goat now, and I sing *Gafr Wen* under my breath. I can see the city and the bay and the beacons arranged before me, and I walk down the hill, holding on to the handrail again.

Through the neat bollards, I walk into another street. To

one side, a drop to Carmarthen Road, always the artery of the town to me, the path of an annual trip to Fforestfach and a week's holiday alone with Gran. To the other, the Victorian terraced houses continue, getting further and further from the road below as the ground dips once more, and the steps have to reach up even further to the doors. Twenty steps, thirty, forty ... The gardens are high above me: small, square, covered in grass. They slope away from their bay windows, looking as if they're ready to slip and slide off at any moment and tumble to the ground below, but still they stick to the earth under them, like the icing on a child's uneven birthday cake I once made: bright green, with lollipops for trees.

Then suddenly these high, climbing houses end, and a string of 1930s terraces appear, continuing the row, on the flat now, their front doors opening straight onto the pavement. How did that happen? It puzzles me, and I can't get an answer in my head. I file it away, to be examined later. So many thoughts already stored, so many questions about my journey to this town.

The road seems endless, deserted except for a guard-cat lounging in front of a door, feigning sleep. Have I followed the route I was given? Is this the way? Then - whiffs of vinegar and hot oils and spices meet me before I turn a corner and see two shops: one with a window advertising everything from kitchen cleaner to corn flakes, the other oozing tempting aromas of cod and chips, hot Jalfrezi, battered sausages. A group of men and women stand outside, talking, features covered for religious or Covid reasons. A tableau of the city's melting pot. They turn when they see me, nod, raise a hand. I smile, and they smile too. I push the 'open all hours' door and hear its clanging bell; I squeeze my way through the narrow aisles until I find the milk, and take it to the counter. More smiles, thank yous, and goodbyes.

I'll find a new way back, along the main road first, comfortable, back into recognised territory. I see the foot bridges in front of me, and a myriad of streets. I turn into another, unfamiliar road. Heading in the right direction, surely? I choose a path, a walkway, past some tangled brambles spilling onto the tarmac in front of me. I don't know where it will lead, but I'm not worried. I've got my phone, and my daughter's not far away. I see some steps ahead, steep ones, leading to who knows where, but I feel brave now, and I start climbing. Halfway up, I turn and look at the view behind me. Is that Pen-y-Fan I can see? Away in the distance, pale blue and misty? I turn again and finish my ascent, and - I'm back on Seaview Terrace, next to the neat bollards at the end of my street. MY street. The road is empty save for a cat and a recycling bag. And I'm home.

David Turnbull

David Turnbull was born in Edinburgh but has spent most of his adult life in South East London. A former chef, he was until recently, National Officer for Unite the Union's hospitality membership. He is currently designing walking tours based in Lambeth with a sci-fi, horror and fantasy theme.

He is a member of the Clockhouse London group of genre writers. He has had numerous short stories published in magazines and anthologies. His stories have also been featured at Liars League London events and read at other live events such as Solstice Shorts and Virtual Futures. His near future dystopian novella HUSks is currently on release and can be found at www.indienovella.co.uk.

His collection of genre stories of 100 words or less 'One Hundred Predictions' is available from Fiction4All, as is his children's fantasy novel 'The Dragon Breath Chronicles'.

Extract from *The Hurdy Gurdy Man*

Don't Sleep in the Subway Darling

"Life sure has a shitty way of slapping you right across the face."
That was about all Kath Dunn had to say about the situation she found herself in. Choking back her tears she wiped rainwater away from her face with the dirty sleeve of her pink anorak. With less than a month to go till her nineteenth birthday she was homeless and sleeping rough in subways and shop doorways.

She'd come to London with high hopes that she'd find herself a job as a secretary, or maybe a receptionist, for a record company. She'd rent a little flat in St John's Wood and deck it out with designer gear. She'd buy chic clothes from trendy boutiques on Carnaby Street and would frequent the bars and clubs on the Kings Road, rubbing shoulders with the likes of Jean Shrimpton and Stevie Marriott.

Back in her hometown near Berwick upon Tweed she'd indulged herself in vivid daydreams of the sophisticated metropolitan lifestyle that she unwaveringly believed awaited her. These daydreams had brought smiles to her face and such a deep, aching longing to her heart that she'd convinced herself that all she had to do was act to make them come true. She knew now, to her detriment, that those were just immature pipe dreams.

The reality had turned out to be a living nightmare.

She'd rapidly become destitute and without a roof over her head. Someone had stolen her luggage. All she had left was her blouse and her flared jeans, her pink, hooded anorak, and a pair of scuffed ankle boots. Her money was spent. She rummaged in the bins behind restaurants for scraps to eat. Her eyes were raw and red from all the weeping she'd done.

Now she sat on a flattened piece of cardboard on the cold concrete steps in front of the Eros statue in Piccadilly. The headlines in the Evening Standard newspaper she'd spread over the cardboard read 'A Serious Crime every 25 seconds.' Knowing what she now knew of London Kath could easily believe that to be the case. The date of the edition was Wednesday 9th August 1969. Kath had lost track of time. She wasn't sure if this was today's date, or the previous day, maybe even the day before. She wondered what it might be like to know once more with absolute certainty the day of the week, the exact minute and hour of the day.

The light afternoon drizzle was slowly soaking through her anorak. Her filthy hand was outstretched and starting to feel numb. She was hoping that one of the tourists milling around in pack-a-mac plastic rain capes might deem to drop a coin or two into it. Beneath the hood of the anorak her ginger hair felt grimy, caked with the exhaust fumes of red buses and black taxis, greasy from the dirt on the pavements she'd been sleeping on. A few weeks back, before her impetuous decision to jump on a train, she'd had it cut in a short bob like Twiggy. She thought it was boss. Now it was growing out at all angles, like the straw on a scarecrow's turnip head.

Kath thought that if she could get enough money to buy herself a cheap sandwich that would be a start. A full stomach might help her to think straight. If she could somehow work out the knack of this begging lark she might be able, in a week or so, to squirrel enough money away to buy a train ticket and go back home with her head bowed. In her mind her parents were distraught, like the ones in that Beatles song about the girl who was leaving home.

But it was like she'd become invisible. The tourists crossing the road to the little concrete island were paying her no attention. She was a blot on their landscape. An inconvenience. Something that was getting in the way of them taking a holiday snap of the statue on their cameras. She thought maybe she'd have been better off parking herself at the entrance to the tube station.

The first time she'd seen Piccadilly Circus it had been nighttime. The gigantic neon hoardings. Famous names. Coca Cola, and Cinzano, and Wrigley's Chewing Gum, and Players Cigarettes. All lit up, beaming bright reds and blues and yellows. For a girl from a little seaside town, it was a jaw dropping sight. She'd felt like Dorothy, swept up in the twister, and transported from the dull monochrome of Kansas to vivid technicolour of the merry old Land of Oz.

That momentary elation was well and truly gone now. The hoarding looked sad and dismal in the slow, persistent day time drizzle. The pavements seemed depressingly grey, and the stark opposite of a yellow brick road. The statue was horribly tainted in dirty white pigeon guano. And in another somewhat depressing parallel with the movie, she was plagued by the nagging thought that there really was no place like home.

She knew if she went back her mother would go on the gin and start screaming and yelling, while her father would sit passively in his armchair, dressed in his postman's uniform, scowling behind his newspaper, and giving her the silent treatment. It would be exactly as it had been before her exasperation with the monotonous predictability of it all caused her impetuous departure. But at least she'd be safe. At night she'd have a warm bed and she'd buy a new transistor radio to keep beneath her pillow, tuned in to Radio Caroline.

She missed her transistor. It was a Sanyo, with pink leather casing wrapped around it and a big dial to show the frequencies. It was her prize possession. She'd bought it with her wages from Woolworths. By the time her valise had been stolen, the batteries were well and truly flat, and it was wrapped in a sock to protect it from being damaged. She'd cried for its loss. Like it was a beloved pet cat that had gone missing. That night in an underpass, plastic bags wrapped round her feet to keep them warm, she imagined she was listening to Radio Caroline. It wasn't so hard to do. She knew hundreds of songs and their lyrics.

The drizzle continued unabated. Tourists passed her by, snapping shots of Eros up on his tall plinth with his little pigeon fowled bow and arrow. The engines of the cars and buses hummed as they circled the roundabout on which the statue sat. She could taste the diesel of their exhaust fumes in her mouth. Her outstretched hand remained depressingly empty. Mentally she tuned out of the moment and into the comfort of her imaginary radio station.

She stuck her index finger into her right ear and imagined it was the earpiece that came with the transistor. *Three One Nine – Radio Caroline,* went the jingle. The DJ on this occasion was Tommy Vance. *"Now here's The McCoys with Hang on Sloopy,"* he said.

The song played inside her head as if she was truly hearing it. She knew all the lyrics. She could hear the guitars and feel the beat of the drums. She began slapping her hand against her damp thigh and tapping her foot against the stairs as she joined in with the chorus. People passing by might think she'd gone nuts, but she didn't mind. She lost herself in the fantasy.

C-A-R-O-L-I-N-E, went the jingle, *Caroline, Caroline, Caroline.*

Now Tommy introduced *Have I the Right* by the Honeycombs and her foot tapped even louder to the pounding beat of Honey Lantree's drumming. But when the chorus kicked in and they sang about coming right back where you belong, she started to get that homesick feeling all over again.

And now it was if it was her subconscious was in control rather than her imagination.

Going back in time on the sounds of the nation, came the next jingle, *it's the Caroline flashback.*

And the song that followed was Buddy Holly, Raining in My Heart. And as Buddy sang plaintively about misery piling up on misery another warm teardrop rolled down her cold cheek. In that moment a shadow fell over her. She became aware that someone was standing there.

"Could I get you something to eat?" The voice sounded deep and well rounded. Like someone with a public-school education. Someone wealthy. Maybe someone with the benevolent trait that some rich people were reputedly keen to affect.

She looked up, squinting against the drizzle that coated her face. He wasn't what she expected. He looked like a middle-aged hippy. Long hair, down to his shoulders, the grey mixed in with the wiry black strands giving his beard a slightly blue tinge. He wore a yellow kaftan, embroidered in flowery patterns, and faded bell bottom jeans that were frayed at the hems. Leather sandals on his feet, exposing thin, hairy toes. He had multi coloured love beads around his neck and his wrists. His nose had a ruddy hue to it. On his head he wore a red beret, tilted at an angle.

"Are you hungry, my dear?" he asked.

Kath didn't know what to say. Other than the police telling her to move along, and shop keepers yelling at her to bugger off when they tried to open in the morning, she hadn't had a single proper conversation with anyone in the ten days since she stepped off the train at Kings Cross. It almost felt as if her tongue was glued to the roof of her mouth.

"There's a café just across the road, a little way along Shaftesbury Avenue," he said. "Come on. My treat."

She looked into his eyes. Hadn't someone once said the eyes were the key to the soul? These eyes were green and looked kindly. Within them she could see little jagged forks of blue vein, like cracks in porcelain, spreading across the whites. The pink bridge of his nose was similarly veined. There was a warmth in the way he looked at her. It was kind of hypnotic. She felt the tension ease from her shoulders, and found herself surprisingly relaxed, a little drowsy even.

He turned and beckoned with shaggy head for her to follow. "Come on."

Kath rose cautiously to her feet. Despite the weather the streets were busy. What harm could it do to follow him to the café? There was no immediate risk that she could see. Her stomach rumbled, urging her to stop her procrastination. Maybe she could explain her situation to him? Tell him that if he lent her the money for a train ticket her father would send back a postal order for the amount as soon as she got home.

A few steps behind him she followed when he crossed the road through a gap in the traffic. He wove through the crowds, occasionally looking back over his shoulder to check if she was following. Kath walked cautiously, watching for his red beret, hood up, shoulders hunched.

The windows of the café were steamed up from the rain. He showed her to a table and asked her to sit down while he went and fetched her something. Almost in a daze Kath pulled down her hood. It felt so good to sit on a chair that wasn't the splintery wooden slats of a park bench. The sounds of the café infused her. The hum of chatter from the other customers. The clink and clatter of cutlery and crockery. The raw, hollow rasping of the cappuccino machine.

A boy with mousy brown, feather cut hair resting on the shoulders of a brushed denim jacket dropped a coin into the jukebox. The arm whirred. She heard the scratch of the needle and knew immediately from the opening chords he'd chosen *Ha Ha said the Clown* by Manfred Mann. He winked at her as he returned to the table where his friends sat. She blushed, realising she was no longer invisible. She lost herself in the music, tapping her fingers on the Formica tabletop.

Her benefactor came back with a steaming cup of tea and fatty slices of lush, pink bacon inside a crispy bread roll. He smiled. Between his moustache and beard his teeth were yellow and uneven. "I do hope you are not vegetarian," he said in his clipped, posh accent. "So many girls are these days. I should have asked."

By way of reply Kath picked up the bacon roll and took a huge bite. As she chewed a massive grin curved on her lips. Who'd have thought that simple hot food could ever taste this delicious? She savoured the salty residue that lingered in her mouth when she swallowed down the bacon.

Once she'd spooned some sugar into the tea, she picked up the cup, blew on it and took a sip. Across the table the kindly hippy sat with one hand resting on top of the other, observing her intently. As she'd first noted he was older than might be expected from his dress and appearance. If she were to hazard a guess, she'd say he was mid-forties. Not that much younger than her father.

"They call me the Hurdy Gurdy Man," he said. "Hurdy for short."

Kath paused with the bacon roll held up to her mouth for a second bite.

"Like in that song by Donovan?" she asked, finally finding her voice.

"Or the earlier one by Schubert," he replied, losing her completely.

"Who calls you that?" she asked and took her bite of the roll.

He smiled beneath his beard and his crow's feet creased at the sides of his eyes. "My girls."

"Girls?" asked Kath with her mouth full. "Your daughters?"

"I have a big house up on Hampstead Heath," he explained. "Too big for me. I've turned it into a kind of hostel for homeless girls. All girls. No boys. They have the run of the place. Except my private quarters, which always remain locked at all times."

Kath swallowed down her second bite of the bacon roll and took another sip of tea.

"What's your name?" he asked her.

"Katherine," she replied. "But I prefer Kath."

"Well, Kath," said the Hurdy Gurdy Man. "There's a vacancy in my big old house. Things didn't work out with one of my girls. Room for a little one, as the saying goes. How do you feel about taking a look?"

"I don't have any money," she warned him. "Not so much as a penny to my name."

"That's fine," he said. "As long as my girls stick to my rules, I don't charge them a single penny."

Kath found herself caught again by the reassuring warmth of his green eyes. Again, she felt herself relaxing, embraced by an odd drowsiness. A hostel would be good. Dry and warm until she raised enough money for her train. Or until she plucked up the courage to ask him for a loan.

"What do you say?" he asked. "Finish up. We'll go and take a look. My motor scooter is parked not far from here. You can ride pillion. We'll be there in no time. If you're not comfortable with what you see, you can leave. No obligations. No questions asked."

Kath stuffed the last of the bacon roll into her mouth, unable to break away from the verdant allure of his green eyes. Before she knew it, she had her hood up again and was trotting behind him, following the red beret through the narrow streets of Soho. He led her between the bustling market stalls to a little street called Duck Lane, where his scooter was parked.

The scooter was resting by the curb on an outstretched leg-stand. Kath thought it looked fab. It had red bodywork, to match his beret. White mudguards to the front and back. Silver handlebars, a single headlamp, a flat platform for the rider's feet and a twin leather seat so that a second person could ride pillion.

"It's an Excelsior Monarch," said the Hurdy Gurdy Man, as if he expected her to be impressed by the revelation. "British made. Glass fibre. None of that Italian nonsense all the mods seem to go gaga over."

He reached up to adjust his red beret and set it at a jaunty angle on his head, wiry graying hair hanging down to his shoulders on either side. With his beard, he looked a bit like the depiction of Che Guevara she'd been seeing a lot on T-shirts kids were wearing that summer.

Kath felt utterly discombobulated. She could hear the calls of the stall holders nearby in Berwick Street market, and the hum of traffic on Charing Cross Road. But they were like distant echoes in a dream. Unreal and beyond reach. Kath tried to orient herself, turning her head slightly upwards to catch the rain. Then, somehow, she didn't quite understand how it had happened, she'd been bundled onto the back of the scooter.

She had ridden pillion before. Her cousin was a tonne-up boy. He had a Norton. Way more powerful than this little thing.

She bunched her fists into the damp material of the Hurdy Gurdy Man's kaftan. The engine puttered like a lawnmower. And then they were off, zipping up toward Tottenham Court Road.

Her mind was yelling – *What the hell do you think you're doing? You've only just met him. You don't even know his real name.* But the wind blew back the pink hood of her anorak, and when the rain, a little heavier now, stabbed pinpricks against her forehead, her trepidation became lost in the wild elation of the ride.

Hackney, Haringey and our Neighbours

Damien Mosley

Hello!

My name is Damien. You've already heard from me twice already so I'll keep this relatively brief. When anyone asks me to write anything about myself the first thing I do is reach for the copy and paste keys and copy some blurb I may have written a year ago so as not to directly answer the question. That's because it feels weird to talk about myself and maybe, as I said in the introduction, part of that is because I've spent so long not really knowing who I am.

Today though I'd like to say three things. I love books, I love writing, and I love Newington Green and my little axis of North London. And I learned all this probably aged 38.

What draws me to Newington Green is I always have a place to sit. Be it at Belle Epoch, the café on the north of the Green, or on the Green itself and the bench overlooking Mary and her swirls of silver. I've been living in London over 20 years but for the first 15 I never had a place where I could go and just sit, so would spend a lot of my time wandering, perhaps getting a hot drink from Starbucks and doing lengths of Liverpool Road and visiting the posh areas of Barnsbury and Canonbury. There was something about Canonbury Square that felt too quiet to ever sit for long. Highbury Fields would fill me with dread with all its noise and good-looking young people on a hot sunny day – people who were my age at the time – who had these big circles of friends and were enjoying these social media friendly lives. I didn't know the phrase imposter syndrome then so I just felt sad. And angry. I didn't belong and I didn't know why I felt that way.

Maybe it's getting older you realise you don't have to be so angry all the time. No one has a picture-perfect life but you don't need to be jealous of those who do. Some would say Stoke Newington is posh and picture-perfect and intimidating, but at Newington Green I seemed to find somewhere that the me aged 38 suddenly felt quite comfortable. It had a no thrills chip shop which felt acceptable to buy dinner-for-one and spend under a fiver. The coffee shop called Belle Epoch had a backroom which didn't look like it was trying to be hipster, or trendy, or anything else which would trigger my imposter syndrome. There was always a table free for me and usually around me were local residents having a chat and a slice of cake. Soon the lady who ran it would recognise me and ask how I was every time I went in, even noticing when I had not been back for a while. This may not sound revolutionary, but to me it meant something. And on the Green, it didn't feel like Highbury Fields. There was a busyness about it with parents taking their kids to the playground, people my age and older having their coffees to sit outside, buses lining up just over the road making it feel less of an isolated oasis but something firmly in the present, which I strangely liked. I remember the first time sitting on my bench and suddenly realising I didn't have to leave, to wander. I allowed myself to sit, listen to some music and for the first time just be me.

Extract from *Relationship on the Green*

We can't seem to get it right. Or I can't. The worst thing is that we don't even fight or have stand up arguments. Instead it's the little things, a bit like why Polly and I are a couple in the first place, now conspiring against us. Or against me, as at times I'm not sure if she sees me as her boyfriend or that guy she shares a flat with and does everything humanly possible to piss her off.

I had two choices that day. Clean the flat from top to bottom, put everything away from the joint living spaces, and make Polly feel she is returning to somewhere she can feel at home. With someone who listens and respects her space. Or get my hair cut.

The minute I sat down in the leather salon chair I knew it was another mistake.

'Dan? How's it going?' said Ali, his New Zealand accent memorable. He'd cut my hair the last time. Is it weird to suddenly feel reassured by seeing someone you'd met once three months ago? 'What are we having today?'

I'm sure for that split second, while I paused, he could see the look of fear in my eyes.

'Tidier? Maybe the same as last time?'

Ali's face went blank. Of course I remember the only person to cut my hair, but I cannot expect him to remember everyone who would have sat in his chair over those three months. Especially as I had to still wear a mask back then.

'Just shorter.' I grabbed a handful of my unwieldy dark hair. 'Nothing too fancy...'

I saw him smile. I think he now remembered the grown man who still got into a bit of sulk at having his hair cut.

Coming up the stairs of that small salon, after having my hair washed for me – something that also felt alien – and being sat back down, I have to say, it was a rather nice place to get your hair cut. Peering in from outside it had looked more like a florist, with a forest of green plants taking up the window, perhaps brought it deliberately to give it that soothing effect. There was even a 50s style SMEG fridge and a note saying it was stocked *with refreshments from our local neighbours at Yield N16*. It made me smile. In my heart of hearts, I'm not the type of person who despises gentrification completely. I like nice coffee and quiet peaceful tidy-looking places where I can blend into. Hence why I'm in a salon rather than a more manly barbers. But, admittedly, I also get into a cold sweat at paying more than a tenner for a haircut and my sense of imposter syndrome at being somewhere... *hip?*... is pretty obvious, largely from my use of the word *hip*. Ali put a black cape around me.

'Not tempted to grow it out a bit longer? You've definitely got something Beatles-esque going on.'

'The Brown George Harrison.' I don't know why I said it, but Ali smiled. Last time I was in the salon he told me he had been in London two years, originally from Auckland, but his parents were Malaysian. Not being from the place you now call home had bonded us, as much as you can bond with someone a decade and a half younger than you, infinitely more stylish by his long, perfectly positioned, spikey punk-rock hair and arm tattoos – whose idea of a wild night probably wasn't limited to drinking an Americano after five p.m. – and who you were also paying forty-five pounds to cut your hair. I hated being called Brown. No one used that phrase when I was younger and growing up somewhere 99% White, it was jarring when

168

someone pointed out that you were the other 1%. But it seemed to be the in-thing to say and perhaps rather than paying for a haircut, I was actually paying for someone to relate to.

'You sure you want me to take this much off?' Ali held out an inch and a half of hair. 'I could just thin it out a tad. Let you go proper Abbey Road.'

'My girlfriend prefers it short.'

'Ah, I get it,' he laughed. 'Trying to be the good boyfriend?' He began snipping away around my ears.

'You guys had just moved here, right?'

'Yes,' I felt this lift from when you find out someone has listened to you. 'My girlfriend is from Stokey and I used to work here, on Newington Green.'

'How you settling in?'

'Good! I guess.' I was right to get my hair cut. This was exactly what I needed before Polly got back. I'd had at least a couple of hours to get the flat 'Polly-tidy' rather than just 'Dan-tidy'. That forty-five quid was looking a bargain compared to what my mate Patrick charged as a therapist.

'It's quiet here. For London. On the Green.' I didn't know how to put it, but as Ali seemed to be the first person listening to me in what felt over a year, I felt slightly more at ease just to witter. 'It's not too posh either. Compared to other parts. I know it's technically Stoke Newington, but there's a really cheap chip shop next to an organic wine shop whose cheapest wine is sixteen quid a bottle. Council estates down the road from town houses. A nice café next door and a no thrills coffee truck on the Green, which everyone uses and isn't just full of...'

'White people?' Ali said, and then laughed. I smiled again.

'I was going to say *sunbathers*. Even in weather like this.' Ali laughed again.

'You're not all about catching rays, then? I thought that was strange, when I started working here. No one getting their tops off and lying out, but I guess it's more of local community feel around here. A village feel. Unique for London, I guess.'

He positioned my head so I was looking dead straight at the mirror.

'My partner's a bit like that too, about sunbathing. I love it. Going to London Fields, lying out and soaking in the heat. She prefers a coffee, book and a large sun hat. Prefers me with short hair too come to that, but you have to rebel now and again.'

'Your partner isn't thinking of leaving you.'

I smiled. Ali didn't. He just looked awkwardly away.

'So, about an inch and a half off, was it?'

We didn't chat much after that.

Elan Nitpick

The memory of place is one way we make our personal identity. The way that we experience places in the present is never usually the same experience as that had in the past, and they are almost always at odds. They can be familiar and comforting or be made strange and uncanny, not just for the pace of construction and change. This is what the North London boroughs of Enfield, Haringey, Hackney (and Waltham Forest) represent for me, and as a mixed blessing, I have lived or worked in all four.

An Extract from *Conversations, real and imagined, with my family*

Fortunately, people aren't responsible for who their parents are

"Disappointed people, clinging on to bottles
    When it comes it's so, so, disappointing."
    "Your dad liked them," my mum once told me after I asked

her with some twelve-year-old snottiness if she knew who Radiohead was. It was one of the first concretely factual statements I could pin on the person: Dad liked Radiohead. Quite possibly everything up until the release until 'Kid A' I could be sure he liked because my parents were still together then.

There are certain songs you remember through the material circumstances of listening: the time of the year, the visuals of the cover, and maybe how you came by it. Often the material circumstances play some guiding role back in the memory. Sometimes it has been the other way around.

I'm fairly sure that the memory of listening to 'Let Down' for the first time - on the greyest afternoon, streaks of rain on the windows, the depressing flat with its thousands of blemishes and few serious structural problems - is also due to the insistent quality of Thom's caterwauling.

It was nice to know that I could share something besides his malevolent laugh, which according to my mother was "100% him." Where was this jerk? What was he doing? Why did I feel, at the time and no longer, that I needed him to 'rescue' me?

In the great cherry-picking of quotes I thought were pertinent, Adam Philips writes things like: "If someone can satisfy us, they can frustrate us; and if someone can frustrate us we always believe they can satisfy us. And who frustrates us more than ourselves?"

Does that mean we need to find a partner that has the familiarity of childhood suffering? I haven't read much of those well-known psychoanalysts Philips, Klein, Winnicott (but I have had an online therapist, who had no allegiances to one theory or framework), but I've heard if we manage to turn rage into grief we will have made psychological progress.

I was angry, it was true, but I didn't understand that the nuclear family was old-hat, passé. Besides, what if you didn't have a positive male role model? You had the freedom to become whatever you wanted to be, I would later find out in retrospect. I was free to break the chain of the usual Cypriot male seducer that his father and his father's father had been.

But, as a teenager, it seemed that it became less and less likely as the years went by without contact that I had forgotten ever been begotten by a man that looked like me. Even if the picture I have sketched of the disappointed person doesn't account for great variation in human reaction, it has the great advantage of convincing angry people that they can exist in an otherwise different range of emotional habits. (Thanks too, to CBT). Moreover, it seems to be the case that the cynical are reactive in their way because they have been fixed in that circuit of habit, taking safety from the risky, familiar calumnies which create distrust and disappointment.

Yet while the person who is cautious and reserving their time and energy may still have the small victory of a certain degree of inviolability, there is an obvious disadvantage of doing little with their life that is not deemed low-risk. Notably, loving and caring sincerely and wholeheartedly.

Perhaps, then, to take an out-road from this discussion, one of the more relieving dues of non-existence is not having to want anymore. Not wanting to rewrite the past, not wanting better, more self-aware parents...Just as is written on my namesake Nikos Kazantzakis' resting stone, "to want nothing, to fear nothing," Instead, "to be free."

As the weight of all fatherless sons of the past, that yawning, yet restless energy which should be more properly considered as sublimated or misplaced anger impels me forward. For other reasons, several years on from when I wrote the first sentences in this paragraph, I've slowed down a bit now I think.

I said to my dad, "Why are you such a jerk? Where are

you?" Power, propriety, property, authority, knowledge: all those things I used to be not happy with myself for admiring in my early twenties – now I am ambivalent about them – and you have none of them, I thought.

I remember as a teenager when my dad came to visit me and mum, I was pressing my way through his photos on his Motorola flip-phone when I found a picture of his penis. Him laying down on his bed, in his Green Lanes bedsit, with his erect penis. I initially did not mention it to my mum, who was on the rare occasion in the room, giving my dad back his phone without saying anything.

I later shouted out, I think, "Dad has a picture of a penis on his phone!" to which he initially protested before I dived for the jean pocket where his phone was stored. He pushed me away with a delicious smirk. "A woman asked me if I had really a big dick so I had to prove it to her," he told me and my mother. "She wanted me to go and fuck her so I went over and fucked her."

And with a pause, "Thank you for telling your son that Pannikos".

Maybe I can extract from this moment an understanding that being self-absorbed is not harmless or funny; it can hurt people. And also, taking your sexuality too seriously is still a bit funny, a bit arch. There is definitely more to extract from that. Don't become this man, a flighty Adonis.

Maybe I don't understand how his seducer father and teenage life of loose morals shaped him. If there is a disadvantage that comes from not knowing I should probably say something about his formative years: at 15, his schooling ends, and he then begins a stint of bar and restaurant jobs for the next ten to fifteen years in Cyprus and the UK. Now, in his late fifties, he has a slipped disc and consumes large strong painkillers (but not opiates) in North Carolina, one of the forgotten in the dawning glory-time of mass unemployment. I call him every week or so via Facebook messenger to play out a familiar conversation.

For someone who left school so young, he has seemingly not been hampered by a lack of communication skills or psychological manipulation.

Some years ago, when I wrote, then re-visited, this many years later first from a bench in a walled garden of a former landed gent's house, it was August and there was a man with a bald head obscured by a low shrubbed tree sitting on a bench. At first, I didn't notice him until I had looked around to explain the potent waft of marijuana. A cloud crept over from behind the gaps of the small tree. If wasn't for the two small boys with a ball running to the bald man with a football, I may have never registered him. "Daddy, daddy, I need your help. Be on my team," one said. "No, no," comes the urge of the other of the two blonde-haired boys. I can't hear the father's response if he responds meaningfully at all. His arm points and extends outwards. The two little offspring, after in all likelihood imbibing his recreational aromas, run back to another part of the grounds.

As my writing from all those years ago written in the garden I'm holding a book called Elif Batuman's The Possessed, and there was a conversation in which her then-grad-student self and another student, Matej discuss his "current object of study: something called 'the problem of the person'":

"The problem, was that personhood is revealed and constituted by action, such that the whole person is always present in every action - and yet the person isn't 'exhausted' by any single action, or even by the sum of all her actions." (p. 76)

This is probably what's known as an action-centred philosophy of personhood, although I'm not sure. It reads as something possibly esoteric, but it also seems straightforward. For the problem of the paterfamilias then: though he might yet be capable of surprises, he is not exhausted by everything that he is, we can know them in their objects, in the things that they like, and in an overall loose relationship to the factual accuracy of the stories told and retold about them we ask, "What is he?" He is definitely exhausted with his back pain though.

On balance, I still like Radiohead and maintain an ambivalent relationship with that cannabis-based treat but I would like to think, moralising aside, I would do better than these two, even if he now sends me the occasional Western Union money transfer – out of what motive? Benevolence? Guilt? Seeing that his care as a pensioner is assured?

Except that I don't know that I could or would want to be a better father. A lot of adult life is stressful and you end up, as I've found out if you're not holding your attention, on autopilot. Also, the flesh can be weakened by temptation, or in a less religious framing, that adrenaline and noradrenaline (they're not exactly the same, right?) can make you act thoughtlessly and without much reflection sometimes. This is important in the case of my dad as I'll come to. It doesn't matter much anyway, no one of my generation seems to be having children anyway.

A day later, still under the sway of a Batuman's book I remember some sentences registering her relative dissatisfaction at having, more or less, studied Russian for two years without being unable to simply pick up a book and just read it (in The Possessed). Ditto, my own inability to watch a Greek feature film without the subtitles. Under this spell of this disappointing reflection later that night I told myself I should watch Kynodontas (Dogtooth), a film in which it is revealed that adult children are held captive by their parents, akin to something you've heard about happening in Austria some years ago, although not quite as bad as Josef Fritzl.

There's some kind of initial grim irony in using this film to learn Greek, since, at least in the opening scene, audiotapes narrated by the mother insidiously redefine the Greek language. In the bathroom, down to underwear the three (siblings? How would the viewer know initially?) listen to a tape player: "The new words of the day are 'Sea', 'Highway', and 'Roadtrip' and 'Shotgun.'". Analogous in certain ways to Dogtooth, I knew – and we know – of the world through specific media diet and through our social circles. If my dad had stayed beyond my second birthday, I may have actually been fluent in Greek (a slightly unofficial Cypriot version and not the Demotic kind). I might have liked football more, though I still do, and might have been less solitary.

Instead, I knew Dad from the few sub-Kray crime paperbacks, spined and yellowed like a true-crime victim, that had been carried perhaps unknowingly in each move of the several, early flats we lived in. We have had those thoughts, at one time, of the nascent, secret selves that were not immediately obvious to us; that could have become us.

These unknown, unrealised selves are not just some literary conceit though. Some years ago, when I was perhaps a tweenager, I found out that Dad had fathered another family – and perhaps again, not without the same expanded definition of what a 'family' meant. I had heard about the story, that he had become consummate with an American woman, several ears down: first my dad had spoken, casually and confidentially perhaps, on the phone to my Uncle Michael, the droll, serious-minded hunter of rabbits, who had then fed morsels, tongue-in-cheek, to my auntie. My auntie Androula, less reticent, had then jawed on with the news to my mother. This unknown woman, this American, had been cast by someone, as not unlike the role of a temptress to my all-too virile Daddy. She was working for the American government on the island of Cyprus (an agency with one of those infamous three-letter acronyms) and as the vague motions of the story went in Papa's cheeky eagerness to flirt and seduce during his service-industry dealings as a waiter, he had sparked up something.

After, there is something of an ellipsis since, when Dad does respond in person, with a few sentences, a few years after, he mentions how he spent some time in New Jersey. He makes the trip across continents, after how long of knowing this woman exactly? The visits are perhaps worth writing some paragraphs on, but hold on: he doesn't say how long and in what capacity he lived (and perhaps loved) in The Garden State. I don't think to ask. I'm not incurious, I think, but I am quiet. I am not alone in the room as he tells us this. We're at my auntie's house. My mum doesn't allow him to know where we live now, although he keeps asking and has some vague indication.

Anyway, my Dad tends to the twins with this woman who eventually births (conceived where it is unimportant). Did he drive an inconspicuous suburban vehicle through the highways in the sky, rocking a baby carrier on the front seat? Did the status anxiety dynamic, she a government professional, he just a waiter, eventually break them apart? Did he get the finger flipped to him by a balding man who could -yes!- from the rear, actually be Phillip Roth!

Wrong on both accounts. The story goes that, apparently, this government worker couldn't get the indefinite leave she needed from the federal agency she worked for, being apparently childless and unmarried. My dad's genetic material, as it were, fulfils this, again apparently, and she is able to exit for good. It sounds far-fetched. I have only heard what I have heard, some of which is probably untrue. Which federal employees cannot just leave their agency? Perhaps children make them, in the eyes of the ruthless male-headed managers look less useful. This account also overlooks any semblance of any actual real love they may have actually sparked up.

Are the New Jersey twins thinking too, of the problem of the person? They have probably graduated college now and in their first-ever jobs. Moving to New Jersey with a new woman is a fairly large commitment, isn't it?

With my mum, we do know that he gambled away paychecks at the Casino. Perhaps he was feeling lucky. The gambler loves the thrill of aleatory possibility. It's a sickness, a disease, of course, to crave those hits of hormones and stacks of chips. But if gambling away mortgage money is any indication he wears his commitment like he wore his dark five o'clock shadow: up-front though lightly.

Izzy Cole

I live in Hackney in a happy flat with my boyfriend and cat. Living here means a sense of stability and stillness I haven't felt in a long time. Living here also means seeing through the eyes of my mum and her stories of Hackney when she was my age. I feel close to her here even though I never knew her in the context of East London. We lived south of the river growing up, and she still resides there. But there is something of her life here and I enjoy finding it, even when I'm not looking.

Long weekend

Mara began rotting on a Thursday. Her arm was damp. It had a hot, fleshy quality. A thin fuzzy layer coated her skin like fog. She was ripening.

That morning, Mara felt shy about her development. She wondered if other girls might become jealous of the newfound attention she would inevitably receive that day at school. Not all began the process of decay so young. But by lunchtime, emboldened by favorable treatment, Mara adopted her new form with ease. She found that men let her on the bus first, savoring the sharp fruity scent as she breezed past. They insisted she keep the change at the till of her after school job, gave her the warmest, stickiest pastry at the bakery at lunch, turned a blind eye as she dropped smoldering cigarettes in the street.

Mara continued to rot on a Friday. She was looking forward to the close of day, and had been told of a club that would let her in without ID. All she had to do was dress revealingly enough, show blood and bone. As luck would have it, in the mirror that very morning she unveiled peaks of milky rock amongst marbled pink. Folds of pale skin curled over themselves, creating gelatinous edges that shone when they caught the light. There was a depth to her scent now too. Lingering whispers collapsed into stench. She felt most beautiful when others registered it, and could always tell when they did. Older women would turn up their noses or bury them in the bobbled sleeves of their M&S coats. Men's faces softened, became inquisitive, bright. They'd watch hungry eyed, quivering to reclaim some semblance of youthfulness to impress upon her. Mara enjoyed the dichotomies she created, the powers she drew from them.

She met the night in its richest, darkest hour. She danced beneath flickering street lamps, eyes rolling, catching silver coins and tossing them into gutters. Her joy attracted the scrutiny of passers by, those who similarly relished the small hours but had never derived such ecstasy from them. Weary from lives lived beneath the dim light of the moon, they pressed the newcomer for her story. To indulge them in whatever secrets she surely held. Dripping crimson on their concrete city, she offered no more than a smirk.

Mara was still rotting on Saturday. She woke early with a mind swimming in the depths of the night before. Memories of trailing bloody sinew across bitten lips. Bright lights, shadowed corners and fingertips tracing cartilage. She let herself linger in these visions all morning, and in bedsheets that stuck to her gummy limbs. When she finally peeled herself away, both her and the mattress were left strange canvases.

Mara wondered if any of her men thought of her beyond that curtain of night. If she had taught them anything, helped them feel anything. If they were somewhere inside themselves too? If she could truly call these encounters an exchange? A part of her hoped that they might treasure the scarlet stains she had smeared across their throats as they conspired together against homely women. But she knew that they would return to their wives, all dampened collars and alibis. Retreat into the same domesticity they'd claimed terrorized them so.

On Sunday, Mara was well and truly rotten and rested. She revelled in her own filth, in the angles of her body that collected dust and debris. Feverish and heavenly, there could be nothing more gorgeous. More admirable and womanly, than a total surrender to the potential she had always held. To push herself beyond promise. To be *of the body* in its basest sense. To the untrained eye she was deteriorating, but Mara knew better. She always did.

Anu Kumar Lazarus

Anu was a finalist of the 2023 Watson, Little x Indie Novella writing Prize for her novel, *The Blue Monkey*. The special relationship of a brother and sister was brought home for Anu after witnessing her mother's grief following Anu's uncle's death. A delicate fiction formed very clearly in her mind. Prior to this, Anu has mostly written for theatre. She is a B3 Media finalist. Anu has lived in London's East End for 30 years, and works in the NHS, bathed in rich story telling. *The Blue Monkey* is her first novel, and she is working on her second.

More about Anu Kumar Lazarus can be found here - www.sensorinet.com.

Columbia Road Flower Market
London E2

*In January, daffodils and tulips trip spring in too
    early
amongst mimosa and kangaroo paw.
Scattered tourists brush hibernating locals.
March , continentals admire Banksy, banksia,
    buskers,
drinking coffee in Campania , befriending
    bohemia ..
Unconsciously
awaiting the unfurling of the peonies...
Cobbles, towers, parks, nettle industrious folks ,
Sparing, sharing family time
midst poetry, scavengers, perpetual orchids and
    wine.
Giant Poppy, Amaryllis, Hydrangea sneer upon
geranium window boxes
just before school closes,
leaving visitors to air b n bs and sunflowers.
September! Gladioli stems nod nostalgic,
Perennial crops of school blazers
"We shared those years a-go, ago.."
Pubs topple learners to an autumnal street
All yearning to find gold or sex, at least.
The tall Chinese lanterns, orange, signing
fireworks , Chanukah, Diwali, Eid
Then, boxed amarylli claim iced air fair*

And invite yuletide to each one's door
The travellers leave , mother's breathe
and writhe at home
in blood holly - mistletoe wreaths.

Mian Shah

Mian Obaid Shah is an accomplished management consultant with a wealth of experience spanning more than 20 years in market research, consulting, and training. Alongside his professional expertise, Mr Shah has also made significant contributions as an editor for various trade journals. His academic background includes holding an MS in International Economics from the University of Glasgow, and in addition to that he pursued additional courses, including studying at the University of Oxford.

He is the author of several books including A Modern Approach to Applied Market Research and Exemplary Islamic Stories. He also writes short stories and poetry which is being published in Magazines and anthologies. His adeptness in research has greatly benefited his creative writing endeavours, enabling him to develop richly detailed worlds and to introspectively explore his own writing practice.

His literary passion encompasses a diverse range of genres, with particular interests in historical fiction, contemporary literary realism, and speculative fiction. Mr. Shah is currently engrossed in crafting a novel centered around the journey of an Afghan refugee to the UK, delving into thought-provoking themes such as illegal immigration, racism, and the war on terrorism.

Beyond his writing pursuits, he is actively engaged in a community project with St. Paul's Cathedral. He is crafting an article focused on one of the East India Company Monuments, further showcasing his versatility and commitment to contributing to the collective knowledge and heritage.

The Holy Shrine

In the year 1947, during the tumultuous partition of India, a Hindu found himself caught in the throes of uncertainty. His name was Ramo, a quack doctor by profession. Ramo had accumulated a vast wealth over the years, and he feared he would lose it during the chaos of partition. Muslims were fleeing to Pakistan, a Muslim-controlled country, while Hindus and Sikhs were heading in the opposite direction.

Upon learning about the mass killings of Muslims in India, he feared the repercussions. Worried about the safety of his family and wealth, Ramo made a plan. He decided against taking his treasure with him and instead opted to leave it behind, intending to return for it when the situation had calmed. For that purpose, he selected an old graveyard outside the city.

Under the veil of night, he carefully buried his treasure deep within the earth. On top of his hidden treasure, he gave it the shape of a grave. He erected a tombstone over the hidden riches and painted it green, a symbol of sacredness and reverence. He was quite comforted that his treasure would remain safe in the grave and no one would ever suspect it.

Subsequently, he embarked on a journey with his wife and two children to reunite with their relatives on the other side of the border. After a long and perilous journey, they finally reached their destination in India.

Ramo promptly settled in the new town and resumed his business of selling medicines. Weeks turned into months, and months into years, as Ramo patiently waited for the dust of the partition to settle. Eventually, he decided to return to his homeland to retrieve the treasure he had buried there.

"I have to go back," he declared.

"To where?" his wife inquired, engrossed in sewing a sweater for their youngest son.

"To reclaim my treasure! We need it now more than ever."

"How many times have I told you to let it go? What if something happens to you there?" she blasted.

"The time is right. I've heard that the borders will soon become stricter, making it difficult to transport such wealth without attracting unwanted attention from officials. It is now or never."

"Very well, if you insist, I won't stand in your way," his wife agreed after a long silence.

Soon, Ramo started preparing for his journey to his old homeland. He really missed the places and friends where he spent his childhood. But he had to retrieve his treasure without revealing his true identity. Over the years, he had changed so much that no one there would even recognise him. In anticipation of his journey, he also allowed his beard and hair to grow.

Finally, the time arrived for Ramo to embark on his journey. This time, it was not fraught with peril as the riots had subsided. Upon reaching his former hometown, he discovered that not much had changed. Everything remained almost identical to how he left them. A towering oak tree between the White Mosque and the old Temple, under which he used to sell his remedies, was still standing there. He recognised most of the shopkeepers on that street, yet no one recognised him. Dressed in dark black attire with his long hair cascading down his back and a silver beard tinged with dust, he presented the perfect image of a fakir (a mendicant or begger).

After scouting throughout the day in his old city, evening was approaching, and Ramo felt the pangs of hunger. He decided to have dinner before heading to the old graveyard to retrieve his treasure. As he made his way to a hotel, Ramo found himself in a precarious situation when he noticed Ali, his long-time friend, seated behind the counter, busy in conversation with a customer. Uncertain about how to proceed, Ramo lingered for a moment, contemplating his next move. Soon, Ali caught sight of him but failed to recognise him. Nonetheless, he kindly extended a small coin as a charitable offering, unaware of Ramo's true identity.

"No, I want food. I will pay. Can I come in?" Ramo inquired, altering his voice.

"Oh, my apologies. Of course, you may enter," Ali responded politely.

Once Ramo finished his dinner and tendered payment, Ali interjected, "I don't want your money. Just pray for me."

"Thank you. May your business flourish," Ramo uttered, offering a prayer akin to that of a revered saint, and began departing from the hotel.

"Hey! Stop!" Ramo heard Ali's voice, causing his heart to race with fear that his true identity had been exposed. He spun around, ready to face the consequences.

"Please take this food with you. It may help you on your journey," Ali said, extending a small parcel of food to Ramo.

Ramo took the food with gratitude. On his way to the old graveyard, he bought a shovel and a pickaxe to dig up all his riches tonight. The path towards the graveyard was unusually busy. He started hearing drumming from quite far away. As he got nearer to the graveyard, the drumming and Qawwali (chanting) became louder. He could now see some lighting, which was not a good sign for Ramo's mission. He was expecting the area to be deserted.

Ramo could now see a small shrine with a dome standing in the graveyard. He started sweating as that meant that some saint might have died recently, so people built a shrine in his honour. He stopped at the graveyard door. It would be impossible to dig out the treasure in the presence of hundreds of people.

"I haven't seen you before. Are you new here?" A beggar, sitting in the darkness near the door, asked him.

"Oh, yes," Ramo quickly replied. The unexpected shrine had shocked him so much that he couldn't notice him.

"What's happening here?"

"Tonight is the anniversary. Devotees have gathered from far and wide."

"I visited here long ago, but there was no shrine at that time."

"That is because the shrine for the great saint has been recently built."

The beggar started telling stories of how prayers were answered at the shrine, but Ramo wasn't interested in those stories. His sole focus remained on retrieving his treasure. He excused himself, pretending to pay his respects at the saint's grave. Instead of entering the tomb, he began scouring the graveyard in search of his fake grave, where he had buried his wealth. After scanning the entire graveyard, he couldn't find the grave he was looking for and held onto the hope of locating it during the daylight of the next day. He hoped there wouldn't be many people after tonight, making it much easier for him to excavate his treasure without attracting attention. As he ventured closer to the centre, where the saint's grave was situated, the dense crowd obstructed his view, making it difficult for him to see clearly. Exhausted, he settled down in one corner of the tomb, reclining and swiftly falling into a deep slumber.

Upon awakening, it was nearly dawn, and many of the devotees remained asleep. As Ramo sat up and surveyed his surroundings, his eyes widened, and a mixture of awe and disbelief gripped him. Standing up, he made his way toward the saint's grave and sat beside it, gently running his hand over the tombstone. To his astonishment, it was the exact grave where he had previously excavated and concealed his treasure.

Ramo was devastated to find that his precious treasure was trapped beneath the shrine, inaccessible and seemingly lost forever. Despair weighed heavily upon his heart as he tried to understand how his fake grave turned into a saint's shrine. A hand rested upon his shoulder, startling him, and he twisted around.

"Why do you look so shocked? Did you see him in a dream?" a voice whispered.

"Saw who?" Ramo inquired.

"The great saint, who else? He usually comes to the most pious devotee's dream," he explained.

Ramo didn't reply and left the tomb. The stranger looked at him curiously and whispered to his friend, "I think the great saint came in his dream." Soon, the rumour spread throughout the shrine, fuelling curiosity and speculation about Ramo.

Suddenly, Ramo noticed a shift in people's attitudes

towards him. He became the object of great respect, with devotees seeking his blessings and prayers before departing from the shrine. As the day progressed, visitors gradually dwindled, and the shrine grew deserted. Ramo re-entered the tomb, gazing upon the grave, when a tall person dressed in white robes with long hair and a beard approached and sat in front of him.

"I don't recall seeing you before," the person remarked.

"I'm new. I arrived last night," Ramo replied, scrutinising the individual but unable to recollect his face.

"I'm the custodian of this holy shrine. I've heard about you from several devotees. They spoke highly of your piety."

"Really?...That's very nice of them... I'm nothing."

"So, are you staying longer in the city?"

"I don't know."

"I'll be very frank with you. I really like you and would be delighted if you stay here. There are a few more keepers here. I can pay you for the service. I need people like you."

"What exactly would you like me to do?"

"Nothing, just stay here. We want people to keep coming and help raise donations so we can expand the shrine."

"I'm sorry to say, but I know nothing about the saint. Who he was and what he did to become so famous?" Ramo candidly expressed his lack of knowledge and tried to understand who turned his treasure into a shrine.

"I like your straightforwardness. Let me tell you. The person in the grave was a highly revered saint. One day, he was going on a journey but fell seriously ill. I found him lying here. As the night progressed, his health deteriorated, and before he passed away, he expressed his desire to be buried in this very spot. I respected his wishes and laid him to rest here. Then, one night, he appeared in my dream and asked me to build a shrine over his burial site. Now, people come here and pray for their wishes to come true."

"Oh, wow!" although Ramo's face was calm, deep down in his heart, he was shouting, "Liar, fraudster!" He wished to tell him to his face that the grave was fake and it was he who made it. But then he couldn't say so, as he would lose his treasure.

"So, what do you say?" he asked Ramo, eager to secure his commitment.

"I'm very impressed. I will stay here in this shrine as long as I'm around."

"I'm honoured. But I insist you accept something."

"A meal will be enough for me."

"Of course, you'll get free food daily," said the greedy custodian of the shrine, his face beaming with delight at having acquired a free servant for his business.

The custodian of the shrine left, clutching a bag filled with donations. Meanwhile, Ramo became lost in thoughts, pondering how to retrieve his treasure. As evening approached, only two other keepers remained inside the shrine.

"My beloved friends, you must be tired. As now the anniversary of the great saint is finished, so if you want to go out to see your family, feel free to do so. Don't worry, I'm here now," Ramo said reassuringly.

"Go out? Where? This is our home," one of the keepers inquired.

"We have nothing waiting for us outside. Do not concern yourselves with us," the other affirmed resolutely.

Ramo sought solace in a corner, lying down and delving into his thoughts, strategizing and reconsidering plans. Eventually, he succumbed to sleep, unknowingly venturing into the realm of dreams. When he opened his eyes the next day, he found a dozen devotees seated within the shrine. Time was slipping away, and the prospect of being left alone in the shrine seemed increasingly improbable. Ramo realised that his best opportunity might arise during the night, when devotees were scarce. But even at that time, he would not dig in the presence of the two keepers.

After having his lunch, he left the shrine and ventured into the barren wilderness. For hours, he wandered amidst the desolate surroundings, carefully selecting and gathering various herbs. Being an adept quack doctor, he precisely knew what he sought. Upon returning to the shrine, he began crushing the herbs with rocks, skilfully extracting the green paste. Adding water and filtering the mixture with a cloth, he soon produced a green solution. Throughout the process, the two keepers observed him attentively but remained silent, curious about his actions.

After dinner, when there were no devotees in the shrine, he brought the green drink in a brown clay jug.

"My dear friends, I have prepared a special drink for you. My esteemed teacher, a great yogi, passed this recipe down to me. This drink will boost your focus during worship," Ramo said.

"We are deeply grateful for your care and thoughtfulness," the elderly keeper expressed his gratitude.

Ramo poured the green drink into a clay bowls and handed them to his companions. They sipped the concoction, appreciating its taste. Soon, they finished the drink and felt a wave of drowsiness washing over them. Their legs stretched, accompanied by yawns, until they succumbed to a profound slumber, unaware of their surroundings.

Seizing the opportunity, Ramo swiftly made his way to the shrine's main gate. It was hard for him to close the gate, as it had probably never been closed since its erection. After wrestling with it for a few minutes, he eventually closed it.

Wasting no time, he ran back to the tomb. Armed with his pickaxe and shovel, he dug quietly but urgently, determined to reach the treasure. The surface was harder than expected, but he did not lose hope.

As he drew closer to the treasure, a knock echoed from the main gate. In a quick improvisation, Ramo wrapped a white cloth around himself, resembling a ghostly figure emerging from a coffin. With his eyes peeping out and his tongue protruding, he held a flickering candle close to his face as he approached the gate. The sight of Ramo's imitation of a ghostly visage scared the devotees on the other side of the gate, causing them to cry out in fear and hastily flee from the scene.

Ramo quickly returned to the fake grave, and after an hour of digging, he hit a metal box full of gold coins and jewellery. As the first rays of dawn painted the horizon, Ramo emerged from the depths of the shrine, clutching the wealth he had once feared would be forever lost. Exhausted but victorious, he cast a glance at the innocent mendicants still unconscious of the surrounding. He slipped a few coins into their pockets. He threw off his white cloth and started filling the grave. But then he realised to leave it open and expose the greedy custodian who was exploiting poor devotees. He packed up his belongings and fled from the shrine, aiming to leave the city before daybreak.

After a lengthy slumber, the two keepers finally awoke and were shocked to find the grave open and their new colleague nowhere to be found. One of them hurried to the custodian to inform him of the situation. It shocked the custodian when he saw the opened grave. The last thing he wanted was for anyone else to find out about it. If word got out, it could spell the end of his once-flourishing shrine. No one would offer anything to an empty grave. So he ordered the keepers to close the main gate. But before they could carry out the command, a group of devotees entered the tomb.

"What has happened here?" one of them inquired, looking at the ruptured grave of the saint.

"We do not know," a keeper answered.

"Does this mean the saint has disappeared? ... Was he unhappy about something? ... Where has he gone?... Is he coming back?" They started asking in confusion and concern.

"It appears..." the custodian's limited understanding left him unsure, trying to piece together the puzzle, with his brow furrowed in confusion, a hint of fear creeping into his voice "uh, honestly, I have no idea what's going on."

"Was this his miracle? ... Will he return? ... Should we leave the grave open?" they fired a barrage of questions once again.

"No, we can't leave it like this," the custodian replied after a moment of thought. "I request that you don't disclose this to anyone. Let's keep it as a secret."

"Why?" the devotees asked in unison.

"Because the saint may be displeased if his secret is disclosed," he said, trying to convince them to protect his shrine business.

"I know what has occurred here. It was a miracle! The saint revealed his divine power—a genuine miracle! miracle!" One of the devotees exclaimed, overcome with ecstatic joy.

"Yes, undoubtedly a miracle! Of course, it was a miracle." the greedy custodian's eyes brightened up as he breathed a sigh of relief. Soon, the entire shrine resounded with the enthusiastic chant of "Miracle! Miracle!"

The news of the incident spread rapidly, capturing the attention of many who saw it as a miraculous occurrence.

Unaware of the true nature of the situation, the ignorant devotees flocked to the shrine, filled with awe and wonder. The greedy custodian felt a sense of relief at the unexpected turn of events. However, unbeknownst to the devotees, he quietly sent out his closed servants to search for Ramo.

"I want him found, dead or alive. And ensure that every item he took is recovered," the custodian commanded. He figured out from the grave that Ramo had unearthed a treasure. However, he remained oblivious to how Ramo had discovered its existence.

Meanwhile, the once-quiet shrine became a bustling hub, with pilgrims flocking from distant cities. The custodian hired additional keepers and volunteers to collect alms, and as his wealth increased, so did his greed. His men were searching for Ramo like mad dogs everywhere. He wanted to get possession of whatever Ramo had taken from there. The more the greedy custodian thought about the type of riches Ramo had found, the crazier he became. One night, he awoke from sleep and started screaming. His family sought medical help, but to no avail. He had lost his sanity.

"My treasure! Oh, my precious treasure! I need it back," he cried out, running barefoot around the shrine in dirty, filthy clothes.

"Please heal your loyal servant. He has lost his mind for your sake. Please return to your grave, oh great saint!" a devotee was praying at the empty grave.

Heather Finlay

Like many of the people I still know, I came to London for work in the mid-1980s. I hadn't planned to live in London and I always say I came to London for 2 years and never left. We moved into large shared houses in areas that were still cheap like Peckham, Hackney and Archway. Some people I knew squatted. The old London was still around then but it was frayed at the seams. Money hadn't arrived yet in the areas we could afford to live in. We sat in faded pubs surrounded by stuffed animals and listened to old ladies singing at pianos. The old Londoners were still around too. One of my neighbours used to tell us how the women 'on the game' during the blackouts in the second world war used torches to look at men's shoes to see if the men looked rich enough to pay!

But there was a sense of change — Thatcher's Britain was tearing up the rules and we knew we weren't on the same side. My friends and I went on demos and spent hours shouting 'Maggie, Maggie, Maggie. Out, out, out.' The kernel of Ray's story comes from this period but the story is set later. It reminds me of a time in the early/mid 1990s when places like Peckham and Hackney were being redeveloped. Old buildings were being bought up and done up but others were being knocked down and replaced with steel and glass – especially around the City. It was almost as if the fabric of an area was no longer stable, everything was up for grabs. I suppose Ray's story is about change and loss and what that means for us as individuals caught up in it all.

Fragment One

Ray pulled up the collar of his overcoat as he left the flats. The wind always seemed to be coming from the East these days; it played havoc with his joints. He didn't know why the bloody GP surgery wanted to see him again. They were always prodding & poking, checking this & that. Preventative medicine they called it. Preventative my arse – it hadn't done his Marie any good. As he thought of her his ramrod straight bearing faltered and he blew his nose with a spotless white handkerchief. "No use dwelling on the past" he muttered as he drew himself upright once more with a brief shake of his head. As he walked he took in the streets he'd known since childhood. It was all rubbish now, even the old boozer had closed and was being converted into flats. He remembered the smoke-filled evenings ending in a sing-song round the piano. Mind you he remembered the hungry kiddies without shoes too. Young people now have had it easy. He glanced over at a group of boys awkwardly straddling a new piece of 'street art' – whatever that was. Their bicycles lay abandoned next to them & their heads touched as they shared a joke from their mobile phone. Their laughter felt like a taunt to Ray as he walked away from them, he couldn't think when he had last laughed. They hadn't known suffering this generation, he'd been to war and, my god, his Marie had known suffering at the end. His eyes prickled and he blinked to bring the street back into focus. Where had he put his hanky? Behind him Ray heard footsteps running purposefully towards him. He turned. It was one of the boys from the group, looking unsure and holding something out. Ray squinted to see what it was, one of his gloves. "You dropped it, it's a bit cold eh?" The boy smiled as Ray took the glove and with a quick "Bye" the boy was running back to the group. As he stood there holding his glove Ray was suddenly dazzled by a memory of running as a boy, the sheer joy of it. Then running with his own boy, Ralph. Ralph, now a man who looked at Ray with Marie's eyes. It was time to make peace with those eyes and see Ralph again, there'd certainly be no running at his age but... "Damn that hanky" said Ray patting his pockets.

Fragment Two

Ray stood ramrod straight in front of the kitchen sink. His shirt sleeves were carefully rolled up and over his clothes he wore an apron with a faded picture of a flamenco dancer. A souvenir of a never forgotten holiday. He washed up slowly, methodically, everything had its place, just as Marie would have wanted it. He could almost feel her hands on the plates, the cups, her cup. The sounds of dripping water and the rattle of crockery were blunted by the viscous silence that filled that flat. Ray looked blankly through the window where he could just see the sun rising over the furthest buildings. 'I'm a miserable old bugger' he thought to himself. 'Would Marie want me to be like this' but he batted that thought away, no point. He thought at one time that he would be swept away with the grief when she died. That he would be bleached, a battered and scarred version of himself. But his generation knew how to deal with suffering, a stiff back and a strong mind. That's what got him through Korea. He put down the final cup and noticed that there was a small crack down the side.

As he walked into his bedroom Ray took a look around. His small suitcase was packed by the door and the bed was made, the folded back sheet just so.

Then the memory hit him, of himself lying in the bed unshaved and stinking. With Ralph, now a big man, standing over him.

'Look dad, you're not doing so well. Come and stay with us for a little while..... till you're yourself again. There's people you can talk to, who can help.'

All Ray could see were Marie's eye's looking at him and he turned away, couldn't bear it.

'Fuck off, fuck off out of my house. No one asked you to come here.' His voice was muffled against the blankets. For some minutes there was silence and then he heard the front door gently click closed.

The memory left Ray sweating and he placed his hands on the edge of the dressing table to steady himself.

Ray banged his suitcase up the stairs of the bus and sat down breathing heavily. He couldn't see what had been so wrong with bus conductors, they would've helped pensioners in those days. Cost cutting like everything else he supposed. They had always sat on the top deck, a family tradition from Marie and him courting through to taking the kiddies to the Parliament Hill Lido. Those days always seemed to be filled with primary colours. Looking out at the steel and glass buildings that were colonising his streets everything seemed to be grey now. Then, gradually, as the bus moved on Ray felt his thoughts stretch and loosen as the motion of the bus lulled him to sleep.

When Ray woke the bus had stopped outside a small row of shops. These were the type of shops Ray could recognise with names like "Shortcutz" and a butcher that looked like somewhere you could buy a couple of chipolatas. Not like where he lived. There the butcher kept going on about how long the meat had been hung, when all Ray wanted was a bit of mince. The bus swung into motion and Ray began to recognise the streets. Neat terraces of houses each with its own tiny front garden behind a low wall and it was time to struggle his suitcase back down the stairs.

The short walk felt harder than it used to, was he just getting old Ray wondered. But he straightened his shoulders, zipped up his jacket and carried on. The gardens were full of flowers he knew, a Fuchsia there and a yellow Rose in the garden next to it. Then he was at the purple gate and the black and white tiled path. He remembered cleaning those tiles, his poor knees but they'd made the best of it and been rewarded with a beer in the garden afterwards. The house hadn't changed, the same red, green and gold curtains at the windows and yellow paintwork. There were still cabbages growing in the middle of the flowers as there were every year. Ray struggled slightly to open the gate and walked slowly up the path towards the deep green door.

The bell seemed barely to have rung when the door was opened and there stood Ralph. His greying hair was pulled back messily from his face. He was a full head height taller than Ray and he had his mother's eyes.

'Hello son' Ray's voice was hushed.

'Long time no see, eh dad. Come in' Ralph stepped back to

let Ray into the hall. Standing there Ray felt unsteady, unmoored.

'I'm so sorry' Ray said 'I was....I was' Ray felt his words racing away from him.

'It's alright dad' Ralph said. Then Ralph hugged him. Ralph smelled of new baked bread and a smell Ray couldn't name but it was so familiar. In the warmth of that hug Ray felt something in him soften and slip back into place.

Then there was a cacophony of limbs and noise as the children bolted from the kitchen. Ray bent down to hug them but they stopped a foot or so from him, suddenly wary. Milly swaying slightly and Ryan looking down. Then Ray realised his cheeks were wet with tears.

'it's OK loves, I've got something in my eye that's all.' Emboldened they were on him, small sticky hands in his.

'We made cake.' Ryan informed him.

'But we can't eat it until you arrived' Milly added gravely as they started gently tugging Ray down the hall towards the open kitchen door.

'Mum would've loved this, wouldn't she?' Ralph said.

'Yeah.... she would' said Ray and that felt OK

Alice Chadwick

'Green' is an extract from a longer piece on identity, the body and making space (gardens, domestic space, communities). Set around Millfields, Hackney, I've chosen a number of sections which focus on gardens and neighbourhood, ending with a section on communal green space and Covid.

Green

Wall

The house is a narrow Victorian terrace in Hackney. It is not exactly derelict, but it is in a bad state of repair. It has enough bedrooms for our children and is close enough to where they go to school. It has a garden. We feel at once fortunate and frightened. Soft joists, unsteady windows. The seasick lean of the walls.

The front of the house is covered in stone cladding, blocky concrete tiles in pink, beige, uncanny green. The fake-rock is rough and chunky, and gives the house the appearance of a monstrous, thickly iced cake, sifted over with the dust of London streets. Pollen and pollution.

There must have been some tiles left over when the house was finished. *Let's do the wall!* I imagine somebody saying, waving a trowel at the extras, at the brick wall between the front garden and the street. But there were not quite enough, it seems. A third of the wall remains bare red bricks, splashed here and there with bucket spills of lime-green paint.

Recently the wall has started to look precarious, leaning outwards as if exhausted by its own weight, as if its only desire is to lie down flat on the warm tarmac bed of the pavement. Or, as one gloomy dog-walker puts it, like it's about to collapse on a small passing child. At the end of the wall there is an old evergreen shrub. It is plagued by something, this bush, a soft powderous disease which blooms over its dark and clenching leaves.

We are too afraid to take the cladding off the front of the house in case what we find underneath is worse (dry rot, horror-film cracks), and anyway we can't afford to. But the garden wall is possible. Even if it is a diversion, a delusion; planting daisies while the rest of the house falls down. I think a lot about planting. Tulips and a hornbeam hedge. A small tree. Herbaceous perennials, tall and loose and flourishing.

I find a builder who demolishes the wall, excavates the stump and roots of the shrub and builds a new breezeblock wall that stands sturdily up and is level. It is low, about knee height, and rendered flat. There will be iron railings on top – short ones, no spears. I am not after a barricade. I want something porous, although not entirely; something that plants can grow through but which might deter foxes. Flying beer cans. The builder constructs a narrow L-shaped flowerbed from scaffolding boards, lays the foundation for a path and fills the space that remains with pebbles. He heaves a bulk bag from his van and deposits its contents in the empty trenches. Soil of some sort, thin and sandy.

The slabs for the path come from a reclamation yard in Hackney Wick, across the canal from where they are building the Olympic Park. We walk between towers of paving stones – limestones, sandstone, concrete, many different sizes – and chose four Yorkstone slabs that have been lifted, the stone merchant tells us, from the streets of Chelsea and Westminster. They still have chewing gum attached, he points out. The owner is selling up. The community of scrapyards, mechanics, builders' yards, of artists and wilderness, which has given Hackney Wick its peculiar heady energy, is already breaking apart. *It's too much,* he says, glancing out at the cranes. Development, its voracious pressure.

The paving stones are flat and grey, wide and handsome. The builder lays them with a little strip of earth to one side, where I imagine a succession of bulbs.

To suggest that this happens smoothly or quickly is to skim over some months of indecision, of sketching plans on scraps of paper, walking up and down East London streets noting wooden fences, types of gate, what grows well as hedging or in pots. It embarrasses me, the time spent on this small rectangle of London clay, but when it is finished, it looks solid and cared for, as I hoped it would. If a bit raw. The blank wall and bare soil, the exposed pebbles, it looks a bit... I have inadvertently made a miniature beach. I could set up a deckchair, throw chips for the seagulls.

Or have I done my own bit of development?

I stand in the front garden and plant things. People stop at the wall and look. They stop and talk. I plant daffodils and snowdrops. A small magnolia tree. Mexican fleabane, a sort of daisy.

Dahlia

There is a loud knock at the door. I run downstairs. Three ladies stand on the path, smartly dressed in sensible shoes, calf-length skirts, cardigans. They are holding leaflets, shiny wads of them, printed in bright colours with paintings of rainbows, sunrays, flowers. *Good morning,* the one at the front says, but before she gets going, I get in my defence: *I don't believe in God, but good luck and have a lovely day.* They are not so easily deflected. They offer me reading matter. They ask me if I believe in Love. *I have to go back to my work now,* I say. *Enjoy the sunshine.*

On their next visit, one of the ladies, the elderly one who does most of the talking, comments on the front garden. We begin to discuss the flowerbed, what I've planted there, the lavender, the magnolia tree. *It was struggling a bit,* I tell her, and describe the insubstantial builder's soil. *Alright, well then,* she says, after a while of this. *Goodbye.* She begins to move away, but comes to a stop at the end of the path: *It's all the Lord's Garden, isn't it? All His Creation is Holy!* She is beaming. I shut the door.

After that when she knocks, as she does every few months, she dispenses almost completely with God. *Have you been to Lidl?* she asks me. *Lidl in Well Street has very good plants. It has big bags of bulbs in springtime. Now it has heather, all sorts of bright colours.* She has bought some heather for her daughter, she tells me. The women standing behind her, who looks younger, who looks a bit shy, shifts and smiles. *And Lidl also has dahlia tubers. Very good ones in many colours. You know my garden?* she asks. She stands on the stone slabs, in the morning sunshine, her eyes bright with enquiry. *You do know it. The one with all the dahlias in it. Coming through now.* And yes, I do know her garden, I realise. A street away, facing south, baking in the sun, and full in summer of enormous, upstanding, ravishing dahlias; four-, five-feet tall, perfectly circular pom-poms in magenta, deep velvet red, bright Lidl yellow, thrumming scarlet-orange. *One day you will find a dahlia, the root, here,* she says, pointing a crooked finger at the corner of the garden, the bins and recycling bags. *And you will know who has left it for you!*

She has a low, resonant voice, full of good humour and at once ringing with Old Testament warning. I don't believe in God. And yet her garden in mid-summer, in full sail – it is hard not to look and feel joy. The exuberance of fresh growth. Life multiplying and succeeding, its beauty and variety. All its bright colours! *Alright, Bless God. Bless all of His Beautiful Garden!* she says, sweeping her ladies back down the path.

Lamb's Ear

I dig holes and plant a hornbeam hedge, a short row of bare sticks. I put a jasmine in beside the path and spread compost on the soil. When spring comes, the magnolia holds up a single flower, a pale candle lit against the grey sky, then opens its leaves, broad and flat and green. There are forget-me-nots and foxgloves. Hollyhocks. The lavender grows tall and flops through the railings, filling the air with perfume and humming bees. People trail their hands through. The jasmine arches over the path and reaches out onto the pavement. *Foliage,* the Sains-burys man says, whipping it aside.

One day a woman delivers the shopping. It is never usually a woman. She is young and talkative. *What's this plant?* she asks, stacking the crates on the path. *And this one? I LOVE this,* she says, reaching down her hand. Lamb's ear. Its leaves are felted, silver-green, and taper to a point exactly like the ear of a lamb, or so I imagine, the same soft density. *Does it have flowers?* she asks. It does, I show her, small ones half-hidden between the stem and the leaves. The woman lets the leaf go and straightens up. She tells me that she lives near the woods, out east further. Her daughter wants to be in a princess garden and they have planted the back of their house like a meadow.

I lug the shopping into the kitchen. I go out of the back door, find a trowel, a pot and dig up a sprig of lamb's ear for her daughter. Lamb's ear is tough. As long as it has a couple of roots, if it's watered in, it will grow.

When I was small, my friend across the street had a big garden. It lay in the bed of an old river, the lawn running on a gentle slope, the flowerbeds wide and flat. Her parents grew raspberries, almonds, irises, and big clumps of lamb's ear along the sandy paths. I loved the feel of the leaves, soft as duck down; and the blue plastic barrel they kept on the grass for climbing in, for rolling over and over towards the river, the ends sawn off so that our arms and legs could stick out.

The Latin name for lamb's ear is *Stachys byzantina*. It is native to the land lying between West and East – Turkey, Iran, Armenia.

The delivery women's daughter wants *to be* in a princess garden. I am struck by that. She doesn't want to be a princess or have a princess garden. She wants *to be*. In a garden.

Jasmine

A woman stops. She is from about ten houses down. She has a daughter in the same year as my younger daughter at school, although they don't really seem to know each other. In fact, she has three or four girls at my daughter's secondary school. Nine, maybe ten children altogether. She wears a long black robe and a black headscarf, pinned tight under her chin.

Is it honeysuckle? she asks, gesturing towards the climber that is taking over our front path. I am cutting it back. It has become a challenge to get in and out of the gate. *Jasmine,* I say. She looks sceptical. *Are you sure?* I am, because I chose it to make the air smell like Sydney, where my husband comes from, like the other side of the world. I don't mention this, but I say it doesn't smell quite how I expected it to. It smells sweet like honeysuckle, we agree, only with a sharper edge like lemons or breathing the air near to the sea.

She has a pale face, dark anxious eyes behind black-framed glasses, a ready smile. She is thin and birdlike – she probably never gets to sit down, I think – and looks much younger than she must be. Some of her children are in their twenties, one or two are still in the pushchair. Sometimes I see her walking the small ones to school, her high stilettos flashing under her long robe. Her children are immaculately dressed, often in matching clothes, in party clothes even – sequinned cardigans, gathered satin skirts, patent leather shoes – their long hair plaited and shiny. One of her daughters is always running ahead, climbing up lampposts, balancing on the tops of walls, fast and agile. Today the woman is on her own.

Jasmine. And a vine, I say, pulling down the gold-green leaves that are beginning to appear over the fence from my neighbour's garden. The vine leaves are soft and fresh, almost wet to touch they are so newly grown. It is spring itself I am holding, its first tender growth. She reaches a hand. *You can cook with these,* she tells me. *My mum, if she was still here, I would be telling her to come and ask you for some.* She describes stuffed vine leaves. *Stuffed with rice,* she says, *stuffed with meat.*

Her eyes shine. She calls them *dolma,* or something like the word I know but slightly different. *I'm Greek, you see,* she says.

She tells me that all the old people garden in Greece, that's what they do. I nod, thinking of last summer, the little old woman in a blue summer dress, in black ankle boots, watering her tomatoes, her basil and cucumbers, while sailing boats grazed the jetty and people – we – walked along her lane to the beach. My neighbour tells me about her brother who planted a fig tree and now has figs. She looks amazed that this could happen. Perhaps he seems too young to her to grow things. Perhaps he's not usually so green fingered. *They all do it,* she says, *fig trees, tomatoes, cucumber. They all plant it in their gardens.*

She tells me that she is from Cyprus, the Greek part. Before the division, the Greeks and the Turks got on, she says, and could speak each other's language. But then the fighting started. Her father came to London, then he brought his family. *In Cyprus, if you have a daughter, you have to build her a house. My father had two daughters and he was a poor man. He couldn't build a house, but he could give us an education. But imagine me, I have seven daughters! I can't afford to build them each seven houses, I mean each one a house, seven houses!* Impossible, we agree, laughing. Especially now in Hackney. *But my dad wanted education for us,* she says, *and so he brought us to England but* – she is laughing – *but then it didn't work out because none of us kids went to university!*

She lets go of the vine. The branch springs back up into the warm air, the blue sky. *I haven't been back since I was small,* she reflects, *to Cyprus. It's Christian and they don't like it, that I'm Muslim.* She pauses, her face pale, her eyes wide. *I don't feel at home in my own country,* she says, and looks astounded. *I think*

214

they say something behind my back because my husband, he's from India.

I know something of this story, how my neighbour was working for a company and fell in love with a man who also worked there, how she converted to Islam so that they could be married. I find it romantic but also reassuring, that people have to love each other, be together, whatever they are. And they do seem to love each other, the tall, quiet, courteous husband, this quick, tiny woman from Greece. They seem to share a particular way of being alive to the world.

Nobody cares where you're from in Hackney, I think. Or rather: whatever your origins, you belong. I look at her clear face, her dark eyes. Can I see the Greek girl in the woman? Perhaps, now I know that she is there. Her mother picking vine leaves, her brother planting figs. *Anyway, I'm supposed to be at work,* she says. *I'm never late!* I pick up my secateurs, say goodbye. Move along the path.

The woman's own front garden is trim with artificial grass, her back garden full of climbing frames and trampolines. She owns a professional iron, she once told me, because as a child she never had nice clothes and was determined that her own kids would. And they do, I think, hearing her high heels tap around the corner. Her girls like peonies in their full satin dresses, like fireflies in sequins, racing at dusk along the hot Hackney pavements.

Merlin Goldman

I lived in Muswell Hill as a child, on a long, curving road that led through Queen's Wood, which formed a border with High-gate. On school mornings I'd traipse through it, slowed by my sister. If we were lucky, we'd get a lift from a schoolboy's mother. She drove a pale green Mercedes-like car, imported from the Middle East. Of her, all I can only remember is the back of her head.

We'd often have family dinners in Muswell Hill. There were two Chinese restaurants back-to-back. One month it would be the Cantonese, with its bright orange and yellow sauces. Another, the Peking Duck banquet. On our return home, as we entered that dark forest, my father might turn off the cars' engine and lights, and we'd coast home in an exhila-rated silence.

An Extract from *The Carpenter and the Goat Herder* – Chapter 6

When the warlord was dead, the village would get its children back and for him, his belongings, and his peaceful life. Tomorrow, he'd ask the villagers to help him move the wooden figure into his house.

The cart lurched heavily, throwing Kip sideways. His sweaty hands lost grip on the reins. He grabbed for the side rail, but it snapped, sending him over the edge. The donkey drew the cart a little further on, then stopped.

Kip pushed himself up into a sitting position and breathed rapidly. He'd sprained his right shoulder and gashed his left knee. The donkey glanced at him. At least it had stopped. But now he could see why: the axle had split, throwing a wheel. He could repair it, at least well enough to get home, but he would need someone else to help him lift the cart. He limped to the back of the cart and collected his tools. He dragged off a chair to use for spare parts.

Rough hair brushed against his legs. 'That's unlucky,' said a female voice behind him. More goats circled his legs.

'Or is it bad workmanship?'

Could it be her!? Kip thought. He spun round and looked down, expecting to see the little girl goat herder. Instead, a young woman stood in the road as goats jostled around her.

'This donkey always seems to find the biggest holes.'

'They seem to find trouble, don't they?'

Kip examined the woman. She did resemble the girl somewhat, perhaps it was her older sister.

'Do you need any help?' she asked.

'Yes, I do.'

Kip repaired the split hub using a chair leg as an axle rod. The goat herder stroked the donkey's head. She wore a similar dress to the girl before and it caught the light in the same way. She took Kip's bucket to fetch water for the donkey and her goats.

The goat with a collar and bell climbed onto a tree stump and faced the donkey. The goat bleated, its pink tongue shaking violently. The donkey remained stoic.

The goat herder returned and placed the bucket under the donkey's nose. It dunked its head straight in, followed by a few goats.

The girl rolled a green pod between her fingers as she approached Kip. He stopped hammering in the axle rod.

'What is that?'

'A bean creeper pod. It's meant to be lucky.'

'Aren't the seeds poisonous?'

'Don't you ever do anything dangerous?'

Kip picked up the wheel and positioned it opposite the cart. He motioned for her to hold it upright. 'Now, when I lift the cart, you must push it onto the axle.' She nodded.

Kip crouched underneath the cart, wedging his shoulders against the cart's base. He pushed upwards and when the axle aligned with the wheel's hub, he shouted, 'Now!'

The goat herder pushed on the wheel. He lowered the cart which bounced, creaked, but remained in place. Kip hammered on the hubcap. 'Thank you,' he said, climbing back up. 'We should go, the donkey needs feeding.'

'And what about you?'

'I'm usually too tired to cook on market days. Thanks again.'

'Goodnight, Kip.'

It was dark when they got back to the village. The donkey

trotted into the barn and Kip stored the unsold items. Something caught his attention – the smell of ginger. He'd not bought any from the market, just a few vegetables. He probably had some in the kitchen, but that couldn't explain it. Approaching the house, the aroma was now mixed with the smell of stewing meat. Pork, perhaps.

He peered through the window into his living room, but it was empty. The kitchen light was on. Kip tried to remember if he'd left it on. He took the knife from his belt and gripped the front door's, handle. He turned the key and pushed the door open, stepping inside. He tiptoed towards the kitchen.

The room was illuminated. A woman stood by the light switch, tall with long hair, wrapped in a red blanket. It was the carving, come alive. He gazed. 'Better close your mouth unless you're catching flies?'

She glared at the knife and put her hands on her hips. 'I think you're done, don't you?'

They sat at the dining table and ate the pork stew she'd made. It was good; better than anything he'd ever cooked.

Between mouthfuls he'd steal glances at the empty plinth.

He was angry with himself for not noticing it was empty.

'Looking outside will not change anything.'

'But it's impossible.'

'Do I not look real?' She threw out her arm. 'Go on, feel.'

Kip held up his hands, palms forward. 'I believe you.'

At the end of the meal, he cleared the dishes. When he returned, she was adjusting the blanket.

'I'm sorry, that blanket must be uncomfortable. It's usually on... never mind. Let me find you something else.'

'I'm tougher than I look but thank you.'

Kip still had some of his wife's clothing. He grabbed a few items and returned. 'You can sleep in our... my room. I will sleep in the rocking chair.'

She held the clothes to her chest. 'Tell me about your life, so I can place it.'

'What do you mean?'

'I remember parts of my life before this,' she said, looking down at her body. 'The conversations nearby, the wind against my bark. The birds and insects that made a home on me. The rain falling on my leaves. But I cannot place the voices I've heard to those in the village.'

Kip added logs to the fire. 'Do you have a name?'

'Trees do not have names. But now that I am something else.' She gripped the blanket. 'I shall be called Ekundu.' It meant red.

Kip beckoned her to sit. 'Let me tell you about my wife. She had a voice you would remember.'

Denise EL Rawls

I am Denise EL Rawls, a proud dual heritage (Jamaican British) working-class, fledging writer from Hackney. I write stories centring female joy and hope. I am editing a full-length novel which won the High Commended, Writers and Working-Class Writers Prize in 2020.

During the pandemic I regularly walked my dog around Springfield Park and became very attached to the grounds and the parks history. I love that, thanks to the proactive conservation of the house, the River Lea, the marshland and the railway the view from the hill hasn't changed that much over the past 100 years. Inside Springfield House is a display of its history, including some of the people who worked there. According to the 1851 census Isabella Leigh, a 50-year-old British Subject of Jamaica, was the Bros family's cook. We don't have any more information on Isabella, 'Hard Food' is my reimagination of her story.

Extract from *Hard Food*

I am leaving Springfield House today. I have been longing to leave this place for years, now finally, on this crisp October day in the year of 1854 I leave. I've packed my bag and I've Milly's hair ornament safely tucked away inside a layer of cotton. I've made my bed, packed a few provisions for the trip and have been to say goodbye to the cedar tree standing by the servant's entrance of this fancy house. I've stood under that tree's broad branches, breathing in her woody sweet smell so many times while looking down to the river it seemed only right to tell her I'm going. I didn't know they have this tree in England, it is the only thing created under my sun that thrives here.

I am still not convinced leaving will happen until I am away. You see the last time I asked Mrs Boon about her plans to return to Jamaica she shooed me away. "Soon Isabella, we'll talk about it soon" she flipped, "right now we must focus on preparing the house before the first frost."

That was back in September, two years past. Yuletide was coming, the air was damp even though apples were still clinging to the trees in the orchard near the gate-house, waiting to be picked. Early mornings held a fine mist, rolling up from the Lea, carrying the whisper of winter. I was already wearing the sontag our neighbour Mrs Hamley had given me last Boxing Day. A beautiful thing, cream and scarlet, with a thin floppy frill waving along the edges.

I wasn't expecting such an extravagant offering. It is absolutely the nicest gift I have received. Mrs Boon asked me about it when we were discussing the menus for her New Year's Day lunch. She said she would ask Mrs Hamley directly to be sure there was not a mistake, and I was the intended for it. When I saw Milly, Mrs Hamley's cook at the Grocery collecting provisions, Milly told, her mistress delighted in telling mine it was a gift from a gentleman she no longer wished to call at the house and she'd noticed I was carrying a chill. Mrs Boon was horrified on hearing about gentlemen callers prowling around the hill.

Mrs Hamley is a troublesome woman. I like her very much.

I was 46 when I arrived at Springfield House, soon it will be 51 years on this earth that spins slowly around the sun. Never did I imagine me, little Isabella Leigh, born on a creole on a plantation in Jamacia would travel to England as a free cook. I say free, but even as a so-called British Subject I do not have the freedoms enjoyed by men or even the poorest women here, I do suppose I have more freedoms than any negro back home.

Mr and Mrs Boon didn't want to leave me at Duckenfield Hall, they enjoyed my cooking too much. I would not work in another plantation house, there had been enquiries on my service. I would travel to London and become their cook, in their new home which sat on atop a hill in the parish of Hackney.

Mrs Boon carefully explained I'd have a wage and my own room. I had never had my own room before. At Duckenfeld, I slept in the bunk house with Mary and Flo. How I miss them girls. They were so excited for me when I left. I didn't know then that a home is not where you sleep, it's where your heart is most happy.

My room so. It has a window, it's too high for me to see out of unless I stand on a chair, and even then, all I can see is the ground stretching out towards the fine lawn. I am grateful for that window and the air seeping through the crack when its open. No matter the season, if it is what the English call hot, or snow is settled across the gardens, that opening brings the familiar scent of my cedar tree which creaks when the wind rushes hard around the house into my below-stairs world. Some nights I lay in bed wondering if a bough might snap unable to cope against the strain. Some nights I wonder if I will snap too? My room is comfortable. The bed, is off the floor, not like the bunk house. Mistress has provided me, and all the servants with a gown, bedding, sheets and blankets and a thick layer of an eiderdown. It all has 'SH' embroidered on it, tiny blue silk stiches in the corners. The family's stiches are in red, just in case Mistress should ever find the wrong sheets in the wrong place.

One-time back home Mary mixed up the bedding. Boy she got a whooping and was told to burn the sheets. She only burned one, the smoke was all the old mistress was looking for, and Mary, she kept the others. The whites never came in the bunk house so Mary decided they'd never know she kept them. She said as her people died picking the cotton that them, she was entitled. Dear Mary enjoyed those sheets every night, especially when her husband visited.

I can imagine Mary's screwed up face buried into the eiderdown filled with down duck feathers. I think I might die in England if it was not for that eiderdown. Behind the confusion over my bedding would be disappointment and sadness set hard on Mary's face for me not having any flowers in my room. "We are free, we are allowed to enjoy all God's gifts" she would express, thoughtfully turning over the small velvet bow I kept by my bed in her tiny worn-out hands. She was younger than I but she had been worked much harder. Some days when she couldn't play the plantation game, she would speak her feelings. She rarely got whips; the Overseer sent her into the fields, knowing that would hurt her more. Hold Mary's hands and you feel her story.

Over the last few months, my monthly bleed has stopped, hairs grow on my chin. I am getting old, I worry I might die here in England, no kin or gentle word. I am not ready to become an ancestor, I want to see my Molly and the wide blue skies again before my time sets. I want to see the fiery yellow sun dip behind the earth one last time.

When the end of the enslavement of my people finally came, never did I think I would leave Saint Thomas in East Parish, let alone Jamacia. Like most of my people, I stayed working in the big house, for me life was not really different. I was legally free, but I was still a slave in the minds and hearts of the not-so-gentlemen making the decisions about everything on the island. I needed work, somewhere to live, where was I going with no money, no papers, no husband? The law said we were free but we have no real freedom, or the money to buy any.

Negro villages were the only villages I knew and trust me them nothing like the village of Hackney. Emancipation did not bring better lives to we, nor any of that high British government compensation.

All things considered, and I have considered all things many times, I know I am better off than most. Mrs Boon never took a switch to me and Mr Boon, had affection for her. Unlike his father, he didn't force himself on me or any of the servants, as far as I am aware, you never know with these men.

I eagerly agreed to come to England, for three years only. I would return to Jamacia with Mrs Boon when she travelled back to visit the schoolhouse she helped to found while she celebrated the end of slavery. She's very proud of that school. It's set in the old administration building. I hated it. The Accountant took so many young girls there to break them, I couldn't go past without rehearing those poor girl's silent screams. The red bricks hold so much pain that even as a building filled with young souls it can never be anything but a menacing reminder of the hell that happened there.

227

Domestic staff rules here are different than in Jamacia, even though we have the same government. I am paid a wage of thirty pounds a year, provided with a little barrel of beer each week and have coal for my fire. I knew beer, but I had never seen a fire inside a bedroom. If I had known about this kind of cold, I would have stayed in Jamacia. After accepting the dampness seeping into my bones and the yellowing of my skin from the lack of sunshine, I get used to living in Springfield House. I never relish English winters which the Boon's seemed to enjoy. How can you be happy when your breath freezes?

The other servants were suspicious of me, of course. They couldn't understand why the Boons had brought me, a negro woman, back with them from the Caribbean. They said Mr. Boon must have taken me for a lover, or Mrs. Boon for that matter. Oh, they loved making up reasons for my being here until they tasted my rum cake and my salt and pepper chicken; then they understood fully why this high family would ship me, along with their monogrammed linens, to the other side of the world. The staff had never tasted such delights; they would steal spoonfuls from my pots and ask me for the recipes. The wretches cannot read nor pronounce the names of my spices; sharing any details was pointless. The best they could wish for was Mrs. Boon allowing me to dish up leftovers from a party.

The food is decent, but my, I miss hard food. Real crops from red soil. Sometimes I make yellow curry from the scraps of meat without anyone understanding the joy that brings me, but the potatoes—ugly brown Irish potatoes—never a sweet potato or a yam. Potatoes become too dull after eating them every day. And

I don't make flatbread here; the family eats loaf bread made with fine flour, which looks like the powder the mistress puts on her face. I can't eat that bread; it swells me up like a dead cow. But really, what I miss most is the smell of the plantation. The smell of burning sugar cane in the boiling house, of manure on the soil, of orange trees warmed by the sun, all mixed up with the aridness of the negro village when you pass along the track before you get to the big house. I miss the smell of our kind of poverty.

I have witnessed here that many working people have poverty too. And that there are many different kinds of richness. I don't have money, but I have a wealth of persons dear to me. Folk who will hold my secrets deep until they can be released into the sky like a hummingbird drinking on nectar. I've learned that small animals here hibernate; they curl up with the gain of time and their very own place to be. They are warm, secure underground, and they wait patiently, undisturbed, for the winter to be over. I have tried to hibernate my mind, focusing on the tiny things: the shrimp molded into the frieze that runs around the dining room ceiling, the way the light changes throughout the day. If the sun is very bright, it breaks its beam on a curve in the glass by the front door, throwing a rainbow across the entrance hall. This is richness, especially when the days are short and the plane trees lining the front path have become skeletal, their leaves lost to winters, standing naked like enslaved girls being picked over before an auction at the Pera Estate.

I don't see much of the harshness of Hackney. When I go to the village, I go by carriage alone but for the driver, or with Mrs.

Boon. From the high-up window of the wagon, I can see the people with dead eyes. Those who sleep in the shadows and in alleyways, those who spend more time in the alehouse than they should because there is nowhere else to go.

When I meet folk, away from the house, I don't mind them, and they don't mind me. People of good character know I am the negro cook from Springfield House. After the locals got past their curiosity, they began to ignore me, as they do all the servants, as we servants do them.

I've mostly stayed on Springfield Hill. Even on my afternoon off, I don't go far from the grounds. Occasionally, I like visiting the greenhouse over on Big Hill; Mr. Johnstone has produced the most amazing orchids there, and he doesn't object if I go to see the bright pink and orange florae in full bloom, like the brightest garden jewels. Mr. Johnstone's eyes are kindly; he drops his head, nodding intently when anyone speaks to him. He likes to talk about the flowers of Jamaica and the other islands he has taken specimens from. Sometimes, after church, I like to walk through the laid-out gardens to see the water fountain. I have no need to go any further; I don't have a chaperone, which seems ridiculous at my age, and Mrs. Boon doesn't need to send me any further. I've had a very simple, often lonely life here. I am grateful, even though it is taking my breath from me. I've been canny, saving nearly all of my wages, enough, I think, to buy a small parcel of land at home and my gravestone. I wrote it all down for Molly in case God didn't spare my life. Now I just need to survive the return journey.

I am ready for home. I miss the smack of the briny sea tang

hitting my tongue. That taste of acidity when the ocean meets Salt River Bay is like no other. I want to feel the hot, hot sun on my skin, making my face tight and sweaty at the same time. I want to hear deep thunder rumbling over the Blue Mountains before a storm lashes down its big rain, before my feet sink in the warm mud as I run for cover under the broad leaf of a banana tree. I want to eat yam, roasted underground in a fire pit so the skin is blistered and charred, and I get heat bumps on the inside of my mouth from eating too fast. I want to sit with my grown child and comb her hair, feel the soft skin on her plump ears as I gently turn her head from side to side, folding her large curls into fat plaits, finished with that dark green velvet bow I've been holding since my time in England began.

That hair ornament has become a good friend I can tell secrets to. Mrs. Boon discarded it after a party at Easter, not long after we first arrived; she said it made her head look like a rabbit. I think it is delightful and was so pleased when she said I may keep it. It will look perfect on my Molly. I keep it with my prayer book.

Cheryl Cohen

A remorseful estate agent, apologising for being late, gave me a tour of Tottenham Hale. It never occurred to me to turn right off Tottenham High Road, towards the east. I didn't know the area existed.

My flat overlooks the River Lea, with the Walthamstow wetlands beyond. The sun sets over Canary Wharf. My view will always be trees and water.

In the morning, the reflections from the river dance on my ceiling. Coots and moorhens battle for domination with the swans and noisy Canada geese. Neon-blue and green dragon-flies hover outside my window. Walk or cycle along the river path to the marshes, or to Limehouse. It's the other side, the wild side of Tottenham.

Tottenham felt unloved when I moved in. Too much rubbish everywhere, fly-tipping, shabby shops, not enough locally sourced food for my liking. I started a mini-festival to promote local producers called Tottenham Ploughman, which was named after the key ingredients, all sourced within the area. I got to know the lovely local community.

Redemption Brewery is still here, but Wildes Cheese and Flourish Bakery are sadly no more. I'd hate to see Tottenham turn into Stoke Newington, but there's a gentle balance to be found. I'm part of a very supportive local poetry group in Tottenham, run by poet Abe Gibson. Writing is central to my existence; words thrill me, keep me alive, and living here provides inspiration and exasperation in equal measure.

A Collection of Poems

Black mulberry

you soft seductive flirting taste of summer
dark lashes peak behind leaves
bright dark eyes that defy anyone to steal
*   you away*
your fruits rare jewel ripe, red to deep black
like a cat lazing in the sun, you give
a come hither look, then
defy; be
quick to pick before you drop and dribble
you'd rather
splatter blood stained droplets onto the earth,
than be plucked
And if you do relent
fingertips are stained with retribution

ME meets ADHD. A rant.

Panicking in public speaking, deadline writing, escape room failing, duvet changing, dust in corners, voices flailing....brain is tailing, exasperation, blurting talking, mind is bending, interrupting, memory lapsing, squirming busted, conversations, brain is fizzing, noise is busy, climbing ceilings, feeling dizzy, mental effort, side-tracked tasking, pay attention! And the Duvet still needs changing. Where's my wallet, and my passport, what's their name and who are you? What does ADHD stand for? Can't do crowds and can't do noisy, can't do volumes, can't do seats. Don't do coffee, no bright lights. Spilled my tea and cracked the teapot. Dust in corners taking over. Writing projects put on hold. Muscles aching, can't do facing...anything, right now. Restless hands and restless feet, can't keep still and can't keep neat.

Under the bridges of Tottenham v7 Dec 2022

Under the bridges of Tottenham
The water slops and laps with
Warm, fetid breath

Under the pond weed in Tottenham,
The lost shadows of slow running water
Free floating with the current at darkness's edge

As old as flint.

Living In-between lives
Rattlingly breathing in the effluence

Here the echoes corrode. No one cares
In the melting dream darkness
the shrill pop of a coot Interrupts the lost silence
Half there folk, skiddle along shadows
rooting up rust with impatient claws
Peculiar, not particular, there's good pickings
       here

Under the radar in Tottenham
Black clad thieves on stolen bikes. Dog walkers.
Canal dwellers shuttered against the night air.
Wish bloods – Shallow crunchers – Diluted by
       the dawn.

Ice

I wanted a drink when you'd left
But there was no ice
It seemed defeatist
The sound so solid
Determined
Cold and bleak
To hear it hitting the bottom of the glass
splintering on my tongue
Floating, touching, parting, melting.

236

I wanted a drink so I made one, but the ice I
    craved
So nice, so right
Ice is cruel, to be parted, from ice, why didn't
You fill up the freezer before you departed
The sound of a drink without ice
Is defeatist
The sound without ice is an empty room

June 2002

To the man listening to LBC on a transistor radio on the bus

To the woman on her speaker phone telling the
    world about her husbands boils
To all the cyclists crashing through the river path
    with boom boom boxes, crushing the natural
    soundtrack
Acrobats in the park balancing on the high wire
    belting out music from their speakers

Footballers accompanied by a high volume
    discordant audacity

Thank you for sharing your music, your noise,
    your private conversations.
When did it become acceptable to share so
    publicly?

I've got noise doctor
It's ringing in my ears doctor
There's no escaping doctor
From the swarm of sound.
It's on the underground, doctor
On bicycles and park benches, under my bed,
        through my windows

I'm allergic to noise pollution and its spreading
        like a plague.

On the bus the tinny vibes of a You Tube advert
        that emulate from the 2nd seat top right
Are fighting with the football fixture 3rd seat
        from the front
They're clashing with the phone based family
        infighting by the window.
They're all at it doctor.
Elderly pensioners, school kids,
        teenagers, mothers with push chairs.

When did it become okay to air conversations on
        public like dirty washing
Broad brush strokes of pain and panic, shouted
        voices, screaming laughter.
A cacophony of clashed sounds
No one seems to care but me
Maybe I should join in
With the man listening to LBC on a transistor
        radio on the bus

I dream of bringing my Bluetooth speaker

Blast out Ride of the Valkryries at top volume
Say thank you for sharing your music
I hope you enjoyed mine

If every passenger plays music or has a conversa-
	tion on their speaker;
What kind of musical score would arise. Bring
	back conductors.

In the park
I come looking for peace and birdsong.
I find the heavy thud of rap from bench and
	barbecue deep in my belly, and walk away.

I don't want your music. I don't want your voice.
	I only want the silence that used to be my
	choice.

But
I'm wrong
I love it if your music comes from guitar or violin
I love the drift of gentle conversations across the
	breeze.
I love the drum group who gather to share their
	ambient vibes, beat out ancient rhythms, and
	new conversations.
Meanwhile, the man with the transister radio
	holds it up to his ear, frowning at the talk
	show he shares.

Paul Angliss

I am a comedy writer and an award-winning filmmaker. I've lived in Hackney for 30 years. Any time I think of moving on, another hangout in Hackney – be it urban or green – grabs me and I think where else has this and the people that make the place? I live with my partner, Priya, and our solidly Hackneyite daughter, Nancy.

Extract from *Starless and Bible Black*: 1

'Have you considered that your formula for saving humanity by destroying mankind might perhaps require a tweak?'

That tinny, disembodied voice joined its owner, a man appearing on the mobile phone screen with his bushy head at a tilt. He, Dr Wu Xen Pratt, with his hair and beard fitting him like a fuzzy balaclava, was reclining, drearily addressing Professor Breville O'Singh from a green, leather Chesterfield sofa.

'Like, you know, when you promise the people the discovery

of all knowledge in exchange for climate change? Might that need some work? Hard to say.'

The image on O'Singh's phone lurched away from the features of Dr Pratt and whooshed across a stately chamber, appearing as it might to a suddenly nausea-gripped teenage drunk. The shot shuddered. Jump-zoomed in and wavered on a scene of mayhem. A mob heaving in waves against a buckling line of riot police officers shielding the Houses of Parliament. O'Singh now saw that he was watching a television channel's rolling news play out fuzzily through Pratt's phone.

'Though we could of course ask the people. They look like they've made an informed opinion.'

Bottles, glasses and innumerable items that would struggle to get themselves a mention on TV's Antiques Roadshow 400 years hence, exploded skywards from the hordes. Like an ill-timed and uncoordinated pyrotechnic display of junk that rained down on the riot police who, forced to defend the aerial bombardment, suddenly found themselves vulnerable to a renewed surge of bodies.

'But I did not mean it,' whimpered O'Singh. One bulging eye loomed large on Pratt's mobile screen, surrounded by beads of perspiration gathered round a spectacle frame.

It was then that a hollow thud and hollering from distant streets rudely alerted the professor to his immediate surroundings. He flinched and involuntarily ducked his head, though even encumbered as he was with baggage, he did not break step. This was central London of grand stone edifices and leafy squares, for a moment again eerily quiet, tensing itself as if against an anticipatory blow.

'The people know about man-made climate change,' resumed Dr Pratt, staring out again, hair-framing O'Singh's screen. 'What they don't realise is that it is exactly that. Man-made. Made by one man. By you.'

'But what about the truth?'

Pratt slipped into an expression of mingled awe and pity.

'You do realise who you're dealing with?' he drawled.

'What can I do, Dr Pratt?' pleaded O'Singh.

'Nothing. There's nothing you can do. The Government is about to make you, me, the scapegoat; close down the Investigations of the Para-Usual. Truth, the truth we sought, is dead. Admit to yourself, it's over, O'Singh. Humanity shall never benefit from knowledge.'

'Professor! Hey, know who that is?' came a yell from O'Singh's end.

'Who?' came a reply.

'Wow! He's bigger than he looks on television!'

'Aren't people supposed to be smaller than they look on tele?'

O'Singh glanced back. A rabble was spilling from a side street toting placards like so many lance-tilting Don Quixotes. One of their number was dressed as a giant slice of burnt toast for a reason possibly explained in the message daubed on the protest banner she dangled in front of her, back-to-front. The professor had a block's distance between him and the rabble, in front of him the garden square to traverse and make it to Dr Pratt at the Department of Energy, Climate Change and Green Stuff.

'Professor Breville O'Singh!'

'Where have we seen him?'

'Come on. Breville O'Singh. The presenter. The bloke who did the documentary. The one on telly – Everything about Everything.'

Near-distantly sirens stirred into a woeful whoop.

'Wait!' yelped Dr Pratt, tinnily. 'There's something. That's it! The documentary! There is something you might do. Think back, O'Singh. Your very first day on set. From that, from there, learn what is your greatest flaw.'

'My greatest, Dr Pratt? Could it be the very same thing as human beings' greatest flaw?'

'What?'

'Having arms too short to flannel-wash the middle of our upper back?'

'OK right, OK, so think what is your second-greatest flaw?'

'You mean equal greatest?' O'Singh contributed, reasonably. Greatest could only ever be attributed to one thing after all.

'Your equal greatest flaw, your other Achilles heel, is your failure to control knowledge. Fail to control knowledge and the existence of mankind shall forever be in jeopardy. And yet you cannot hope to do that before you figure out how to save the Government. You don't have time. Correction, you have between now and the time it would take you to get yourself over here to realise. Before the minister here decides to swing the axe on us. Before the mob discovers that you're the foe.'

'Oi, professor!'

'It is him! That's him!'

'Even you could not supercompute your way out of this. Could you? Could you, professor?' came the strained voice of Dr Pratt.

'Professor O'Singh!' sang the giant toast.

'Better get yourself here sharpish, O'Singh,' sighed Pratt to the linen of Professor Breville O'Singh's trouser leg, for the professor's arm had fallen to his side. The mighty academic had succumbed to a sudden paralysis, bringing to a conclusion as he did, the mobile phone conversation that would shape the destiny of humanity. An exchange between a most misunderstood polymath and his colleague, a nonchalant doomsayer – a man who up until that moment had dressed himself in a pantomime dog suit. Why that was, and whether that suit was Pekinese or Great Dane, whether bespoke or off-the-rack, we shall see. What we would later learn is this. That the fate of mankind has never rested on an event quite as pivotal since it embarked on that evolutionary venture to become more ambitious newts. To wriggle itself out of the swamps and try its luck on land. Or perhaps since it decided that it should shun the foliage, drop down out of the trees and have a global poke around. What, it thought, was the worst that could happen?

At this momentous juncture our collective fate rested on this: how Professor Breville O'Singh would process what happened on the set of that documentary. Within, of course, the time it takes to cross a London Square, albeit hastened by what might be an appreciation society or a baying mob intent on his offal.

The documentary...

Candyman: 2

The most important lessons humankind could ever hope to learn on a scale of those grasped by our ancient relatives – the obliging newts, the entrepreneurial, tree-shirking apes – were those Professor O'Singh was about to preach. How, miraculously, we can be empowered to know what we already know... that we did not know we already knew. Think about that. All of this in that documentary Dr Pratt spoke of – 'Everything about Everything'. Professor Breville O'Singh promised to show us the path to all knowledge. Whereupon we might seize upon and explore a random subject and in doing so reveal previously untapped knowledge. And then further discover that that knowledge itself might be explored and yet more knowledge revealed. And ad infinitum until we come to know everything. And that is how we achieve all knowledge. 'Everything about Everything' was to be the documentary to end all documentaries. For, indeed, what else could anyone learn after that?

The masses would become aware of our potential saviour, our potential destroyer, sometime just before the Westminster Riots. In the early Stone Age, to be less imprecise, moments before his image swam into focus. For the announcement of Professor Breville O'Singh to the big stage, his grand introduction to a breathless television audience, was as a blur. This was to be the opening shot of the documentary. The blur resolving into a jerky handheld camera image of a bear-shaped man, or perhaps a man-shaped bear. Professor O'Singh. A figure as imposing as a Cassius Clay. Albeit one that looked sorry for the imposition, for the professor was apologetically large. Here was he with this seismic opportunity.

The professor stood back from the cave, hands clasped behind his back awestruck by the cavepeople, who in a spirit of curiosity, were violating the studio set-up. Here for O'Singh was a priceless opportunity to observe what Stone-Agers made of twenty-first century living.

The professor pouted thoughtfully, adjusted his spectacles and peered down at an immaculately typewritten script he held now in front of him. 'EXTERIOR. CAVE ENTRANCE. NIGHT,' O'Singh read aloud, the description of the scene setting at the top of the topmost page. 'The CAVEMAN sits nobly upon a boulder chipping a flint spearhead. He glances at his CAVEWIFE across the cave tending a cauldron suspended above a fire.' Looking up, he espied the male cave-dweller, the

troglodyte, grimacing intently, chewing a lens cap while preci-
sion-dismantling the studio camera. Heedless of the camera
operator by turns lunging tentatively at the caveman and clapping his hands vigorously in non-congratulatory
discouragement.

'The CAVEWOMAN stirs the cauldron, gracefully, medi-
tatively,' read O'Singh, returning to the script. Across the floor
at the side of a make-up artist sat frozen in her canvas chair, was
the caveman's spouse, picking what she had decided to be nits
from her victim's hair. Virtual nits.

Again, the professor surveyed the contrast between script
description and the activity on set. At that moment in time, as
his dream was being destroyed, O'Singh sensed that he was
blessed. That his time, this time, had finally come.

'And while we have them here in this moment in the 21st
century, they are taking our studio apart,' he marvelled, under
his breath in his soft, South African lilt.

There was O'Singh's first lesson, surely? The audience had
only just met the professor but already they had a window into
the professor's slippery control of knowledge. The longer he
allowed those pesky cavepeople to disrupt the production, the
less chance the show had of making an awe-inspiring impact, of
luring the optimum audience and empowering the people to
exponentially increase their knowledge. For the longer the hold-
up, the shorter the time there would be to capture the visuals.
Think how the truly epic documentaries influenced so
profoundly. Sir David Attenborough and his legendary Life on
Earth series with its glorious scenes. The iconic footage of Sir
David hunkered down with a troop of gorillas in the misty,
verdant highlands of Rwanda. By contrast, Everything About
Everything was threatening to weigh heavier on narrative,
lighter on illustration. If O'Singh failed to take control, this

episode would soon enough be fit only for radio. Hell, if that caveman was to wrap his molars round the sound-recording equipment, this show would be imparting knowledge on a level with the medieval town crier. 'Oyez! Oyez! I am sitting here alongside the dominant male silverback!' And how well would that go? David Attenborough with the apes. What did he do in their company up the Rwandan mountains? He kept his voice to a whisper. Gorillas respond to unnecessary noise. It upsets them. And you don't want to upset a gathering of primates weighing 200 kilos a piece, collectively a metric tonne of monkey sinew. 'Oyez!' at 140 decibels, lustily ringing a hand bell in a silverback's shell-like. Those gorillas are going to go apeshit. Even if we fail to understand the connection between the faeces of a large primate and a highly excitable state, we figure that this is a serious situation all the same. That town square with its weekend farmer's market is about to be equally upset. The traditional, quirky themed food stalls tipped over by an enraged whoop. That Cockney-Spanish fusion street food – its paella, mash and liquor – slopped all over the cobblestones. People panicking to escape that square, slipping on locally sourced, organic, artisanal, free-range donkey cheese. Those down to slum it for the weekend in their second home country retreats scrambling to get to their four-wheel drive urban tractors parked in adjacent streets, convinced that thieves are breaking into them. They are not to know that the monkey whooping is from the frantic apes and not their car alarms. The whole thing is a disaster, documentary-wise.

O'Singh became aware then of a man at his feet wielding a handheld camera, hungrily capturing his reactions. The very same cameraman that had begun recording the professor as a blur on set presenting his first episode, his first subject – Alphabetti Spaghetti. The academic had arrived. And yet. And yet.

O'Singh's triumph was built on rickety foundations. Those unruly cavepeople were disruptive, but in truth they were merely the spoilers of knowledge. The outright exploiters, the grabbers of knowledge, the professor did not see that first day on set.

'O.M.G.A.!' exclaimed a figure, diminutive in form, dressed as a nineteenth century explorer.

'What is even the point of having a chauffeur?' she griped, stepping out from the shadows into the studio glare, take-away coffees in hand. A chauffeur – a French driver! Have you even seen how the French drive?'

'Persil, you poor sweetheart,' mewed Mike Baby, tripping across the set to greet his collaborator. The show's producer-director was sporting a teddy bear design T-shirt. A brand of toddler chic favoured by ironic creatives.

'What is it with London? There's more speed bumps on the roads than the flat bits!'

The profoundly aggrieved Persil Bland raised the veil from her pith helmet and propped one leather-booted foot upon a fake rock. Voluminous khaki pants tucked into the boots and an open-necked shirt completed the Victorian explorer look.

'The actors are those we met yesterday, are they not?' broke in O'Singh, who had tracked across the studio to join the documentary makers. 'Our scene players?'

'At your disposal,' answered Baby, bowing with a gallant flourish. His exaggerated movements gave the impression that he was being controlled by a puppeteer.

'What are they doing? Can't you stop them?' demanded Persil.

'They're method actors,' replied Baby, reasonably.

'What do you mean "method"? Get off me you freak!' she

shrieked, rounding on the cavewoman, who had stolen up to tug at her shirt.

'It means,' replied Baby, stamping his foot to repel Persil's assailant, 'they actually become the characters they're asked to play.'

'So, have we begun the documentary already?' asked O'Singh, referring to the cameraman closely attending his every word and deed.

'Yep, that's my man,' said Persil, proudly.

''E and 'is assigned director are what we call the "second unit"; commonly used to pick up all the filler shots we need for the offshoot doco,' said Baby, nonchalantly imparting his wisdom.

'I see. I hope rather it will not be, well, a little off-putting,' said O'Singh, tentatively, hoping to convey that the cameraman was manifestly off-putting.

'Better get used to it!' sang Persil. 'The making of the doco's what's going to grab us the ratings.'

Persil disengaged from the two men and surveyed the set with an air of proprietary satisfaction. All of this was what she had set in motion, what she had made possible.

'They're like monkeys at a wildlife park,' she remarked of the cavepeople, referring to the precocious primates that rip windscreen wipers from cars on English country estate safaris.

O'Singh edged out onto the set with a look of intent.

'What are you going to do?' called Persil after him. 'How are you going to get them to do what you need them to do?'

'We will need to work with them,' said O'Singh in a low whisper, returning just briefly to charge Persil with the script. 'Gain their trust.'

Attaining the mocked-up fire, the professor lowered himself down onto one knee, where he began poking around the hearth beneath the rock-hewn cooking pot. Flames licked up around the bottom of the vessel.

'Ug!' grunted O'Singh, staggering to his feet. 'Ug! Ug!' he directed at the cave people.

Backstage, the caveman and cavewoman broke off from their foraging on instant coffee granule spillage on a catering tabletop and gawped at the professor pointing at the fire.

'Ug!' they replied in unison, then 'Ug!' at each other. They scampered back to the set and over to O'Singh to sniff at the hand that had lit the fire. To the fire itself then, where they circled the flames. But in venturing too close, the caveman recoiled suddenly from the heat and darted off, whooping, hotly pursued by his cave wife, alarmed by her cave husband's reaction.

'Ug!' repeated O'Singh. The cave couple had gone to ground underneath the backstage catering table. 'Ug!' O'Singh continued to grunt, reassuringly, until the Stone Agers had huddled themselves into a calmer state.

Little by little they returned. O'Singh reached for a wooden spoon and stirred the contents of the pot, checking all the time that he had the cave people's attention. Persil and Baby exchanged looks. O'Singh raised the spoon laden with wriggling Alphabetti Spaghetti pasta letters up to his mouth and slurped, exaggerating his enjoyment of the literal snack.

The cave people closed in. O'Singh dipped the spoon, scooped up another portion. He proffered it to the cavewoman, nodding encouragement for her to try. Uncertainly, she hobbled forward, seized hold of the utensil and bolted the contents, dribbling surplus letters down her chin. Her jaws worked to a standstill. Her eyes opened wide.

'Ug!' she exclaimed, excitedly, 'Ug!' She plunged the spoon back into the pot for another helping and thrust it toward her cave husband. 'Taste it,' she was saying. And as he did so, O'Singh crept back to Persil and Baby.

'I believe I may well have invented fire,' said O'Singh, impressively.

Persil and Baby peered across to the cavepeople, now clumsily, greedily sharing the spoils.

'And perhaps conceived what would later become known as the TV dinner... post Logie Baird and the invention of the television, of course,' added O'Singh.

He waited expectantly for a reaction.

'So, cavemen really did live in caves?' marvelled Persil, first to speak.

A sharp crack, the clapping of hands, was the cue from Baby. The documentary crew that had drifted onto set at first by dribs and drabs, leapt into action, dragging, shifting and replacing props.

Harry Penfold

There is something of Singapore about Hackney; everything flows through it. The towel-dried Lords at Aubert Park, the Friends of Shakespeare and murders at Crobar. Barbara Cartland painted by George Grosz.

Every morning at Highbury Fields, a man known locally as the Fool of Oban sings the Marseillaise. While making his own way towards the public pool, he might suddenly yell and step backwards, stand stock still like a cricket stump or break into a jitterbug yodelling all the while.

I often saw him at Kingsland Waste, with his pale oval face an egg, and his eyes staring as if pressed against a window pane. He wore a black bowler hat, and a penny-sized badge on his blue dungarees which said 'I love Balboa'.

He would stand on one leg on the diving board with his hands stretched over the edge, whilst a deep pedal note you could hear in the water rolled like a ball in his gut.

Once in the pond, his head was filled with show tunes and the Bucks of the Kingdom of Fife. He spouted nonsense to the tune of an Irish strathspey.

The Fool quoted Colette to the tune of Auld Lang Syne; sang a ballade about Glenlogie; then belched like a bugle, fired a broadside, and found a refrain in Tolstoy. Rolled on his back like a pink otter and splashing to keep time, he threw his voice like a discuss into the sky.

'He turned into toothpaste tonight / I had to sing the blues just to keep him talking', sang the Fool.

Sometimes, rarely, then often, he revealed what an innocent he really was. I recall one early morning, at my flat on Ockendon Road, he showed me a very fine moth he had caught by the wing. 'I wish I had hair', he confided, 'it's a symbol of youth, to me'.

Confronted with the questions of his epoch, he could only laugh and cry nonsense, then sing a rigaudon. Every word he sung and spoke was evidence that our humiliating age had not won his respect.

'Merde! The first word of the day should be merde! A child's first word should be merde!'. At that, he went up like a flame at a curtain on a late Victorian stage.

This is the Hackney I want to set down; a writer and lawyer.

A Dedication to Tim Revell

In London not long ago, I went to a private gallery run by a local artist. He had transcribed the mottos of Chinese thinkers in handsome *dazibao*, then proceeded to outline, for my benefit, those phrases he revered the most, drawn in thick black paint on the wall.

There was the measure word for a book, the pronoun *he*, and the past participle *le*; and as he lectured on Yan Yuan, who travelled a thousand *li* to learn the art of fencing, the character for 'laughter' danced behind his back, drawn upside down, offensive as the Cross of St. Peter.

The signs I would betray my firm were hanging around me. They stuck out like the Sabaoth in the black sewer of the law. I wrote letters of recommendation for clientele 50 years dead; for Alexandru Iliescu, a solicitor and Communist.

Among the associates assembled in that suspect institution, I always wondered which were on the point of becoming ghosts. Some carried their cubicles with them. In pictures stranded from their time, they peer out through that box's ghost like portraiture slain in its frame.

Their social activity made them unnatural. It was out of time, unrehearsed; they took their cues from one another.

Most of them were comfortably drunk, their conversation like bad writing. Everything was in italics and everyone was unredeemed, and you thought did Christ die for these, these young professionals you were taught to admire, who are so grotesque at parties?

Each star had shuffled up to eminence, first in their own eyes and then in those of the small circle around them. They were famous in their way, a student's fame, which did not extend more than two streets to the north, two streets to the south, three to the east and one to the west of this flat on Ockendon Road.

In kitchens and lofts, laid across London's parks and fields, they were famous; and if not here than in Leicester, York, Bristol, Reading, Durham, Newcastle, Manchester, the university towns breeding legends nobody knows which define young lives forever.

I could stare at their portraits for hours, absorbed by the fantasy they create.

My picture has been a private affair, an *andachtsbild* almost. The woman who drew it only ever knew the back of my head, which she loved with the warmth of her heart; but she took to a stranger and left for the States with two paintbrushes in her hand.

She was last seen beneath a Hollywood actor, the now-supplanted darling of the Halloween circuit, famous for inhabiting monsters. You would not recognise his face, though his masks are familiar.

Friendships often die with the habits that sustain them. There are times we are so close to certain people that we believe there is a lifelong bond between us; then they vanish from our thoughts overnight.

We may be on terms of the most intimate friendship with someone, and then we think they've let us down, someone we respect and admire and consequently scorn and banish from our arms. Unwilling to ordain them with hatred as we pursued them with love, we erase them from our lives.

Chris was an old friend who knew nothing about me. His face was rumpled to suggest more vice than he could fairly lay claim to; and thin, unnaturally thin, his cheeks as concave as two bowls.

From his nose to his chin was a parabola; in profile he looked like Augustus.

The way he talked, everything open, his mouth a valve; the tough air he put on when discussing sport and war; the way he cursed, the creativity with which he damned, his sentimentality; a man sore, who debated the low brow all night and then, when his friends had left and he was alone, dreamt about Daedalus; his contempt for the rich; my oldest friend, who saw the world but nothing in it; a thousand and one evenings on which quirks and ticks were charted endeared that man to me.

All Chris had lay in his tongue. He spoke sounding brass and tinkling cymbals; things without life, giving sound.

Chris, then, standing at Speaker's Corner. He leant into the crowd before pulling back sharp, rocked by his own ebb and flow.

'Roll up, roll up - a command and request, I'm running out of Amber Leaf. Step right up, ladies and gentleman, friends and family, and those I have yet to know, gather round, gather round; stand where you can see me, sit where you can hear me.

"Music is the ultimate teacher". Said Kandinsky.

The art I love is a nameless thing; so abject, yet alive; the first twentieth-century man of the nineteenth century. He owed so little to the *Belle Epoque*, and so much to Lenin, that I cannot imagine him existing at all before 1917.

Alexander Scriabin. Europe may never again dance so ecstatically; not without tarantism and the dance of Saints Vitus and John.

There was only one voice in Scriabin's work, and that was his own, all nerve and a holy flame; and like all men who talk to themselves, this appeared madness to those who heard it.

He dreamed ahead of the musical vanguard, the Gouty Strauss and syphilitic French, that belched and filched the soporific renaissance for feelings yet retired. There was Mendelssohn, precise, beautiful, sensitive without being weak, but entirely conventional; Berlioz, whose passion was always legible, a Romantic in possession of a classical education; and the lucid nonsense of Erik Satie, who said nothing so clearly he was always understood.

Scriabin upended each of them to inspect their heels, the way a master would his horse. He saw the pin holes of waltzing stilettos and embossed stamps of military marches, their heels blistered and calloused.

There is nothing more forgettable, more mediocre, more fashionable than Scriabin's early work. Preludes without allusion; etudes without aspersion; he was the darling bauble of the dandy hall. His second symphony concludes with the flat champagne of a rusted jubilee. It lacks the fraud's self-awareness, the knowledge that he is dancing in clothes cut too small for him.

In this and this alone Elgar, that satirist of genius, was Scriabin's superior.

But that which survives the age is often what defiled it, the stone arrowhead in the cadaver's side. Scriabin was sick in his person, at war with his age and himself, and rejected by both.

He was that generation of tormented artists, of Munch and Spilliaert, who had little to say but everything to express.

When I think of his deformities, the sarcastic styles he chose, the grotesque and flatulent works he cranked to tedium, I feel an exhilaration.

"I am God", said Scriabin. It is ridiculous because it is true, just as announcing at noon that the sun has risen is ridiculous.

Scriabin had no desire to compose for everyone, as I have no urge to talk to everyone. In this, he recalls Henry Miller who holds every reader to ransom.

Miller walks you through a corridor of sacred relics – baptismal fonts, crosiers, reliquaries from Limoges – to convince you of certitudes which do not require proof, then desecrates the vestibule in which he told you to worship.

He gives you a psalter stained red with ink, with the pictures of saints cut out. You are shown the minus and plus side of the fence Miller stands above and provides a ratio between, and told to choose one.

You cannot have both, nor pretend either is the other, nor

can you plead ignorance. If you do not step forward with him, then you elect to stand still on the spot, in the monotony and sterility which drove Miller to desperation; the reasons you, out of favour with yourself, turned to Miller in the first place.

What drove them, Scriabin and Miller, together alone? Their coming together – their common cause, their contrariety – is the deepest mystery of the modern age. I cannot escape the feeling that they hold the secret to life, in much the same way as the relation of Cézanne to Pissarro seems the key to French painting; and that if we could understand what they said to no one but themselves, we would have in our hands that secret name which people once called god.

Their art was to overthrow, to sow strife and ferment, to bring up the bodies trapped in the mud with their sulphurous fumes; and if they shuffled, if they were confused and blundered and brought the axe down on their own limbs, why, I call that nourishing progress'.

Chris's set pieces are less impressive from the back. You can see the masking tape which holds his ideas in place, illuminated by the lime light. He read from a script sellotaped to the floor and his costumes looked pale and worn.

Irina joined me in the stands. A skinny woman of twenty-five, she must have once been very feminine, appealing and soft, but now was nothing but angles.

We watched the crowd that Chris addressed, four people sunk in a sofa. They groped themselves and then one another, as if searching for something lost.

Irina turned to me. 'Do you think anyone can follow him?'.

'That's not how his speeches work. He doesn't lead a crowd from A to B. He stands behind them and shrieks and clangs, trying to cajole them, like a beater driving birds towards guns'.

'That's not fair. He's not malicious. He just casts his net too wide, so that you can see all the holes in it. That's why he's so passionate. He's excited at meeting his arguments for the first time'.

There was something unsettling about Chris, when he shook ideas like an upended purse to see what fell onto the floor. But he had a maternal streak. It ran through him, a lone grey hair in a youthful fringe of freshest straw.

Later he would stop talking, and walk up to the four people now sleeping to place pillows beneath their heads. This no one would have known, had I not stayed with him to the end.

This scene recalls Mantegna's *Lamentation of Christ*.

Whenever I come across that group of men who are hopeless, who are good for nothing but talk about transport and names unknown, I want to inject a little Bang, or Hasheesh, or whatever berserkers use into them, to see them run howling down the street like a Malay Amok.

Men like Chris hang damnation and rot on our noses, without caring if we agree so long as they're allowed to talk. They'll talk about someone right there in the room, who stares unaware in front of them and then walks away bored, and carry on talking about that person because they weren't pinning them down for their sake.

When the images fade and the evenings despair; when the food and drink has gone, thousands of hours in which we named things and faces, and groped what could not be said - there will be silence, and no one to say it.

Save but a few, a lifetime of words is tombless, with no remembrance over it.

'Our life was to give name'. Said Gunnar Björling.

I lay in bed making a story of the evening, pairing words to events where nothing had been said, like the soundtrack to a silent film.

As I dressed Chris in suits of armour, and mounted him on a horse, I found myself haranguing nothing as he had done before.

'Chris was always a prudent rebel that raged when permitted, without upsetting the tableware. He was no hypocrite, but he could read a room. He knew when to tickle and jibe, when to jam the brakes and come up abrupt.

I wish he hated with greater ambition, that his satire never curtsied.

Oh Chris, you blast your bugle from the contented comfort of a pot-bellied armchair. You scandalise, when permitted, and preserve the stagehands you mock. Your attacks; they neither wound nor kill, but embalm.

You fatten your life like a calf, to grow rich from its butchery and therefore stand it better. Your pen is a cleaver which falls on lifeless bodies long deceased.

I deride your work, your chronicle; your petri dish of frozen blood.

What you call destruction is mere insulation; and if you have delusions of grandeur, it further proves the historical fact, that more madmen take themselves for Napoleon than anyone else except Christ.

No arsonist sounds the alarm. The sentence must flay and estrange. Only then, perhaps, will we double-cross ourselves'.

The words fell like feathers to the side of my bed, where they rose to the air as vapours.

'Beneath the reality in which we live there is hidden a second, quite different world'. Said Friedrich Nietzsche.

The Metaphysical paintings of de Chirico have, I have said,

an almost hypnotic effect, such that to readjust, to focus, after *The Revolt of the Sage*, demands physical toil.

By imposing impossible tasks on the naked strength of the will, de Chirico discovered how far it is in our power to dispense with the illusions of sense; that logic, like fashion, is an affection an artist can cast aside; to look upon everything in the world as enigma; to live in an immense museum of strange things.

Sweets and biscuits with remarkable shapes, wind and rough sex, serene eyelids wrapped in a paper napkin, sandal clasps, all framed by an isosceles and the bend of a manikin's arm. Here we have arrived at the metaphysical aspect of things.

It was an impossible task for his naked strength to venture further beyond the line he so thickly hewed across the mind. Logic remains a rough grass grown almost to the knee, its seed sowed deep in the ground, through which we can scarcely catch sight of the painter's incentive which set at Asiago.

Yet his century-old thought is quite new.

I am certain his paintings are waiting to be read. No one has read them; with their fingers too, as well as with their eyes, no one has read *The Revolt of the Sage*. It is new, about to be found, as the lost poetry of Greece was found and will be found.

They are aghast times, when I find myself surrounded by grave goods: white porcelain plates; beetroot in vinegar; middle C played with the forefinger in a warm conservatoire. They strike me but do not amaze me, since the chain of memories which link them together explains the logic of the scene.

But let us suppose that for a moment – and for reasons that are inexplicable – the thread of this chain is broken. Who knows how I would see the plates, the vinegar, the beetroot, the piano keys; who knows what terror and, perhaps, what sweetness and consolation I would feel contemplating the scene?

I have since set the stage on which Chris will perform, a

Victorian opera house. This trespass on the past creates a feeling of intrusion; yet the scene has the clarity of the present.

On various workbenches draped in gold, decorated with stucco ornamentation, cartouches of pan-pipes and tambourines, the mask of Comedy, the upholstery in garnet blush of the proscenium theatre, the appurtenances of the stage are lovingly displayed.

There are several posters in the style of the Edwardian Circus, that London's Egyptian Hall might have displayed, and newsboys peddled with voices like horns in the days of Maskelyne. Each promises wonder, suspense and intrigue on the yellowing tinge of old paper.

The posters are so vivid they are committed to my memory.

Chung Ling Soo dressed in a red *jifu* robe, his hands in his sleeves, stands on a hand which offers him to the globe. At the bottom of the poster is a slogan written in handsome calligraphy: 'A Gift from the Gods to Mortals on Earth to Amuse and Mystify'.

The disembodied head of Alexander, 'The Man Who Knows', with his eyebrows thickly made up. He wears a red turban, fastened with a feather, which hides the best part of his act.

A white dinner table stands centre stage. It is covered in closely written words drawn in a black marker. From a distance, one can make out the names Kandinsky, Björling and Nietzsche.

The cast sit at this table on iron garden chairs with their backs to the audience.

The table is crowded by empty glass milk bottles, dirty tea spoons, saucers and cereal boxes. The mood is comfort amongst rubble; there could be a radio reading test match scores beneath an air raid siren. Elderly audience members would recognise this as 1950s Britain were it not for the chairs, which evoke Dulwich and a baroque fountain in which women tip pitchers of water.

The cast bawdily hold forth as the crowd take their seats. Each voice intertwines with the other, searching for its pitch, redolent of musicians tuning their instruments before a performance.

The audience cannot read the actors' lips. Similarly, the cast cannot see the crowd, nor hear them clearly when they leave through the foyer. Their scripts are muffled and obscure, concealed, overheard.

In decoration, the foyer resembles a commercial gallery beside Truefitt & Hill. Chinese characters draw in thick black paint have been rudely cut from its walls.

These flaws have the closeness of sacred relics. Their tone is that of an empty classical niche which once housed a chipped Madonna.

Above these chiselled marks, the Chinese character for 'laughter' is drawn the right way up, whilst everything else – posters promoting *The Merry Widow*, a ferrotype of Henry Irving – is upside down. The foyer's walls display some form of *craquelure*.

The atmosphere of the performance is two people, embarrassed, speaking a language which is strange to them. If it had a title, it would be *Le Rappel*.

This, then, is what I have found to say about that night.

J Haynes

I am originally from Lambeth, now residing in Mildmay/Dalston for the last 5 years. (Perfect vicinity to express your creativity, with all of the sights and sounds but anyway...)

I am in joyful membership with the Neighbourhood Theatre Company at Young Vic Theatre, a creative community hub for mostly local people who are 25+ and from Lambeth and Southwark. We take part in all kinds of projects, workshops, and discussions and other bonuses.

MayFest 2023 was fantastic! It was a week of celebration of our various talents in the form of a scratch night, variety night (where I performed a poem), acting masterclass, quiz night, Sip N Paint and a one man show ("Something to take the edge off" by Errol McGlashan who will be at The Camden Fringe. Never a dull moment, very funny for such a heavy theme. Truly a masterclass on how to tell a story without yawns from the audience. Right, enough about Errol. This was all fed back to the Young Vic by the way.

Getting back to the Neighbourhood Theatre Company.

Getting back to me. Last year we took part in a 6-part podcast to celebrate Taking Part 25. Taking Part is the community outreach umbrella that oversees the creative projects that local people can get involved in.

The Podcast culminated with *"A Hymn To Creativity"* written by me under the pseudonym J Akre. It is performed by 4 people, 3 of which are Neighbourhood Theatre Company members, the 4th is the producer of Neighbourhood Theatre Alisha Artry. Journeys: The Podcast is available on Spotify.

The poem was really a celebration of culture and communi-ty. *What constitutes a community? where a community gathers, who are the community, what do we eat?, where are we going as a community? what about the future?* I try to elude to many of the shows and workshops produced and took part in over the years. The poem begins with the voices, writings of local people who were invited to write on a wall of what "home" means to them, which was an interactive exhibition conceived by Taking Part team.

There is a nod to Shakespeare. There is a nod to *"Juicy"* by The Notorious B.I.G. There is a nod to the future of space travel with the mention of space shuttle "Atlantis". It was well-researched and hard work, but I enjoyed every minute of it. You are welcome to use an extract of it or its entirety.

A Hymn to Creativity

"REST"
"The sound of sirens"
"Shoes off"
"Smells of cooked food
Its chaotic and silent
I can sit in my bedroom and breathe"
"Kids and cats"
"Any basketball court"
"Canal Saint-Martin"
"The long drive..."
"Our ever-growing pile of shoes at the door"
"Constant shouting from mother"
"The furry carpet"
"Where my Nan is"
"Walking around Volkspark Friedrichshain"
"My mother's terrible lasagne"
"London"
"Safety"
"Seeing old friends as if no time has passed"
"You feel loved"
"It turns out everything I always thought was
      home,
was actually just my mum"
"100% myself"
Fun
Fun
Fun
Whoa

Pestle and mortar - the aroma
black peppercorns, cumin seeds, cardamom
dried sumac, rock salt, toasted sesame seeds
> *thyme, oregano - Za'atar*
wheat no meat, meat no wheat
sugar, no sugar, no dairy, dairy
Hairy husks of a coconut
Puna, saffron, ramen
Tea, no tea, tea snobbery
Blue Mountain Coffee
Plain hot water
Fasting
RSVP look, touch, listen to local voices, smell,
> *taste foods from other cultures, to get to know*
> *each other. Better.*
We nuke daily psychological trauma
with the unfolding blossoming power of good
> *thoughts*
and a posture of dignity.

We eat fish and chips by the sea
Because we got sole
Scotch bonnet in my bag though

Meet greet EAT
sumptuous veg frittatas, stewed meats, jollof
Juices, quiches and cheeses
Asylum Seekers we reach
Welcome home refugees
Journeys...
end of year celebrations
On The Cut

Differing optics, backgrounds, beliefs, opinions,
       passcodes to mind states
sensory deprivation, respect is mandatory
beyond perception is optional,
first nations, dub, progressive, folk, pop
ascension's melody
choruses humming
griots
every last one
The neuro-finials of interpretation
whose view of the world is distinct;
The wheelchair users who will not be defined
because they sit

Women carrying brightly decorated cakes
Strictly Halal. No Haram.
Men serving fellow worshippers' refreshments at
       the gate
lectures in a non-religious space on the same day
a quiver of arrows in buggies
"Thank you for the seat"
"Anytime", curls of crochet for a kippah; we smile
faith, no faith
living libraries
masters of the everyday
all Identities

Thoughts
Suspended acoustics
Stained glass windows
Clasped hands
A tube station

A trip to the shops
A community of believers
Whatever the zeal
Late nights at a museum
Tallit without ceasing
A friend
A mother
Father or father figure
Brother
Aunt, cousins
Grandmother
Cloud formations
A bus stop
Book clubs
ASMR
Soothing vocal intonations
Vintage fairs
*Gardening centres looking for brand new
    secateurs*
Gestures of understanding
Sacred texts
A poem
An article in a magazine
Streaming T.V
Digital messages
Freephone numbers

Help
Ask Clare
Ask Maria
Ask "Ani"

In memoriam.
On a wall opposite the Houses of Parliament.
single kisses, triple kisses, Oxo's rips', miss you
photos crammed into crevices around the frame
to seal a memory, to put faces to names
special section: young people, babies -children
weathering red hearts restored lovingly for the
    loved
movingly beautiful tokens of lavish affection
a stele worthy of a royal civilisation

Unpacked
working with people under the societal radar
circumventing the law without breaking it
Interesting fact: only playhouses and theatres
    were allowed into prisons
from the 12th Century, but they weren't knitting
    pullovers
or thanking their lucky stars,
young men survive and thrive right out of prison
but still affected by The Criminal Justice System

Car boot sales
Market traders
"You buy, cheap!"
"Yu tu teef!"
market vernacular but we understand each other
punnets of plums and peaches
bruised raspberries and potluck avocados
plantains from Guatemala
from Electric Avenue to East Street
beggars with a home begging

beggars refusing to leave
rummaging through nickel free earrings
that don't irritate your earlobes
wear silver or even better wear gold.

We mimic sounds of the city
on Leake Street
we watch couturiers' spray
haute graffiti
Inhabitants of Illyria are surprised
by cannon poppers, who pop cannons
filled with confetti
The Cultural Olympiad
Statelessness, borders, territories
we abseil down the clock tower of self- belief at
    Caledonian Park
shifting minds and places like the people in
    Calais
but the tide turns when a school responds.

We go between sofas, pavements, no fixed
    addresses, to uncertainty
but here in this place of wood, steel and exposed
    concrete
we show up faithfully when we're called
telling our stories under our own lampshade
to be a singing bread roll
art is our home
we're not displaced

Sometimes you've got to go back to move
    forwards

So you know what NOT to write:
give a robot a script
no idiosyncrasies nor nuances
not human, but humanlike
"show me, don't tell me" Ola told me
orbit brainstorm "Do Not Censor"
there are no beavers building dams in this river
let go at The Sea of Tranquillity
geologize on planet idea
Jettison
story tell the images
"Dr Rendezvous" will meet you there.

The upcycled teenagers and other wing walkers
living from the inside out, refusing to grow up
Invisibility unenabled
cuppas, chats with newly formed friends
organising dates to meet up again
where and when
non-verbal children with educational needs
sensory gardens, houses built
The cleverness of trees
a battalion of choirs from all over
sing at The QE2 about coffee in Norwegian
Unplugged performances in community centres
from Rotherhithe to Stockwell

Free internet at libraires
A reassuring presence
A hand on the back
Local radio
Football clubs

Bear hugs
A good pub
Cheers!
A windowsill
A lit candle when it rains
A warm bath (with a rubber ducky)
A cemetery
The Peace Garden at The Imperial War
A walk between trees
Asteraceae under feet
Cinema club
Cleaning
Volume turned all the way up
Anonymity
Stillness
Deep breathing
...and yes,
carnations can sing before you speak again.

Still young
soothed by melody, awakened by song
we learn verbatim compositions
about people living with neurological conditions
like Parkinson's, Aphasia;

We perform for the "Nunhead Massive" at the
    cafe Dementia
we rehearse, rehearse, rehearse - until we get it
    right
we sing with gusto
we sing with gusto
like a lark ascending

but then get shot down like game
when we don't.

Two zero two zero ZOOM
singing and dancing in bedrooms, kitchens,
      living rooms,
subsidized learning and ticketing
Inter-generational handmade silent films
at The Cinema Museum.

Legs in blue stockings, sexuality stripped bare,
      lethal heels, movement, umbrellas
talk sex
work
while wearing very little;
see me now as valuable
glorious bodies of water
oceans, lakes and streams
going after dreams
alchemizing...

Youth exchange to New York or Zimbabwe
Do they have yellow cabs there?

The show. The wizards behind the scenes staging
      it all.
Thank you, Jo

American Dream 1.0
Gentrified, because we own no buildings
like the owners of buildings
living in communities near Heathrow

no paintbrush bristles dripping with paint
to smear with misunderstandings
no more social housing
If you didn't know, well now you do
Zig zig argh!

Generation fingertips
performance access, stage noise captioning
visuals and headsets, verbal commenting
space farers, vertex
lively imagination
storyboard a narration
If you didn't know, well now you do
Zig zig argh!

Pump out the dry ice Tobias
Raphael made a poultice
a cure for no belief blindness
spittle and sand
If you didn't know, well now you do
Zig zig argh!
If you didn't know, well now you do
Zig zig argh!
(Okay my eyes are burning Tobias, cut the
    dry ice)

Unstate myself with auricular assurance from
    smiling rogues
and towns troubled with unruly boys and
    ruffians
I pray thee please deliver me from smiling rogues
    and cowards

for "late eclipses portend no good"
lighten the atmosphere with a slick lyric
"The capon burns, the pig falls from the spit" not
        very vegan is it?
"Let it be so! By all the operation of the orbs"
        Lear said, "from whom we do exist and cease
        to be" Lear said.
To wield worlds into matter that speech enables
to mitigate low sound and reverbs
empty heartedness
hollowness
gilded butterflies out of cages.

A conclave of feminine defiance
loudly chanting and brandishing sticks,
on the main stage.

Everything is changing...

The disappearing pie and mash shops
the pale blue dot
Us
seen from billions of miles away
from Neptune
"The Sojourner" space rover "Perseverance"
        scarifies the surface of Mars
for signs of life
just in case.
Then,
splashdown Atlantis – we made it!
we have the permission to explore
more and more and more

Yet, we are moved
for who we are is not out there
It's in here
It's not them, it's us.

We look up in awe at the International Space
    Station
at the majesty of who we can be,
and we alone are choosing to become
because it is a choice
even if we decide not to choose.

Iqbal Hussain

I studied Mathematics at a small Welsh university, far from the cobbled streets of my childhood. But I chose to earn a living with words. For many years, I worked as a journalist, on publications ranging from the Guardian to the Young Telegraph. Recently, I've turned to fiction, writing short stories, often based on my cultural heritage. My debut novel, Northern Boy, a coming-of-age tale about being a "butterfly among the bricks", will be published in Summer 2024 by Unbound Firsts.

I've lived in London for more than thirty years. It's my home, even though I'm a Northerner at heart. Maybe that's why I've always stayed in the north of the city, moving around variously from Turnpike Lane, Wood Green, Walthamstow and now Chingford. No other city can match London for its vibrancy, mix of people and sense of community – no matter what outsiders often say about Londoners being standoffish. The community in E17 was unmatched, giving it the unofficial name of Awesomestow – because it really was awesome. I was there before it got gentrified, and I was there during and after.

Yes, things were lost, such as the arcade at the top of the High Street, but many more things were gained, such as the reinvigoration of formerly unloved areas such as Wood Street and St James' Street. Walthamstow is soon going to be home to a branch of the Soho Theatre, which will again do wonders for community cohesion.

I'm a little further away now, in the leafy environs of E4, where my partner and I have found a whole new community, mainly thanks to our labradoodle Milo and his film star looks. It's great to still be in London, but to have the huge wilderness of Epping Forest on our doorstep. Walks through the forest mean we've seen woodpeckers, muntjac deer and even the fabled stag who makes an appearance now and again. I go back to my old haunting ground of Walthamstow often, as it's just a short bus ride away, to visit friends and to marvel at what new shop or brewery or florist has opened. And that's what I love about London, and being a Londoner – it's a never-ending season of change, with something new to surprise you even while you mourn the passing of something old.

Extract from *Northern Boy*

Mother was in no mood to be toyed with. The bramble roses around her head had slipped and dangled from her ears like mini pom-poms. She was rarely seen without a bloom in her hair.

"Beta, you will grow horns if you continue to play with girls."

I blinked at the absurdity of her comment. And how did she know I'd been next door dancing to Super Trouper with Shazia?

Mother pinned me with a severe expression, her kameez

rimmed with white where she had leant into the chapatti-floured edge of the kitchen counter. "I am telling you for your own good, young man. You know what happened to the Rizwan's middle boy?"

"Who – not Smelly Arshad? I haven't seen him in ages. Good riddance, too."

"Smelly-welly nothing. He was like you. He used to play with girls. Now they say he cannot leave the house. Because of horns! His poor mother."

I scoffed, but I sounded more like a Bollywood heroine than a villain. While I had a grown-up vocabulary thanks to my love of reading, my voice was like a girl's. Any aura of macho-ness was further diminished by my clothes, which consisted of a green t-shirt with Tweety Pie on it, yellow cardigan, red shorts and blue Jesus sandals. I had added a candy bracelet and a chunky, fuchsia-coloured ring borrowed from Shazia.

"It is no joking. Who is going to marry you if you look like an ox?" Mother slapped a freshly rolled chapatti on to the tava, sending up a plume of flour as it hit the hot griddle. "Or a ..." She let the sentence drop even while her eyes lingered on my jewellery. I crunched one of the sweets from the bracelet.

In her mango-coloured salwaar kameez and jewelled sandals, she was a peacock amongst the Formica. She no longer noticed the lopsided units and peeling linoleum floor or the overflowing Elephant chapatti flour bag serving as a makeshift bin. A well-trodden path was worn between the work surface on which she rolled her chapattis, and the cooker, its gas burners lined with crinkly tin foil that had long lost its sheen.

Nibbling away at another piece of bracelet, I said: "I'm sure I saw him with his dad a few days ago."

"Saw who?"

"Arshad!"

"Oh yes, Arshad. Did you see what he had on his head?" She deftly turned over a chapatti, using her fingers rather than tongs, a skill that always amazed me.

"A cap," I said, swivelling the ring around my finger. "That's nothing unusual."

"And why do you think he was wearing a cap?"

"Because it's the fashion," I said slowly, as though Mother was being particularly stupid. I crunched another two pieces off the bracelet.

She tossed the chapatti into a rattan changher. "It is a funny fashion, wearing it backwards so his hair sticks out the hole. 'New York Wankees' – what does it even mean?"

Chuckling, I skipped to the bedroom I shared with Nabila and Taleeb. With Nabila out, I wanted to style her mop-haired Cabbage Patch doll so she looked like Agnetha in the Smash Hits poster on the wall next to my bed. I imagined Agnetha watched over me while I slept, my very own guardian angel with blonde hair and blue eye shadow.

Half an hour later, having been thrown out by Nabila who was back early, I returned to the kitchen. I tap-danced across the lino, relishing the clippety-cloppety sound of my sandals.

"There is a very nice park for you to play in," said Mother, steadying me by the shoulders. "Just like in Lahore! Shazia's brothers will be there. But, no, you must get under your sister's foots." Flipping open the Saxa tub, she poured salt into the pan.

I sighed. "Hussain and Hassan will be playing football, which you know I hate."

She brushed this aside with a flick of her hand. "All boys play football. Just like all girls love to sing." She promptly demonstrated the truth of this: "The weather is amorous. Oh heart, somewhere, find him in just this state."

While she sang in Hindi, I translated the words into English in my head. The song was from the film Pakeezah. Mother adored all things Bollywood and had even named me after her favourite playback singer, Mohammed Rafi. I joined in with her, harmonising with the melody. I'd always done this, rarely singing the tune itself.

"Get them to show you," she said, stopping. "Playing with balls is good for you."

Ignoring her, I thumped out a rhythm on the counter-top, adding beatbox noises with my mouth to give vent to the disco number that had just come into my head.

Like an unwelcome party guest, Taleeb strolled into the kitchen. "What's that about playing with balls? You don't mean 'her', do you?"

I looked around to see who he was talking about, before realising he meant me. I shot him a death glare. "What would you know about it?" I said.

"Try being a man, for once."

"I'm ten years old!"

"Just wait till you get to Everton."

A shiver ran through me at hearing the three dreaded syllables of the hated school. "You don't scare me," I claimed, despite the quiver in my voice. I stood with my hands on my hips, legs akimbo, just as a Bollywood actor would face off a bully.

"The skinheads are gonna love you."

My stomach flip-flopped. Why did he always have to mention the skinheads? They weren't pupils, but thugs who apparently hung around the school gates at the end of the day. They were my bogeymen – as were the football hooligans who flooded Blackburn at the weekends when Rovers played, meaning we weren't allowed to go into town on those days. As much as I didn't want to believe Taleeb, I knew the skinheads were real – I'd seen reports on Granada Tonight of the National Front going on marches. Last week, Mr Khan's shop window was daubed with the NF symbol, leaving me terrified, knowing they had sympathisers in our midst or that they'd breached our neighbourhood.

I looked over at Mother. Oblivious to our spat, she stirred the curry and continued to sing. "The weather is amorous. I wander alone; someone take me in your arms."

Taleeb opened the fridge and swigged milk straight from the bottle, before belching.

"Puthar, please! Not in my kitchen," exclaimed Mother.

"He's disgusting," I said, my fear of skinheads temporarily forgotten at the sight of Taleeb behaving like a junglee. "He's got the manners of a P-I-G."

"Rafi, must you say the name of that unclean animal in my kitchen?"

"You mean him?" I said, indicating Taleeb.

I hid behind Mother. Startled, she spun round. A dollop of turmeric-tinted curry flew from the spoon, landing with a satisfying splat on Taleeb's white school shirt.

"Watch it!" said Taleeb, jumping back. "Bloody hell. You've ruined it now!"

Tutting, Mother rummaged under the sink, fighting through a stockpile of Vim and Dettol to get to her trusty Daz. With this Holy Trinity, she took on the world and all its ills.

Without undoing the buttons, Taleeb tugged his shirt off over his head. I looked enviously at his taut frame, comparing it to my own pudgy tummy from too many sweets.

Catching me staring, he balled his shirt at me, hitting me in the face. "Does he have to be my brother? Can't we send him back to Pakistan?"

He said this in such a calm voice it caught me unawares. For some reason, it hurt me more than if he had smacked me. As much as I hated him, I still wanted him to like me.

I ran out, tears not far behind.

Acknowledgments

A huge thanks goes out to all the writers who have contributed to this anthology especially J. R. McMenemie, Kate Pasola, Alana Beth Davies, Angela Kay Austin, Damien Mosley, Penny Walker, M Delahunty-Light, Kooi Chock Glendinning, Ken Jones, Natalie Reiss, Rae Bennett, Sarah Ferner, Sarah Lerner, Farva Kaukab, Phoebe McIntosh, Ruth Valentine, Anne G Dilley, Richard Abbot, David Turnbull, Caroline Anjali Ritchie, Nick Toner, Elan Nitpick, Izzy Cole, Anu Kumar Lazarus, Mian Shah, Heather Finlay, Alice Chadwick, Merlin Goldman, Denise EL Rawls, Cheryl Cohen, Paul Angliss, Harry Penfold, J Haynes, and Iqbal Hussain.

A huge thanks to Newington Green Meeting House for all your encouragement and the hosting of our events, particularly Caroline, Nick, Banu and Amy. Thank you to Hackney Libraries for introducing us to so many talented writers and creating a space where people can learn about writing and share their stories.

And thank you to the residents of Hackney and Haringey. For creating somewhere that so many of us can call our home.

Ruby Basu lives in the be
her husband, two children,
the world. She worked for
and policy lead in the Civi
of four children, Ruby connected strongly with
Little Women's Jo March, and was scribbling
down stories from a young age. She loves creating
new characters and worlds.

Nina Singh lives just outside Boston, USA, with
her husband, children, and a very rumbustious
Yorkie. After several years in the corporate world
she finally followed the advice of family and
friends to 'give the writing a go, already'. She's
oh-so-happy she did. When not at her keyboard
she likes to spend time on the tennis court or
golf course. Or immersed in a good read.

THEIR FAIRY TALE
INDIA ESCAPE

RUBY BASU

PART OF HIS
ROYAL WORLD

NINA SINGH

MILLS & BOON

First published in Great Britain 2024
by Mills & Boon, an imprint of HarperCollins*Publishers* Ltd,
1 London Bridge Street, London, SE1 9GF

www.harpercollins.co.uk

HarperCollins*Publishers*, Macken House, 39/40 Mayor Street Upper,
Dublin 1, D01 C9W8, Ireland

Their Fairy Tale India Escape © 2024 Ruby Basu

Part of His Royal World © 2024 Nilay Nina Singh

ISBN: 978-0-263-32122-7

01/24

THEIR FAIRY TALE
INDIA ESCAPE

RUBY BASU

MILLS & BOON

To Pixy, the Beth to my Jo.

CHAPTER ONE

CONNOR PORTLAND STOPPED his car at the end of the road—or what he'd been calling a road. He'd been driving up hills along what was effectively a dirt track for the last few miles, but now even that had become too small to support much more than a bike. At the side of the track, the grass had been cleared, whether intentionally or by constant use, and looked like somewhere he could park safely without risking his tyres getting stuck.

He got out of his car and started to walk along the path, barely noticing the incline as he looked around him at the fields of purple plants and, further in the distance, the mountains surrounding Lake Thun.

As he continued walking, what looked like a mini castle came into view, with a medieval-looking stone building in between two bergfried towers, one square and the other circular.

Although it was the only building for miles, the castle blended seamlessly into the picturesque surroundings. Nobody looking at the fairy tale building would imagine it was the living and working premises of Lachance Boutique, an up-and-coming haircare brand. How could such an unusual building have developed Essence, by Lachance, loved by people who knew and used it and proclaimed by them as a miracle haircare product—and the reason he was in the area.

His phone rang, almost surprising him. In the vast quietness of his surroundings he had forgotten about things like mobile phone reception. He answered the call, then listened to his assistant's latest update. It was no surprise to hear that she'd managed to rearrange his flights and hotels to accommodate his meeting with Lachance.

He had planned to leave the following day, for his next site visit to Munich, and then spend a couple of days back in England, taking a break. Perhaps visiting his brother and sister, before heading out to India for a week or so. Now it sounded as if the best solution would be to rearrange his plans and remain in Switzerland, drive from there to Munich, and go straight on to India after that. He would have to give up his intended break, but that was nothing new. He didn't mind working—it was the constant travelling he tried to avoid.

Usually, once he'd started his annual inspections, travelling round to various offices and distribution centres in Europe, he preferred to keep going—if he had to live out a suitcase he would rather get it over and done with.

He briskly gave his assistant some further instructions before ending the call. He looked around again at the view. What was he even doing here?

Not usually an impulsive man, instead of returning to his hotel in Geneva, Connor had driven to this small village in Sigriswil, where Lachance Boutique was based. Was he hoping that by spending some time in the area he would be able to find out more about the brand? There was very little research available online.

It was a small family company, which had somehow

managed to develop a once-in-a-lifetime product that many companies were desperate to get their hands on. He already knew some of his usual competitors had approached Lachance with deals which had been firmly rejected.

His company's potential deal with Lachance Boutique wouldn't be make-or-break for his company from a financial perspective—it was too large and successful for that to be a concern. From a personal perspective, though, it would be a massive step in the right direction towards a promotion from Director of European Operations to Global CEO. And promotion meant more responsibility, more money and no more business travel.

In some ways the prospect of no longer travelling for work was more attractive than the financial package and new challenges the promotion would bring.

Connor had spent his childhood moving from town to town, following his father from one job to the next. His family had moved to wherever his father could find work, although he never seemed able to keep any job for long. Sometimes Connor had felt his father didn't even try to stay in one place. That wasn't what Connor wanted for his life. He was content living in London—where he could be there to support his brother and sister while his parents continued moving, travelling round the world rather than being restricted to Great Britain, now he and his siblings had left home.

Unfortunately this change of plan meant he wouldn't have time to spend with his siblings, but they probably wouldn't mind—it wasn't the first time work had to come first. The greater shame was he wouldn't be able to fit in a trip to Adysara, to catch up with his old university friend Rohan.

A movement in one of the higher fields caught his attention. He narrowed his eyes to bring the figure into focus. He could make out a small, slim woman. He watched as the woman reached up and loosened her bun, his eyes widening as long, luxuriant black hair flowed down her back. Even from a distance he could tell the length was touching her waist.

He huffed out a laugh as the wind caught her hair and threw it about her face, watching her fight against the flying strands. He had never cared much about people's hair before, but found himself tensing up when she gathered her hair behind her, hoping she wasn't going to put it back into the bun. He relaxed when he saw she was twisting the strands into a long braid.

There was something familiar about her. Could she be the woman he'd noticed the previous evening? He'd stopped for a meal in the village, before driving on to his hotel. As he'd left the restaurant he'd heard a joyous peal of laughter and instinctively sought out where the sound was coming from. She'd been standing next to an older woman who was opening the door to a house. The only illumination had come from the porch light, but he'd been able to make out her huge smile even at that distance.

With hair like that, she had to use Lachance products. But for some reason work was the last thing he wanted to think about when he looked at her.

Without really understanding why, he walked in her direction.

Rina Lachance sighed deeply as she lay in the field of rampion and gazed up at the cloudless sky. Another frustrating day in the lab. She didn't mind the repetitive task of distilling the essential liquids needed to create their signature products, but she hadn't come up with any new products for almost half a year. Where was her inspiration…her creativity?

She watched as a cloud shaped like a lion slowly floated across the sky. She was sure she'd seen that exact cloud passing before. She'd been staring up at the same sky for the past sixteen years, ever since she'd come to Switzerland to live with Aunt Maria after her parents had died.

There was such a lot of world covered by that same sky and she'd seen so little of it.

For a brief moment Rina allowed herself to imagine what her life would have been like if that terrible car accident had never happened. Would she have travelled more? She'd seen photos of herself when she was very young, posing with her parents in front of various tourist attractions in Italy, Greece and Peru, but she couldn't remember going to any of them.

She could barely remember her parents.

She had very few memories of her childhood before moving to Switzerland.

According to Aunt Maria, her doctors had said it wasn't unusual for someone who had been through a traumatic experience to try to block out painful memories.

Rina sometimes wondered whether she'd inherited her mother's sense of adventure. Her mother had moved from India to England when she was ten, and then, while at university, had spent a year studying in Switzerland— which was where she'd met Rina's father.

Rina had moved to Switzerland when she was ten and she hadn't gone anywhere out of the country since then. She'd barely left her village.

She expelled a breath of frustration. What was the point of thinking about what might have been and where she might have visited? Her aunt would never let her leave Lachance tower. Rina had suggested they travel together, to get new ideas for products, but her aunt wouldn't go. There was nothing she could think of to say that would persuade Aunt Maria that nothing serious would happen to her if they went abroad.

Rina stretched out an arm to her side, stroking the purple petals of the flowers. There was only so much she could do with the liquid she extracted from these plants. Even if she came up with a new method of extraction there wouldn't be any significant difference in the end product.

Essence, by Lachance, had taken off in a way Rina could never have imagined. Her initial goal had been rather self-serving—she'd wanted to create a product that could tame her own wild mane. But, although their distribution channels had been small, the amazing effects of the product had spread by word of mouth, with many companies offering to buy the product or be granted a licence to produce it. So far her aunt had turned down every proposal and, if Rina was honest, she hadn't been particularly interested in any of the offers they'd had so far. Even the companies that were prepared to accept a licence rather than buying Essence outright wanted their licence to be exclusive. And they wanted to keep the product exclusive too—which meant it would be out of the budgets of most people Rina wanted to help.

Rina had hoped that the success of Essence might lead to opportunities for her to leave Lake Thun and finally travel the world, but her aunt was happy to maintain the status quo.

If only she knew what words could convince Aunt Maria that she needed more...

Rina needed to get away. She was feeling more and more stifled every day. There was so much to do outside their village, but she didn't think she could leave if it would make Aunt Maria unhappy. Rina could never disappoint her aunt—she owed everything to her. Aunt Maria had happily taken her in and raised Rina after her parents had died.

And, in the circumstances, Rina understood why her aunt was so overprotective of her. Aunt Maria had lost her fiancé in the accident which had killed her brother and Rina's mother. She had stayed by Rina's hospital bed for almost a year, as she'd recovered from brain injuries which had seen her in a medically induced coma and then had undergone extensive physical rehabilitation. Aunt Maria had occasional panic attacks since the accident, which was part of the reason she preferred staying close to home. Although her aunt had made Rina take counselling after the accident, Rina had never managed to persuade her aunt to do the same, and every time she mentioned it even now she knew she was beating her head against the wall.

Rina wished she could persuade her aunt that she was fully recovered, but she still had the occasional headache—which caused her aunt's anxiety to heighten.

No, she couldn't leave, knowing how much it would upset her aunt. But every day it was getting harder to stay.

CHAPTER TWO

RINA'S WATCH BEEPED. She sat up. Only twenty minutes of her break left and she still had to eat. She brought her braid over her shoulder, to make sure there weren't any leaves caught in it, and as she stood up she noticed a man standing next to a tree, staring out over the view of the lake.

She didn't blame him—she often stood in the same position, taking everything in. But he clearly wasn't local. She recognised everyone in the nearest village—there weren't many of them, and people rarely moved into the area. It was a popular area for hikes, but it was unusual for tourists to be on their own—they were usually part of a walking group. Perhaps he had got separated from his companions...

She approached him slowly.

'Are you lost?' she asked.

There was no response. She tilted her head. It was possible he didn't understand German, so she repeated her question in French and English.

Rina sucked in a breath when the man turned round. *Oh, he's finally here!* she thought.

But she didn't know where that idea had come from. She wasn't expecting him—she wasn't expecting anyone. And she'd never seen him before, despite that inner sense of recognition. If they'd previously met there was no way she would have forgotten him.

He looked like a romance book hero, with his dark blond, almost brown hair lifting in the breeze across his forehead. His eyes were a startling green, their colour so vivid they looked as if they came from a child's painting. She'd never seen anyone with that colour eyes in real life before.

She put her hand to her chest—had her heart actually skipped a beat?

As he observed her he blinked, then did a double take.

What had caused his reaction? Perhaps she had flowers and twigs in her hair. She resisted the urge to check her braid again, and willed herself to stand still under his silent examination.

'Sorry, I was miles away. What did you say?' he asked when he finally spoke.

At least now she knew he spoke English. Luckily she spoke all three languages equally fluently.

'I asked if you're lost,' she repeated. 'This path won't lead anywhere but more hills and fields.'

He shook his head. 'I'm just taking a stroll.'

Rina looked back at the path he must have used. It wasn't the gentlest incline. She glanced down at his shoes. They were sturdy, but not the usual choice for people planning to walk for miles. She looked over his casual clothes, momentarily distracted by his strong forearms which were displayed by the shirtsleeves he'd rolled to his elbows. Again, although he wasn't wearing the kind of clothes regular hikers chose, he was dressed in a similar way to many of the tourists who came to the area.

'You came to this area for a stroll?'

She tilted her head. Their village wasn't known as a tourist destination—and, unlike much of the area around Lake Thun, it had very little of interest.

'I came down yesterday from Geneva. I passed through this area on my way to my hotel and wanted to see if it was as beautiful in the daytime,' he explained.

She supposed that made sense. She had half wondered if he had come to the area because of the company, but her aunt hadn't mentioned any upcoming meetings so there was no reason to suspect that. He turned to the lake again, but she was sure he kept stealing glances at her.

'And *is* it as beautiful in the daytime?' she asked, her voice husky.

'Even more so,' he replied. 'Today I can fully see the breathtaking lake, majestic mountains, beautiful people... *Very* beautiful.'

Now there was no doubt he was looking at her.

Her throat went dry. Were they flirting with each other? She had to admit there had been a flirtatious tone to her question, and she was delighted he'd reciprocated. A brief flirtation with a handsome stranger would be the perfect antidote to her humdrum days.

She was trying to think of something witty to say when he surprised her by asking if she lived in the area. She nodded.

'I had dinner in the village restaurant. You live in the house opposite it, don't you?'

Rina didn't reply. She didn't want to lie to him, but she didn't want to mention the tower. Even tourists had heard of Lachance, and often treated her like some kind of genius when they found out she developed all the products—she didn't want to risk opening that line of conversation. She *had* been in town the previous evening, for her regular catch-up with one of the residents. It was possible he'd seen her.

He held up his hand to stop her replying. 'I'm sorry, that was too personal,' he said.

Her eyes widened at this interpretation of her reluctance to reply. Aunt Maria had drummed into her the fact that she needed to be careful about the information she shared with other people. Her aunt always claimed Rina was too trusting, but she knew it was really because of her aunt's overprotectiveness. Although she had to admit it hadn't crossed her mind that he'd been 'too personal'.

'I could promise you I'm not a stalker—but I'm sure that's what a stalker would say,' he continued, his face widening into a big grin which crinkled the corners of his eyes and made him look younger and very approachable.

Rina couldn't help returning his grin.

The previous evening she had noticed a large figure leaving the restaurant, but she hadn't been able to see his face. Staring at him now, she thought that was probably a good thing, or she was certain his handsome features would have pervaded her dreams.

She hadn't felt this kind of attraction before. It was making her have unrealistic thoughts—such as trying to come up with reasons to spend time with him. And she didn't even know his name.

'Do you know anything about that tower over there? The receptionist at my hotel mentioned it. It's unusual.'

He nodded in the direction of her home.

Rina smiled. 'Of course. Everyone in the area knows about Lachance Tower. But unfortunately you can't take tours of it. It's a family home and business—not for tourists. It was constructed to be a mini replica of Oberhofen Castle on the shore of Lake Thun. Have you seen it? It has a museum too.'

He shook his head. 'I haven't, but it sounds interesting.'

'I could show you around if you're not familiar with the area?'

She tried to sound nonchalant as she made her offer—she'd made similar offers to previous visitors she'd come across—but this was the first time she knew she'd be disappointed if he refused.

There was a brief flare in his eyes. Was it surprise or interest? She was too much of a novice at male-female interactions to interpret it properly.

Instead of responding to her offer he said, 'I'm Connor Portland,' and put out his hand.

Rina gave it a quick clasp, knowing that if she held on longer than a moment she would be reluctant to let go. She'd never felt such an intense reaction to someone before.

'Pleased to meet you, Connor,' she replied. 'I'm Rina La—' She cleared her throat, managing to remember at the last minute Aunt Maria's warnings about giving strangers too much information about herself, particularly when she had such a distinctive name. Instead, she used her mother's maiden name. 'Rina Lahiri.'

'You must find it very peaceful out here, Rina,' Connor said, briefly glancing around him before turning back to stare at her.

She shrugged and gave a rueful smile. 'Not much traffic. You said you came down from Geneva. Is that where you live?'

He shook his head. 'London. I was in Geneva on business.'

Rina felt a pang of envy. Having the chance to travel for work was something she dreamed of.

'Do you come to Switzerland a lot?' she asked, knowing her question wasn't solely out of politeness.

'Not really. Once or twice a year.'

She couldn't help feeling disappointed in his answer. Her reaction was disproportionate, considering she'd only met him a few minutes before and they had hardly had the most riveting conversation.

'Do you travel much?'

His lips formed a thin line. 'More than I'd like.'

She couldn't imagine anyone not enjoying the chance to explore different countries. But perhaps he had someone at home he didn't like being away from.

'Where do you usually travel?'

'Usually Europe and the States although I occasionally go further afield if I need to.'

'Really? Have you ever been to Japan or Brazil?'

'I've been to Japan on business. But not Brazil.'

'What about for pleasure? Do you go abroad on holiday?'

He furrowed his brow. She supposed she was asking an unusual number of questions about travel to a complete stranger, but as someone who'd spent practically her entire life in one place, she could only live vicariously through the experiences of others.

'I only travel when strictly necessary.'

She wasn't sure whether his short response was because travelling was somehow unpleasant for him or whether it was because he didn't want to continue the conversation.

'You're very lucky,' she said in a subdued tone.

'I *am* lucky,' he replied, but she got the impression he wasn't talking about travel.

He had an unusual smile on his face, as if he was thinking of a secret joke, when he took a step closer to her and reached towards her. She froze for a second, hardly daring to breathe. Was he going to kiss her?

She felt foolish and also disappointed when he reached up to her head instead.

'You have something in your hair,' he said, holding out a purple flower.

She blinked, certain she hadn't imagined the sensation of a caress along her hair as he'd pulled out the flower.

'What is this?' he asked, 'It's very pretty.'

'It's rampion. Rampion bellflower.'

'I've heard of rampion. I hadn't seen it before, though.' He looked around over the fields full of the plant.

He'd heard of rampion? Rina narrowed her eyes. Could he possibly know about Essence, by Lachance? Many of the businesses that had offered to buy her formula had tried reverse engineering the product, and they knew a key ingredient was rampion, although they didn't know about the unique extraction technique that made Essence so effective.

She couldn't deny Connor interested her—a lot—and she wanted to find out as much as she could about him. But suddenly she didn't want to know why he was in the area or what he did for work. Because everything would change if he was in the area because he wanted to do business with Lachance Boutique.

She inwardly rolled her eyes. Now she was thinking like Aunt Maria, suspecting that everyone she met had ulterior motives. He'd told her he was in the area for a stroll, and if he already knew about Lachance Boutique he wouldn't be so curious about the tower.

She changed the conversation and told him more about the area and the other places of interest nearby. He was leaning back, resting his elbows against the fence, his pose perfectly casual, but she could tell he was paying attention to her from his astute questions and observations.

She didn't know whether to look at his face or at his relaxed figure—both were too distracting for her peace of mind. She wanted to spend more time with Connor and get to know him better, for however long he was in the area, but she didn't even know how long that would be.

'It sounds like I will need a tour guide to get the most out of my visit,' Connor said, when Rina finally ran out of places to mention.

There was something in his tone that made her heart beat a little faster. Did he want to spend more time with her?

'I can show you around. Will your wife or family be joining us?' She grimaced—her question had not been subtle at all.

His mouth quirked. 'I'm on my own.'

She tried to contain her grin. 'I can meet you tomorrow.'

'Are you sure you aren't busy?'

'I'm on holiday,' she replied.

It wasn't true. In fact she hardly ever took any real time off work. But, apart from being surprised, she doubted her colleagues would care. Her aunt would be another matter, though.

'Do you work round here, then? What do you do?'

'I help out my aunt.'

Hopefully, her aunt would approve of the vagueness of that answer.

He nodded, but didn't ask her to expand.

'How long are you in the area? I can plan out the best itinerary for however many days you have.'

He didn't reply immediately. She could almost see the thoughts flashing through his brain as he worked out actions, consequences and rationale.

Had he ever tried just living in the moment? Or was he, like her, prevented from giving in to whims and impulsive actions by what he owed other people. Did they share that in common?

'Two days,' he said finally, flashing her another flirtatious grin that made her breath catch. 'You can play my tourist guide for both days if you're free.'

She clapped her hands like a sea lion after performing a trick.

'Perfect,' she replied. 'Why don't we meet tomorrow on the Sigriswil Panoramic Bridge? That's a great place to start our tour and easy to find.' She glanced at her watch. 'I need to go now. But I'll see you there tomorrow. Ten o'clock? You'll be there won't you?'

She didn't know why it was so important to check— she just knew she wanted to see him again.

He nodded. She expelled a breath, smiled brightly and walked away, giving him a small wave. She walked towards the lane, heading in the direction of the village rather than the tower. She closed her eyes briefly, imagining what her aunt's reaction would be when she told her she was taking a few mornings off and working out what reason she would give for her hasty action.

The only thing Rina knew for sure was that she didn't want her aunt to know about Connor. She was drawn to him in a way she hadn't experienced before and she didn't want anyone to ruin that feeling—especially not her suspicious aunt, who would never understand, and Rina couldn't explain, why she instinctively trusted him.

Connor would be her perfect secret.

Connor walked to his car, deliberately not turning to look behind him. He had a feeling if he caught a glimpse of Rina again he would not be able to stop himself returning to her, wanting to grasp a few more moments talking to her.

He'd been frustrated earlier, when he'd realised he'd lost track of the woman, but she must have been lying down in the field, based on the flowers in her hair. He couldn't explain the pleasure he'd felt when she'd approached him—beyond the basic pleasure of seeing a beautiful woman up close.

In some ways their conversation had been very standard—the kind of questions that strangers asked to get to know each other a little better. And yet it had felt far from ordinary.

What was it about Rina that kept him chatting, wanting to prolong their time together, even agreeing to meet her again to tour the area—something he'd had no intention of doing before she'd brought it up.

Before getting in his car, he pulled out his phone to call his assistant, informing her he would be taking the next couple of days off. It was unusual for him to take time off, particularly before an important presentation, but he knew his team was capable of finalising things, and he would be available for them if necessary.

He expelled a breath after he ended his call. He was acting completely out of character, rearranging his timetable so that he had the chance to meet Rina again—particularly when he knew a relationship with her was out of the question. It wasn't just the long distance; he didn't do relationships.

Moving around so much as child, he'd learnt not to get too close to anyone. There was never any point forming an attachment when he'd known he'd have to move on at short notice. He'd learnt that the hard way—ending friendships because his father had lost yet another job and the family had to move on. Soon, the necessity of saying goodbye had been the only certainty in his life.

The first time Connor had experienced any stability was during his undergraduate studies. Even with his disrupted schooling he'd demonstrated academic excellence from an early age, so when the time came to take national exams he'd performed well enough to get into the best university. But he'd never been sure where home would be during the holidays.

His younger brother and sister hadn't been so lucky. They had struggled with their education because his parents had suddenly decided they were going to homeschool the two of them, which inevitably meant they were left to their own devices. Connor had tried to take their education into his hands, along with everything else, but he'd had to leave them when they insisted he go to university. He never forgot their sacrifice for him, encouraging him to pursue his education, so supporting them now by financing their homes was the least he could do in return.

He'd had girlfriends in the past—career women who understood his drive and passion for work—but none had ever lasted for more than a few months. He wasn't good at making commitments. His unstable childhood prevented him from getting too close to anyone, always prepared to pack up and move on. And he never wanted to lead anyone to believe there was a future with him when he knew that wasn't possible.

But he was getting ahead of himself. Just because he was interested in Rina didn't mean the interest was reciprocated. For all he knew Rina could be the kind of person who liked acting as a tour guide and wanted to do a good deed for a solo traveller.

He paused. He hadn't imagined the gleam of attraction when she had given him a once-over, nor her flirtatious responses to him.

First things first, he would return to his hotel and effectively put in two days' worth of work, so his team would be in the best possible position while he took time off to tour the area.

He shook his head with a laugh—he could hardly believe he was making all this trouble for himself just because he'd unexpectedly met a beautiful, interesting, intriguing woman he wanted to spend more time with. His gut instinct told him he wouldn't regret it.

What was it about Rina that captivated him in the brief time they spent together? And even before they met, when he'd heard her laugh the previous evening? He could spend his time trying to analyse it, but he was only in the area for a couple of days. Instead he would enjoy getting to know her more…maybe leaning into their flirtatious behaviour.

And if their flirtation led to her offering a brief fling before he left Switzerland, then he wouldn't mind that at all.

CHAPTER THREE

RINA TWISTED HER braid as she walked up to their designated meeting spot in the car park near the Sigriswil Panoramic Bridge. She wasn't sure if she was worried Connor wouldn't be there or that he would.

She didn't know why she was so nervous. This wasn't the first time she'd acted as an unofficial tourist guide for visitors. But they had been families, or couples. Never an incredibly handsome single man. At least she assumed Connor was single. He hadn't specifically told her that, simply that he was here alone. For all she knew he could have a wife and family back in London.

Rina stumbled over the idea Connor might not be single. It shouldn't matter to her whether he was or not, but she really hoped he was. Surely he would never have flirted with her or agreed to meet with her again if he was in a committed relationship with someone else?

Why was she even thinking about Connor's relationship status? The only reason for it to bother her was if she was hoping that there was a possibility he was really interested in her, that he didn't flirt with every woman he met and imply they were beautiful.

She knew nothing would come of it—he lived in England, and she could never leave Aunt Maria or Switzerland. But that didn't mean she couldn't enjoy spending time in the company of the most gorgeous man she'd ever seen and find out more about all the travelling he did. She could hear about all the places she'd only dreamed of visiting.

And if he did happen to show he wanted something more with her, she would turn him down—firmly but politely.

But there was no way a plain, boring young woman who had barely left her own backyard could hold the interest of someone as handsome and sophisticated as Connor.

She sighed with relief when she saw Connor leaning next to a car up ahead. As she walked closer to him his features became clearer and stronger. She giggled—the uncontrollable giggle she gave when she saw celebrity photos of someone so good looking they didn't seem real. She'd wondered whether she had exaggerated how hand-some he was in her memories. But she could see now she had not. And the image in her memories didn't even do justice to the sheer magnetism of his physical presence.

She quickened her pace to reach him.

'Hi, Connor.' She greeted him with a small wave.

She caught the twinkle in his eyes as she approached and his wide grin made his pleasure clear. Although it was a natural smile, she had a feeling his mouth wasn't used to stretching that much.

'Is there anywhere you particularly want to go?' she asked.

'Not really. I'm at your disposal.'

She cleared her throat at the inappropriate thoughts

that came to her at the idea of having him truly at her disposal.

'Have you been across the suspension bridge yet?' she asked. When he shook his head, she gestured in front of her. 'Why don't we do that first? You're not afraid of heights, are you?'

'I don't think so.'

She bit her lip. 'Well, I can protect you if you do feel scared.'

His brow quirked, but he didn't reply as she led the way to the start of the famous Sigriswil Panoramic Bridge.

Once they reached the middle of the bridge they stopped to take in the breathtaking views of Lake Thun and the surrounding mountains, and then looked down into the bottom of Gummischlucht gorge.

Connor commented on the surprising amount of tourists taking photos of the bridge itself rather than the views.

'This bridge became quite famous recently, because it was a filming spot for a very popular Korean drama,' Rina explained. 'Have you watched any Korean dramas?'

'I've watched a few, and some Korean films, but I don't remember watching one where this bridge features. Would you recommend it?'

She shrugged. 'I enjoyed it, but I don't really know what your tastes are.'

He gave her a small, almost shy smile. 'I hope you'll have a better idea once we've spent more time together.'

'I hope so too.' She cleared her throat. 'Would you like me to take a photo of you?' she offered.

Connor raised his eyebrows, as if he had never considered photos. Perhaps he wasn't someone who needed those kinds of reminders. If she ever got a chance to travel she would probably be so busy soaking up the atmosphere, trying to be present in the moment, she would also fail at taking photos to capture those memories.

Connor took his phone out of his pocket. 'Can I take a picture of you standing over there?'

Her eyes widened. Did he want a photo to remember her?

'To give a sense of scale,' he explained.

Something about the hurried way he spoke made her think that wasn't the real reason.

She gave him a nod, then went to stand where he indicated, feeling stiff and awkward.

'Smile!' Connor encouraged. 'You look like you're facing a firing squad.'

Rina laughed.

'That's more like it,' Connor said.

She didn't know how many pictures he snapped before he brought his phone down.

'Excuse me.' An older gentleman walking arm in arm with his wife spoke to them. 'Would you like us to take a photo of you both together?'

'That's not ne—' Rina began, but at the same time Connor spoke.

'Thanks. I'd appreciate that,' he said.

He gave his phone to the man, then came to stand next to her.

'Closer together,' the man instructed.

They both moved closer, bumping their sides. Rina gave a nervous laugh, which stopped abruptly when she felt Connor's arm around her.

The man took a few shots, then handed the phone

back to Connor. Rina hurriedly passed her own phone to him—she wasn't going to miss the opportunity to have a photograph of her and Connor together.

After Connor had reciprocated the favour, by taking a few photos of the elderly couple, he indicated to Rina they should continue across the bridge.

He entwined her arm with his. 'This part looks high. I'm a little scared. You promised you'd protect me,' he said with a gleam.

'Of course,' she replied, even though there was no difference here from the height of the bridge they had already crossed.

Being close to Connor's side and soaking up his warmth made Rina feel as if she was the one being protected. She gave a slight sigh.

'Is everything all right?' Connor asked immediately.

'Oh, yes,' she replied, slightly surprised that he'd been attuned to her enough to hear her small exhalation. 'It's breathtaking, isn't it?' she added, trying to give a reason.

'Very.'

Warmth flooded her cheeks when she noticed he was staring at her intently, not at the view. She tried to calm her erratic heartbeat.

'What's your favourite view?' she asked.

He barked a laugh. 'I'm not sure.'

'Tell me about some of the top views from your travels, then.'

He didn't have time to say much before they reached the other side of the bridge. At Rina's suggestion, they took a ferry to Thun, where they toured Schadau Castle before finding a restaurant for lunch.

At first Rina felt awkward, sitting down opposite Connor, looking directly at him. There had been less intensity when they were walking side by side. She kept hoping he would initiate some conversation, and when he didn't she looked around the room and out of the window. Each time they caught each other's glance they would smile, but say nothing. They'd talked about the area and the sights while they were walking, but now she wanted to get a chance to know more about Connor on a personal level.

She couldn't really ask him about his family, because then he would ask about hers, and when she explained she lived with her aunt it could lead to him discovering they were Lachances, and the Lachance name was too well known in the area for Connor not to understand its importance. She couldn't ask about his work, either, because that could encourage him to ask more about what she did for her aunt, which would lead to the same issue.

She sighed and bit the inside of her cheek.

'Is something wrong?' Connor asked.

'No, why?'

'I thought you sounded irritated.'

She smiled quickly. 'No, probably just a bit hungry. Walking must have built up my appetite. On the bridge you mentioned you've watched some Korean films. What other films do you enjoy?'

That was a safe topic, and he'd said he hoped she would get to know his tastes better as they spent time together.

After lunch they walked around the town.

'It's very beautiful here,' Connor said. 'This area is simply stunning.'

Rina gave a murmur of agreement, then breathed

deeply, concentrating on staring ahead of her at the view she'd seen countless times before.

She sensed Connor staring at her.

He gently covered her hand. 'What's wrong?' he asked in a gentle tone.

She raised her eyebrows, surprised by his astuteness. 'It's hard to explain without sounding ungrateful and petulant,' she replied.

Connor smiled. 'It's okay to be ungrateful and petulant in front of me. I won't think less of you.'

The sincerity in his tone made her laugh. 'Okay, then,' she began. 'I grew up in England, but I barely remember living there. I moved to Switzerland when I was ten. Since then all I've seen is Switzerland—and even then not much of this country.'

He nodded his head in apparent understanding. 'You want to travel more.'

'Yes, but not only that. I want some adventure. I don't know how to explain it. I guess I just want a chance to live life to its fullest before I die,' she said.

He didn't say anything, only looked at her unblinking. It was refreshing to tell someone her deepest wishes. She didn't have any close friends to talk to, and her work colleagues all felt so lucky to be part of Lachance Boutique they couldn't understand her yearning to leave.

She waited for Connor to respond, unconsciously worrying at her bottom lip, hoping he wouldn't laugh at her comment.

'Apart from travelling, what do you want to do for adventure?'

She shrugged. 'I'm not a thrill-seeker, but I would

like to try sky-diving or deep-sea diving. Perhaps learn the trapeze.'

Connor laughed. 'Why the trapeze?'

Rina grimaced. 'I know it's a bit random, but can you imagine flying through the air, relying on your own propulsion against gravity, nothing more than a net below?'

'Terrifying,' Connor said, shaking his head. 'I like having my feet on the ground. Although I have been deep-sea diving.'

'You have? Where? What was it like?'

'It was fun.'

Rina waited for him to say more, but Connor remained silent.

'You're so lucky, getting to visit so many places with work,' she said. She noticed him press his lips together. 'Don't you enjoy it?'

'It's a necessary evil. I travel more than I want to, and each time I get a promotion the travel increases. But I'm hoping soon I will be able to reduce the amount.'

Rina wanted to ask him more questions, but it felt too close to asking about his work and, arbitrary though it was, she was enjoying their hidden backgrounds.

'But you must enjoy travelling for leisure?' she said.

'Not particularly.'

Rina couldn't believe her ears. 'You don't?'

'I don't enjoy the feeling of living out of a suitcase.'

Rina couldn't help feeling there was something behind his statement—a reason he felt travelling for work was the same as living out of a suitcase. It sounded like a different kind of impermanence.

'Roots are important too,' she said.

'Very important.' After a moment's pause, he asked, 'Why did you move here?'

'Pardon?'

'You said you moved to Switzerland when you were ten. Why did you move?'

'Oh, that. I lost both my parents. They were killed instantly in a car crash.'

She tried to speak in a calm, dispassionate manner. So many years had passed; she believed she'd grieved fully for her parents, but recently she'd started to think about them and miss them. Perhaps it was the lack of inspiration in her work, perhaps it was the sameness of her existence but she couldn't help wondering what might have been if they had lived.

'I'm sorry,' he said.

He reached out and put a hand on her arm. He clearly meant it as a gesture of comfort, but her physical reaction to his touch was not comfortable in any way.

'It was a long time ago,' she said, moving away to get her heartbeat under control. 'Shall we carry on?'

She walked away without waiting for him to answer.

The next day Connor drummed his fingers on the steering wheel as he waited in his car. He was early. He wasn't due to meet Rina for another half-hour but he'd left himself plenty of time to get there. Because he didn't want to risk being delayed by traffic—not because he was in a hurry to see Rina. At least that's what he told himself.

He took out his phone, scrolling through new messages and emails that had come in during the hour since he'd previously checked.

There had been a flurry of activity in the team.

His meeting with Maria Lachance had been confirmed for the following day, which meant they were working on the final touches to his presentation. Usually he would curtail his leave to work on it too, but he knew his team didn't need him to micromanage them as long as he was contactable. And, with the meeting being tomorrow, this was the last day he would get to spend with Rina.

His heavy feeling at that thought was unusual and unexpected. Two words that described Rina, now he thought about it. She was different from the people he usually spent time with—open and free of artifice. Optimistic, with seemingly boundless energy, but not exhausting—which he often found was the case with people with similar personalities.

He wished he could spend more time with Rina, but that wasn't going to be possible. He felt there was so much to learn about her and she would be someone worth getting to know.

Perhaps he should arrange to stay in the area a little longer, in case there were issues to deal with after his meeting with Lachance Boutique.

He pinched his forehead. Was he really considering rearranging his entire schedule for the chance to spend a few more days with Rina? What was he hoping for from that? This wasn't the beginning of a relationship. He knew from experience that he was incapable of making the commitment necessary to sustain a lasting relationship. After a short while he always began to get restless and unsettled, ready to move on. Leaving was inevitable, as far as he was concerned. His childhood had instilled in him the idea of impermanence. Relationships were doomed because he was metaphorically packing his suitcase from the moment they began. He might be settled in one location for the most part, but that sense of intransience he'd grown up with hadn't changed, even though it was focused on a woman.

Once he left Switzerland he wouldn't try to keep in touch with Rina. There was no point. Work would inevitably get too busy and any contact would cease. It was better not to create any false expectations on Rina's part. They'd indulged in a brief flirtation, but it had never gone beyond that, they'd never give in to their attraction.

Perhaps it would be better if he cancelled today's plans with Rina—sent her a message to say that something had come up.

Even though he knew that would be for the best, he was still reluctant to take that step.

Five minutes later there was a knock on his window. He glanced up to see Rina, beaming at him. He took a sharp intake of breath. He now understood what it meant when someone had a smile that lit up their face and the day. At least the decision of whether to cancel their plans had been taken out of his hands.

He gestured for her to move away, then carefully opened his door.

'You're early,' she said, still grinning at him. 'I thought I'd be twiddling my thumbs, waiting for you, but you're already here.'

He nodded, unable to resist responding to her joyful expression with a grin of his own. He guided her round to the passenger side and opened the door for her.

It took them less than an hour to get to Mülenen, where they took the funicular to the summit of Mount Niesen.

Connor pointed at the staircase running beside them. 'Have you ever walked up those stairs?' he asked.

She shook her head. 'It's only open a few times a year. For some races.'

'You're not interested in taking part?'

'I would enjoy the challenge of doing the steps, but I'm not interested in the race.'

She scrunched her nose and he had to resist the urge to tap it…she looked so adorable. He forced himself to pay attention to what she was saying.

'I don't want to be part of a competition. Sometimes that takes all the fun out of it.'

'You don't think a little competition can make things more exciting?' he asked.

'Well, of course it can. For other people. I like watching competitive sports. I don't really want to be in them.'

So she wasn't competitive by nature. Connor automatically stored the information away with the other small nuggets she'd shared, helping him learn more about her. And the more he learned, the more he liked her. He had, by choice, always dated career-focused women—women who wouldn't ask much from him but who had a driving edge that occasionally made them come across as harsh. Rina wasn't like that. But he wasn't going to act on these nascent feelings when nothing could come of it. Particularly not when he was leaving Switzerland in a few days.

He closed his eyes briefly. Why was he even thinking about whether anything could come of this attraction he was certain was between them when they'd only met a few days before.

'Have you ever come here to watch the races?' he asked, in an attempt to keep their conversation prosaic.

'No. Perhaps I should. It's one of the few things to do around here.' Her smile was forced.

Connor could sense Rina's need to break out of whatever she felt was confining her. He might not share her desire to travel, but he could understand why she had such wanderlust. Perhaps if she had had his childhood, or had to travel so much for work, she would feel differently.

He immediately chastised himself. His childhood might not have been ideal, but his parents had chosen to take him and his siblings with them rather than dump them somewhere and travel alone—although they were doing that now. But even though he'd hated their nomadic existence, he couldn't imagine losing them when he was ten.

'It's a good job you're not afraid of heights, after all,' Rina said, bringing him back to an awareness of his surrounding and the motion of the train as it continued its ascent, as well as reminding him of the feeling of her body pressed close against his as they'd crossed the Sigriswil Bridge the previous day.

When they reached the summit, they spent some time gazing over the panoramic vista of Lake Thun. Even though they'd had an incredible view of the lake from the bridge, there was something about seeing it from this new height that made it more magical. Without fully understanding why, Connor reached for Rina's hand, as if clasping it would ground him in an otherwise fantasy world.

He huffed. And now he was thinking about magic and fantasy worlds! Despite the scenery around them, life wasn't a fairy tale, he wasn't a prince, and he didn't think anybody would describe Rina as a princess in need of rescuing.

They were two strangers who'd met by coincidence and happened to get along. Perhaps it was because that was unusual for him that he was giving it more importance than it deserved.

After they'd finished at Mount Niesen, they drove to a nearby town to have an early lunch. Connor desperately wanted to ignore the vibrations from his phone, but with the meeting taking place the next day, he couldn't leave his team in the lurch—they would only be contacting him if it was urgent.

He got up to excuse himself, but Rina held a hand up to stop him.

'Why don't you make your calls here? I can take a walk along the main street. There are some stores here that I like to visit when I come. Send me a text when you're ready to head back. I can tell you're busy, so we shouldn't stay out too long.'

Connor watched Rina leave. She didn't seem upset that they wouldn't be spending the rest of the day together as they had originally planned. Had she offered to show him around only out of politeness after all? Perhaps the attraction was one-sided—although he was certain from the way she kept stealing glances and looking at him from under her lashes she did find him attractive.

But any attraction between them was a moot point.

He forced himself to turn his attention to the various emails and calls he had to respond to. After twenty minutes it was clear he would need to return to his hotel and work, cutting his day with Rina even shorter.

He sent her a text message and she responded within seconds, telling him where he should meet her.

He found her laughing with a store owner, trying on

some Swiss hats. She looked happy and carefree. Wistfully, he wished he could wrap up her joy and keep some with him as a good luck charm. Instead he would have to say goodbye to her.

If she was disappointed to hear that he had to head back to his hotel she didn't show it. In the car she kept their conversation on neutral topics, talking about the area, making him wonder whether she was also carefully avoiding any further personal confidences.

The silence between remarks gradually got longer, the closer they got to his hotel.

Although he offered to drive her back to her village she refused, telling him she had some errands to do in the area and needed to visit the library.

When he finally parked, neither of them moved. Instinctively he knew he should get out to open her door for her, but once he'd done that it would really mean goodbye. Unless…

'If you're still in the area in a couple of hours, would you like to meet for an early supper?' he asked.

'Supper?'

'Dinner,' he clarified.

'Oh, I know what it means. I just didn't realise people still used that word.' She giggled.

Unable to resist this time, he affectionately tapped her nose. 'Cheeky.' He paused, suddenly serious. 'Would you like to meet for dinner?'

She inhaled. He wished he could guess what was going through her mind.

'Would it be like a date?' she asked.

He stiffened. They had spent a lovely day together, and

admittedly he had been more than a little flirtatious, but he didn't want to give her the wrong impression.

He shook his head. 'Not a date. Even if it wasn't out of the question because I'm not here for much longer, I don't have time or space for a relationship in my life. It's a simple request for companionship so I don't have to eat alone.'

She grinned, and he found himself disappointed that she seemed pleased with his response.

'I completely agree. I'm glad we're on the same page,' she said.

'So, dinner?'

She didn't reply straight away. He wasn't sure whether it was because he'd been a little more curt than he'd intended in his question.

Finally she nodded. 'Okay, then, that would be lovely. Text me when you're free and we can meet for a spot of "supper",' she said, using a fake posh accent for the last few words.

Rina was nervous again. She couldn't understand why having dinner with Connor felt different, more intimate. They'd eaten lunch together, and after the initial awkwardness of sitting opposite each other they'd been easygoing with each other.

Perhaps it was the dim lighting, making the restaurant look romantic—not at all appropriate for not-a-date. They should have met at a cheerful café or diner instead.

Rina looked through the menu. All the dishes were expensive—more than she'd usually spend on a meal. If this was not a date then she should expect to pay for her dinner or split the cost.

'Choose whatever you want,' Connor said. 'This is my treat, as a thank-you for being my tour guide the last couple of days.'

'You've already thanked me by buying lunch while we were out,' Rina replied.

Had he noticed her concern over the prices, or was he being generous?

'I'm very grateful for having my own personal tour guide.'

She didn't mistake the emphasis Connor placed on the word *personal*.

'Do you think you might come back to the Lake Thun area?' Rina asked.

Connor pressed his lips together. 'I have no immediate plans. Not for another year, probably.'

Rina bent her head, staring at her cutlery. Whatever these last few days had been, it was clear Connor had no interest in extending their friendship. She didn't regret spending those days with him, getting to know him better. It had been a brief interlude in her otherwise repetitive life. In a few hours it would be over, so she had to make the most of this time.

While they made their choices and ordered their meal Rina tried to come up with a topic of conversation which would be interesting, but not lead them down an intimate path. Something neutral. It was incredibly difficult to think of something. They'd already talked about films, and what they did for entertainment, and bringing up what they did when they were free in the evenings wasn't something Rina wanted to think about.

Connor put his elbows on the table and rested his chin in his hands, staring at her intently. 'What do you think of this restaurant?' he asked. 'The guide says it's excellent. Have you eaten here before?'

Rina giggled. 'No, never. Obviously I've heard about its reputation, but I never had the chance to eat here before. Thank you for inviting me.'

'No, thank *you*. It's the perfect way to end my holiday...having dinner with such an enchanting companion.'

Rina swallowed. Connor was being flirtatious again. And she liked it!

Her imagination immediately went to the end of the evening—seeing him standing next to her in the illumination of the streetlight as she waited for her bus to arrive, his head bending slowly towards her, his mouth getting closer...

'Bon appetit.'

She almost groaned when her thoughts were interrupted by the arrival of the waitress with their first course.

Connor's lips twitched. She narrowed her eyes. There was no way he could have worked out the direction of her thoughts, was there?

'Tell me about the best restaurants you've eaten at,' she said, finally finding a neutral topic.

'I'm not really a foodie,' he replied. 'A steak tastes much the same whatever country you're eating it in.'

'You stick to what you know?'

'It's easier in some ways when I'm travelling. I do experiment with different recipes when I'm at home, though.'

'You cook?' She raised her eyebrows.

'Why does that surprise you?'

Rina tilted her head. 'Actually, it doesn't. Of course you would cook. You are the perfect man after all.'

Now she was the one flagrantly flirting—was she going to bat her eyelashes at him next?

The corner of Connor's mouth lifted. 'Is that what makes me perfect? My culinary expertise?'

'That's not the only thing,' she said, her voice turning husky.

'What else?'

Rina bit her lip. 'Well, you're fairly easy on the eye too.'

Connor laughed as he sat back in his seat, thoroughly at ease. 'That's quite the compliment. Thank you.' He mimed tipping a hat at her. 'How else am I perfect?'

She couldn't help the broad smile spreading across her face. 'What makes you think there's anything else?'

'Because you haven't mentioned my wit or charm yet.' He spoke in a serious, matter-of-fact tone, but there was no hiding the humour causing a twinkle in his eyes.

She pressed her lips into a pout. 'Hmm… I'm not sure I noticed that.'

'Really?' He smirked. 'Maybe I need to try harder, then.'

She dipped her eyes, then looked up at him from beneath her lashes. 'Maybe you do…'

She noticed him gulp, but their eyes remained glued to each other.

She had no idea how long they'd been staring and no idea how long they would have continued if they hadn't been interrupted by the staff clearing their dishes and bringing the next course.

Over the rest of the meal both she and Connor kept to light conversation, with no more meaningful glances. Rina tried to convince herself she was happy with the way the evening had gone, but it didn't work. If this was the last night they would have together she didn't want a quick, polite goodbye. She wasn't exactly sure what she did want, but it was something more than that.

As they left the restaurant, Rina turned to Connor to begin their farewell.

Connor spoke first. 'It's still early. Do you fancy taking a walk towards the lake?'

A walk in the moonlight next to a handsome man sounded perfect to Rina. So perfect she could hardly form words, merely nodding in response.

They walked close to each other. Occasionally their bodies would come into brief contact before one of them hastily moved away. Was he finding their touches frustrating, even as much as they heightened the tension in the atmosphere?

Her heartbeat became more erratic when Connor's arm brushed hers as he pointed something out to her, then casually slid his hand down her arm to grab hold of her hand.

Connor felt the warmth of Rina's tiny hand enveloped in his. These were the last few moments they would spend with each other. Technically he was at Lake Thun until Monday, since Maria Lachance had asked his company to keep the day free, in case she had any follow-up questions. He could conceivably spend the weekend with Rina. But he'd already told her he was there for only two days. And in the long run what would a few extra days matter? There was no chance of a relationship between them.

Rina had made it clear she would never leave Switzerland, and he couldn't imagine trying a long-distance relationship where he was constantly travelling to and fro—it would bring back too many memories of his nomadic childhood.

And something told him that if he spent extra time with Rina he would crave even more. It was best to say their goodbyes that evening, as planned.

'I should head to the bus stop now,' Rina said.

There was unmistakeable regret in her tone.

'Let me drive you home,' he offered. 'I don't like the idea of you taking public transport alone so late.'

He would never get tired of hearing the crystal tones of her laugh. 'I'll be perfectly safe. Even my aunt doesn't worry about me travelling back on my own from here.'

'Please,' he pleaded.

He fully accepted that his offer wasn't purely out of concern for her safety—he wanted to prolong their time together, and he couldn't deny being in the close confines of his car with her was alluring. Maybe it was the fact that their brief time together was ending before he was ready to move on that was making it more difficult than he'd anticipated.

They spoke little on the journey back to Rina's village. He pulled the car to a stop in the lane near her home and got out, going round to open her door for her.

They stood next to the car, staring intently at each other; neither of them speaking. What was there to say? That he had a good time? That he enjoyed her company? That he wished he could be there longer?

All those things were true, but so true they didn't need to be said.

Unable to resist one final touch, Connor reached out

and ran his fingers over her hairline, down over the nape of her neck and brought her braid to the front. Such glorious hair. Such a glorious woman.

He didn't know whether he moved first or Rina did; it was likely they moved in perfect synchronicity. But their arms went round each other, drawing them closer together, as his mouth covered hers hungrily. He groaned as she returned the pressure, demanding more, which he happily gave her.

CHAPTER FOUR

THE FOLLOWING DAY Rina was back working in her laboratory. The feelings of dull routine which she'd managed to dispel while she was spending time with Connor were now back in full force.

But she was trying not to think about Connor. And she was trying even harder not to think about their kiss. She didn't have the words to describe how amazing it had felt being in Connor's arms, exploring each other.

Rina watched as the vapour she'd extracted from the rampion began to condense in the flask to form the quintessence of Essence. Even the excitement she'd felt when she first cracked the extraction didn't hold a candle to the sensations that had wrought havoc in every fibre of her as she'd eagerly, greedily kissed Connor.

The only downside was the realisation it had been a kiss to say goodbye when it should have been a kiss to signal the start of something special.

What was he doing now? He'd told her he was travelling to Munich on business after his stay at Lake Thun. Was he on his way already? She wished she had a reason to leave with him. She wanted to visit Germany as much as she wanted to spend time with Connor.

Although she could empathise with Connor not enjoying all the business travel—it sounded as if it took some of the joy out of travelling—she had never been out of the country. She would love to leave Switzerland and see a little more of the world. But the chances of her aunt agreeing to that were slim. Rina had suggested they go abroad for vacations in the past, but Aunt Maria wouldn't leave—the idea was enough to cause her panic attacks to start. Any time Rina even raised the possibility of her going on her own she could see her aunt begin to tense and Rina hadn't the heart to pursue it.

She sighed and turned back to her flask, checking to see whether there had been any problems in the distillation process. But of course there hadn't. She would never want something bad to happen with her work, but sometimes she wanted something different—*anything* different—to happen.

She wanted to experience the joy she'd felt when she'd extracted the exact properties she'd needed from the rampion to make Essence work perfectly. But inspiration had been missing for ages.

She watched as the gases condensed in the cooler flask and the liquid dripped slowly into the end container. She could almost feel her own life energy dripping slowly away in the same manner.

Her self-pitying thoughts were interrupted a few minutes later by her aunt's personal assistant.

'Rina, Maria has asked you to go to the conference room. The representative from Newmans is about to give his presentation.'

Rina recalled her aunt moaning over breakfast that morning about having to meet with someone from Newmans—yet another company that wanted Lachance Boutique, or at least Essence by Lachance. Rina didn't blame Aunt Maria for refusing all the offers they'd received so far. None of them had seemed to understand the ethos of Lachance. Many saw money signs rather than an underlying need to help people. There had even been companies that hadn't understood the importance hair could have to some people. Still, Rina remained hopeful that a company would help her realise her vision of seeing Essence available more widely—probably unlike her aunt, who was comfortable maintaining the scale they currently produced—all part and parcel of her reluctance to deal with change.

It had become obvious from the consistent attempts at persuasion by companies they'd previously turned down that it was easier to meet representatives from these companies face to face, so she and her aunt could clearly outline their objections and reasons for refusal. They'd found they tended to take no for an answer in person rather than by email. Her aunt was a force to be reckoned with. It was hard to win any argument against her. Rina knew that for a fact.

Shaking her head to clear her thoughts, Rina took off her lab coat, checked her hair was mostly still in its bun, and then walked to the conference room. It was an impressive name for what was basically a small room with a dining table, but they made the best use of the space inside their tower, and she always believed the cramped dimensions added to the family atmosphere during staff meetings.

Rina knocked on the wooden door quickly, then poked her head inside. Her aunt was seated at the head of the table. She gestured for her to enter.

'This is our head of product development, Katrina Lachance. Rina, this is Mr Portland from Newmans.'

Rina froze. The last person she'd expected to see again,

and the one person she wanted to see again the most, was making his way towards her. When she thought about seeing Connor again it had never been in their own conference room. Was it her imagination, or had the room become smaller with Connor taking up almost all the space?

She was unsure how to react to seeing him again. She didn't want to face questions if she confessed they knew each other. Luckily, she was able to follow Connor's lead when he held out his hand.

'Pleased to meet you, Miss Lachance.'

'And you, Mr Portland.'

'Why don't you begin now,' her aunt ordered.

Rina tried to concentrate on Connor's presentation, which he was giving in fluent German. Why had he hidden his language skills from her? It made no sense. He had let her do all the talking when they'd visited places and in restaurants, even let her translate. Or had she assumed he couldn't speak the language and taken it upon herself to take over?

Why had he hidden the reason he was really in the area from her? He'd given her the impression he was taking a few days' holiday, not waiting for a business meeting.

Slowly she began to replay their meetings and interactions. Had it even been a coincidence when they'd first met in the fields near the tower? Had Connor always known who she was—the niece of the woman who ran Lachance Boutique and the developer of the coveted Essence. Was that the reason he'd been happy to spend time with her? Otherwise, why the secrecy?

What else had he hidden from her? There was probably a lot about him she didn't know. Even though she'd felt closer to him in a few days than she had to anyone before, she really didn't know him that well at all.

Hopefully the heat rising in her cheeks wasn't visible on her face; a combination of anger and humiliation that she, who prided herself on being a good judge of character, had been so taken in by him.

He wasn't going to get away with it—she would find a way to speak her mind to him. But for now she had to concentrate on business.

Slowly what Connor was saying began to penetrate. She sat upright, paying closer attention. Finally someone had come up with a proposal that fitted almost exactly with how she envisaged the future for Essence and even Lachance Boutique itself.

Rina glanced at Aunt Maria to see if she appeared at all interested. Her aunt's smile was difficult to interpret. Rina could only cross her fingers and hope that her aunt would give them a chance to discuss the proposal together rather than reject it outright to Connor's face, as she often had in the past.

Rina felt slightly encouraged that her aunt might be feeling positive about the proposal when she listened to the questions her aunt asked. Usually Aunt Maria's questions were all to do with the reasons she had for objecting to the proposal, phrased in such a way that they could be interpreted as pressure-testing its strengths. Good company representatives could work out by that stage that they weren't going into business with Lachance Boutique.

She rolled her eyes at the idea of how good a company representative Connor was. All the charm, all that attention. Wining and dining her to get a business deal. She was almost tempted to turn Connor down, because she didn't want to be in business with someone who had deceived her. But she would be spitting in her own face if

she acted rashly. Newmans proposal was simply excellent—too good to reject because of her personal feelings
for their representative.

'Rina, do you have any questions for Mr Portland?'
Aunt Maria asked.

'I have a few,' Rina replied. 'Is it okay for me to ask in
German, or would you rather I spoke in English?'

Connor cleared his throat, and she didn't miss the
faintest lift to his lips. 'Either is fine, Miss Lachance.'

She nodded, then went through the questions she'd
noted during his presentation. He was able to answer
confidently and fluidly.

Once the question-and-answer session ended, Connor
began to pack his things away. Rina tried to come up with
a reason to ask Connor to stay behind—she wanted, in
fact needed, to give him a piece of her mind.

'Mr Portland, would you like a short tour of the place?'
Aunt Maria asked, taking Rina by complete surprise.
'Not only is it our business premises, but it has interesting architecture as well. I'm sure you've observed our
tower? It creates a lot of interest in this area.'

When Connor accepted, her aunt turned to her.

'Rina, I have a call to make. Please would you show
Mr Portland round?'

'Of course, Aunt Maria.' She raised her eyebrows but
her aunt's face remained impassive. Her aunt had never
offered a tour to anyone from another company. Could
this mean she was actually thinking about accepting Connor's proposal?

Rina banked down her excitement and concentrated on
the prospect of confronting Connor. She had to know the
truth—she had to know whether he had always known

who she was. She had to keep a clear head. Right now, she had to think of Connor as the representative of a potential business venture—not the charming man she'd spent the last two days with. And she wasn't Rina Lahiri, pretend tour guide, but Katrina Lachance, head of product development and part-owner of Lachance Boutique.

'This is my laboratory,' she said, when they reached the closed sliding glass doors at the end of the tour.

Her aunt's assistant, Agatha, had accompanied them on the tour, which had made any private conversation difficult—for which Rina was grateful. There were too many questions that she had, none of which were appropriate for a business setting, the most pressing one being, had he known who she was? Was that the reason he'd wanted to spend time with her?

'How many people work in your lab?' Connor asked.

'Three, including me.'

'Only three? And you make all the products yourself, here?'

'We make the products. But we outsource packaging and distribution.'

'There would be huge potential savings on economy of scale if you accepted our proposal.'

'The decision on whether to accept your proposal will be solely down to Ms Lachance,' Rina said, wanting to make that clear to him.

She watched him closely for signs that the information affected him, in case he had got to know her because he thought *she* was the decision-maker, but she couldn't perceive any surprise or any other reaction from him. Was he a good actor or had he really not know who she was?

'I appreciate that, Miss Lachance.'

Did he place particular emphasis on her surname? This time it was Rina who cleared her throat as heat rose in her cheeks again. At least Connor hadn't lied about his name.

'I'm afraid I can't show you around the lab,' she continued. 'Proprietary products. I'm sure you understand.'

'Of course. But can you tell me how it feels, working in a circular room?'

Rina raised her eyebrows at the unexpected question. 'I feel like a magician in my tower. It's magical.'

Connor's lips quirked. 'I see. So there aren't any particular challenges posed by the shape of the room?'

Rina closed her eyes, wishing the ground would swallow her. She looked over at Agatha, who was covering her mouth with a book. It was bad enough to say something silly in front of Connor, without a colleague witnessing her embarrassment.

'Not at all,' she replied, deciding to embrace her comment. 'As I said, it's magical working here.'

Connor's mouth curved as he gave her an almost imperceptible wink. She couldn't help giggling at his charm, reminding her of the man she'd spent the last few days with and the man she'd kissed so passionately. Her giggles stopped abruptly as she caught Agatha's look of astonishment. This wasn't the same man. This was Connor Portland, businessman and representative of Newmans, who probably had more interest in Essence than in her.

'I shall leave you here, Mr Portland,' she said, putting out her hand. 'For now.' The look she gave him made it clear there was unfinished business between them and she *would* be seeing him later. 'Agatha will show you out.'

She wasn't sure whether their hands had remained

clasped much longer than necessary because she hadn't wanted to let go, or because he hadn't. When he finally released her hand she twisted it inside her clothes, as if that way she could preserve the warmth and sparks of electricity that flowed through her.

'Connor.'

Connor turned when he heard Rina's voice behind him. He hadn't gone back to his hotel after his presentation. Instead he had come to the place they had first met, hoping she would somehow know to meet him there. And here she was.

He lifted his arms subconsciously, then forced them down by his sides. What was he doing—did he expect her to run into his embrace?

He remembered the lightness in his chest when he'd seen her walk into the conference room. Intense pleasure at seeing her again so unexpectedly, followed by shock at the realisation of who she really was and how important she was to his company. It had taken a tremendous effort to hide both reactions, but he'd worked out quickly, just by her posture, that she wasn't comfortable letting the people in the room know they already knew each other.

When she had told him she helped out her aunt, he had assumed she was referring to the older lady she'd been standing next to that first evening he saw her. He had never imagined she would be related to the owner of the company. And not only that. She was the creator of Essence, the miracle hair product. She was a genius. Somehow she had discovered a way to use the rampion that grew so abundantly around here in a hair product with the most amazing results.

He shook his head slowly, marvelling at the stunning, incredible woman in front of him.

She was glaring at him.

'What's wrong?' he asked, furrowing his brow.

'You're really asking me that? As if you don't know.'

He shook his head; he didn't know. If anything, he was the one who should be angry she had lied about her real name. But he wasn't. From what she'd shared about her aunt, it was a protective measure, and Lachance wasn't exactly a common surname. In this area it would be a complete giveaway about where she worked and lived.

'You seem annoyed with me,' he said, trying to keep a level tone.

'That's an understatement. Why didn't you tell me who you are?'

He blinked, bewildered by her question. 'I did tell you who I was, Rina Lahiri—or should I say Katrina Lachance.'

Her mouth twisted. 'Are you angry that I didn't tell you my real name?'

He smiled. 'No, I can understand that. I guess it was part of the reason you didn't talk about your job.'

'That was convenient for you, wasn't it?'

He furrowed his brow, perplexed. 'I'm sorry... I don't understand why it would be?'

'Because otherwise you would have had to admit why you really spoke to me that day.'

'You're the one who approached me,' he pointed out.

'Because I thought you might be lost. But that could have been part of your set-up.'

'Set up?' What was she talking about. 'I didn't know who you were, but perhaps I should have guessed you

worked for Lachance. You have such beautiful luxuriant hair. I might have assumed you used their products.
I didn't know you'd developed them.' He looked around
him. 'I already told you... I saw you in town my first
evening here. I thought you lived opposite the restaurant.
You never contradicted me.'

'So you didn't approach me because you knew I was
part of Lachance Boutique and thought spending time
with me could help you?'

His eyes widened as the reason for her attitude and
questions finally dawned on him. She suspected he had
agreed to go sightseeing with her with ulterior motives.

'No, I admit I was there because I wanted to see Lachance tower, but I never thought about the business when
I was with you.'

And that truth was alarming to his usual work-driven
self.

She bit her lip. 'So you really didn't know who I was?'

'I really didn't.'

He smiled with relief when she nodded, apparently accepting his response. He almost reached for her again,
but a glimpse of Lachance tower was a visual symbol of
the altered relationship between them.

'But now you know who I am. And I know who you are.'

'Does it make a difference?' she asked.

'Does what make a difference?'

'That we know now. Does it matter that I'm the prod-
uct developer for Lachance and you're Director of the
European Division for Newmans. Why can't we still be
Rina and Connor?'

'We *are* still Rina and Connor,' he said emphatically,

but then paused for a moment. 'But it does make a difference.'

She sighed. 'It does?' she asked somewhat ruefully.

'Mmm.'

'Why does it have to?'

'It makes a difference because now there's a business relationship between us.'

'A potential one.'

He quirked a brow. 'Until your aunt makes a decision on our proposal there's a business relationship between us.'

'And what was there before?' she asked.

'What?'

'Before today? What was there between us? Are we friends or was I just a tourist guide to you? A tourist guide that you happened to kiss.'

He grimaced. It was a simple question with a complicated answer. What *were* they? He knew he liked her. He enjoyed her company. They were definitely on their way to being friends. But he was also attracted to her—a little too much for his peace of mind. For that reason alone, even trying to cultivate a friendship was probably a bad idea.

The business aspect was almost a minor additional factor.

'I don't know,' he replied eventually. 'Can people really become friends in only a few days?'

'What does the number of days matter when you feel a connection to someone? Friendships can be instantaneous.'

His eyes had widened at her use of *connection*. So she'd felt one too. Spending time with Rina was making him feel out of sorts, act out of character. He had to be sensible. There was no future for them. There couldn't be. He wasn't capable of offering commitment even to someone who lived in the same town as he did. Trying to make something work long distance would be impossible for him, and Rina deserved more than a brief affair. She was different from the kind of women he usually had affairs with—special in an indescribable way. Having a physical relationship with her would be wonderful, but he knew emotions would develop—hers, perhaps his—and that would be too messy for him.

He steeled himself not to react to her wistful expression. 'I have enjoyed your company,' he began, 'but I'm leaving for Munich soon, and then I'll be heading to India.'

'India?' her eyes widened.

'Yes, we have facilities in Mysuru and Bengaluru.'

The way her eyes brightened and lit up her face made him catch his breath.

'You're going to Mysuru?' she asked.

'Yes.'

'My mother grew up in Mysuru. I've always wanted to go but I never got the chance.'

'It's very beautiful there. I hope you get the chance to visit one day.'

He could almost see her brain ticking away. He didn't have to wait long to find out what she was thinking.

'Let me go with you,' she said, grabbing hold of his arm.

'What?'

He glanced pointedly at her hand, but she didn't remove it. Thankfully he was still wearing a jacket. If the sensation of the warmth and weight of her hand through its fabric was enough to evoke such a strong reaction in his body, he dreaded to think how he would have reacted if she'd rested her hand on his bare arm.

'Please. Let me go with you. I could come with you to Munich and then we could go to India together.'

A myriad of thoughts crossed his mind—the most startling of which was his urge to say yes. For that reason alone he had to say no.

'Rina, be serious.'

'I *am* being serious, Connor. Why can't I go with you?'

'You're being impulsive. You need to calm down and be sensible.'

He didn't mistake the hurt in her eyes, but she recovered quickly.

'Connor, I have always wanted to go to Mysuru. And you're going to Mysuru. Doesn't that sound like fate to you?'

'I don't believe in fate. It's a coincidence.'

She tutted, then sighed deeply, as if she was being extremely patient with him. 'Coincidence is just the cynic's name for fate. Anyway, you still haven't given me an actual reason why I can't come with you.'

Connor didn't think he'd ever met such a stubborn person. He didn't know what to make of it. He hoped she didn't want to go because she was hoping for a relationship with him. He had to make it clear to her that was impossible.

'I'm going for business, not for pleasure, Rina. I simply won't have time to entertain you.'

Rina tilted her head. 'I don't need you to entertain me. I can sort out a guide at the hotel.'

'What hotel? There are logistics to consider before travelling.'

'I'm sure I could get a flight at this time of year.'

'What about a visa? You'll need one for India. Those can take time.'

Rina shook her head. 'No, my mum sorted that out for me when I was a child. I have a card that means I can travel to India at any time. She always planned for us to visit every couple of years. And I'm sure I can sort out a hotel online. I can organise everything if you let me know your flight details.'

'Then why don't you organise to travel on your own or with your aunt another time? When you can plan it properly.'

'Because that will never happen.' Rina wrung her hands. 'I've wanted to travel so many times, but my aunt hasn't wanted me to. She worries about me, so I usually feel too guilty to pursue it.'

'What makes you think this time will be different?'

Rina practically deflated in front of him. 'I don't know if it will. But I know it never mattered so much to me before that I have to seize the opportunity. I just know that it's probably now or never for me. This could be my only chance.'

Connor paused. He wished he could help her, but it made no sense for her to travel with him. He was going to India for work—he couldn't take his girlfriend with him.

And Rina wasn't his girlfriend. He didn't know how to define whatever it was between them. They'd made a strong connection from almost the moment they'd met, but he knew it wouldn't last. He would never feel comfortable making a commitment to a girlfriend—he was too used to moving on. And even if a commitment was possible for him, Rina longed to travel...longed to explore. He travelled out of necessity—he would only clip her wings.

He shook his head. 'Rina, I—'

She placed a finger against his lips.

'Please, Connor, don't say no. Not yet. Think about it. Please.'

He felt the lingering warmth of her finger. He resisted the urge to run his tongue where her finger had been. Another sign that spending more time with her wouldn't be wise.

He didn't want to disappoint her, but there was no point giving her false hope that she could come with him.

'It's not a good idea, Rina,' he said, adopting a tone of finality.

Her shoulders slumped and she bent her head. He hated to see her that way, so different from her usually bubbly personality. But what could he do? He had to turn her down.

He reached out to touch her shoulder. Her head lifted at his touch. He stared at her, unable to hide the regret in his eyes.

Finally she grimaced, then asked, 'Will I see you before you leave?'

'I hope so. I'm going to be busy dealing with some of the points you and your aunt raised today, but I'll make time to say goodbye.'

'Okay. I'll see you then.'

She gave him a small wave before walking away.

He was sure he heard her mutter under her breath, 'Yeah, we'll see if it's goodbye.'

He barked a laugh. He should have known she wouldn't give up that easily.

CHAPTER FIVE

THE NEXT DAY Rina sat on her stool, watching and waiting for the extraction process to finish, the same as she'd done many times before. It might be a weekend, but that didn't mean much to her when her days all rolled into each other.

She *had* to find a way to convince Connor to take her with him. He was travelling to Mysuru. Connor might not believe in fate, but for her it was a clear sign that this was her chance to travel to India and visit the place her mother had lived as a child. Perhaps her only chance.

But even if she managed to convince Connor, she still had to convince Aunt Maria. She expelled a breath. One step at a time, though. She'd concentrate on Connor— that was her first hurdle.

There had to be something she could use to persuade him. She hardly had any time to come up with a compelling reason to tag along if she was going to get all the logistics sorted. She pulled out a notebook, ready to compile a list of ideas, but had barely managed to write a title before the intercom buzzed.

'Rina, do you have a moment to come here?' Aunt Maria asked.

'Sure.' She made sure her work was safe on its own, then went into her aunt's office.

'We didn't get a chance to speak properly about yesterday's presentation,' Aunt Maria said once Rina had sat down.

'It was good,' Rina said, pleased she could be truthful. She tried not to sound too enthusiastic—she didn't want to raise Aunt Maria's suspicions.

'I do feel it's the best one we've seen so far. And Mr Portland is very impressive.'

Rina nodded. 'But...?'

'I'm still not sure. It's good that the company's happy to start with a licence for Essence and doesn't want to take over Lachance.'

'That's true. So what aren't you sure about?'

'Do we really need it? Aren't we doing fine as we are?'

Rina sighed. This was the nub of the problem between their differing visions for Lachance Boutique. Aunt Maria was happy with maintaining the status quo, while Rina was of the firm belief if they didn't grow and improve they would stagnate. Someday, some company would be able to replicate Essence's formula and method, and then Lachance would have no chance to compete. If Rina couldn't come up with a new product what would happen to Lachance then? And since she'd been feeling wholly uninspired recently, she didn't hold out much hope for developing something new any time soon.

'Is "fine" enough?' Rina asked.

'It has been for many years.'

Lachance Boutique had been created by Rina's grandparents. Her aunt had joined the company, but Rina's dad hadn't followed in their footsteps since he'd moved to England after he'd got married. Aunt Maria was right that the company had done well for years, but it sometimes seemed to Rina that her aunt had forgotten they had almost been on the verge of changing direction or even closing before Rina had created Essence.

'But if we could get Essence into more hands... Wouldn't it be wonderful to think of people in more countries, even on different continents, using our product? But it's not something we can do on our own.'

Aunt Maria stiffened and pressed her lips together. Rina hoped she hadn't gone too far. She knew from years of experience her aunt could be extremely stubborn once she'd made up her mind.

'I know that's what you want,' her aunt said. 'But is it really necessary?'

'We both agree that Essence shouldn't be a luxury product. But at the moment we can't sell it any cheaper. That keeps it out of a lot of people's price range.'

Her aunt inclined her head. 'I agree it's not ideal.'

'If we give Newmans a licence then we would have...' Rina tried to remember what Connor had said. 'We would have economies of scale.'

Aunt Maria smiled. 'It sounds like you actually paid attention to yesterday's meeting.'

Rina shrugged. 'It was the first time any of these business proposals chimed with me.'

'I agree that if we did go with any company it would be Newmans, but I still don't think it's necessary at the moment. Did you have any further discussion with Mr Portland when you gave him the tour?'

Rina willed herself not to blush, thinking about Connor and the way he'd looked when he'd grinned at her response to his question about the shape of her laboratory.

'Not really. He asked questions on how we were running the labs and our distribution. Then he said he was travelling to some of their other sites soon. They have a global enterprise.'

Her aunt tapped her chin. 'I would love to see how these companies actually work—see how their employees actually feel about the company and how it's run.'

Rina tried to contain her excitement at Aunt Maria's words.

'Why don't we?' she asked.

'What do you mean?'

'Why don't we go with Mr Portland and inspect his sites?'

'We can't just go like that. That's not how things work. Everything needs to be properly organised. We could maybe arrange a visit later in the year.'

Rina knew if they didn't take the opportunity now her aunt would never go.

'But wouldn't it be better if we went before they had time to plan anything. If we do this as an impromptu visit, we can see the facilities as they really are,' Rina said, sitting forward as her excitement built. 'Otherwise they'd put on a show for us, which would defeat the purpose.'

'Possibly.'

Rina held her breath, crossing her fingers that her aunt would agree.

'But,' her aunt continued, 'there's no point unless we are serious about their proposal. I have to admit Newmans impressed me more than any other company we've met with. But I'm still not convinced this is the right direction for Lachance Boutique.'

Rina sat back, deflated.

Her aunt turned back to the papers on her desk which was her way of indicating the conversation was over.

'I'll see you for dinner,' Rina said as she rose from her seat and left the room.

She made her way to the kitchen. She wasn't particularly hungry or thirsty, but since food and drink weren't allowed in the lab having a break would give her a few more minutes to gather her thoughts.

Her aunt's suggestion of seeing how the company really operated was excellent. So excellent, in fact, it was the perfect excuse for her to go with Connor. She clapped her hands as she expanded on the idea in her mind. He wouldn't say no if he believed Lachance might accept his company's proposal. And if the facilities were good Rina would definitely use all her persuasive powers to convince her aunt to seriously consider Connor's proposal. She would finally get the chance to travel—her dream come true.

Rina took a few centring breaths. She needed to be sensible. Her honesty compelled her to admit that the business advantage was secondary to getting to travel with Connor. But she had to determine how much of her excitement was to do with the prospect of travelling and how much was to do with the prospect of spending more time with Connor?

She liked Connor—enjoyed his company, found him attractive. *Very* attractive. She giggled again when the image of his gorgeous face appeared in her mind. But she wasn't naïve or foolish. She knew that there was no future with him. As much as she wanted adventure and excitement, Rina knew her duty was to remain with Aunt Maria. She owed her aunt too much to leave for a long time.

And Connor hadn't given her any indication he was interested in more than friendship from her. He'd even questioned whether their friendship was real. She shrivelled a little at the memory of how much that had hurt her.

But visiting Mysuru— something she'd wanted to do her whole life. Her aunt would never take her, Rina didn't have any close friends she could travel with, and she didn't want to travel on her own. If she waited for a time when her aunt felt happy to let her travel she could be waiting all her life. And getting to visit the birthplace of her mother was worth pushing the idea with Aunt Maria. She might never get this chance again.

She had no concerns about travelling with Connor— she trusted him. She'd already spent enough time in his company to know that he was a decent man with integrity. She had to seize this opportunity with both hands.

Without hesitation, she took out her phone to send Connor a message, asking him to meet with her as soon as he was free, offering to go to his hotel if it was easier. She sighed with relief when he agreed to come to their field in an hour.

The time it took before she saw Connor approach her in the field felt like the longest time of her life. She would still need to tell her aunt of her decision, but her priority was to convince Connor. And the best way to do that was to make it part of a business proposal.

She gave another quick look over the file she had prepared before she'd come to meet Connor. It outlined the rationale for her to accompany him on his visit. Although he already knew she had personal reasons for wanting to go to Mysuru, she was pleased her business rationale was solid in itself.

He had to say yes.

She had fully expected him to refuse when she'd first mentioned her proposal, but it had still been disappointing to see his immediate negative reaction. He clearly wasn't interested in spending more time with her now that he'd mentally compartmentalised her as a business contact—so it was a good job she wasn't after any kind of relationship with Connor. She just wanted a travel companion, someone her aunt would consider trustworthy. She needed to stack the deck in her favour when she spoke to her about her plans. She was adamant she would be travelling with Connor.

She handed him the file. 'Read through this. It explains everything better than I did.'

She watched Connor closely as he looked through her file. He frowned once he'd finished.

'Do you mean that unless I take you with me, you won't be prepared to consider our offer?' he asked.

Rina furrowed her brow. It sounded as if she was extorting him when he put it that way.

'No,' she replied forcefully. 'Lachance Boutique would still do their…um…due diligence before accepting any proposal. Newmans' proposal happens to be the one we're most interested in at present.'

'There's no guarantee your aunt will accept our offer even after your visit.'

'No, there isn't,' she admitted, and then played the ace in her hand. 'But she listens to me, and my views carry a lot of weight.'

'What is it you're trying to say?'

'I don't understand all the legal stuff myself, but I'm part-owner of Lachance Boutique.'

'What does that mean for Newmans?'

'It means I can use my influence to convince my aunt to grant you a licence at a fair market value. I already know she's open to your business proposal, and I can sway her decision in your favour.'

'What makes you think you can persuade your aunt to give us a licence when you can't even persuade her to let you travel on your own?'

Rina's mouth gaped open. 'That's unfair. Aunt Maria doesn't want me to travel because of the accident. There is no correlation between that and me trying to persuade her to give you the licence.'

'What accident?'

'I told you my parents died in an accident. I was in it too.'

Connor inhaled sharply. 'You were in the accident?'

Rina nodded. 'We were on our way to the airport to collect Aunt Maria. She wanted us all to go on a trip straight after collecting her, otherwise I would have stayed home with my mum. I think she's always felt a bit guilty about that. That's why she gets panic attacks at the thought of travelling, and why she worries about me travelling.'

'Aren't you concerned about worrying her, then?'

Rina bent her head. Perhaps she was making the biggest mistake in her life, but her gut was telling her she had to go to Mysuru with Connor. She had to grab the opportunity of living out her dream, regardless of the consequences. Rina loved her aunt, and didn't want to deliberately hurt her. But she had to believe that Aunt Maria loved her too, and in the end her love would be strong enough to accept Rina's need to travel. Hopefully, once Rina returned unharmed it would help her aunt to worry less about her.

'Of course I am. But I have to do this.' Rina expelled a breath. 'Connor, I'm sure I'll be able to convince my aunt to accept your proposal. And, really, I'm the best—probably the only—chance you have of that.'

'You think she would turn us down otherwise?'

She nodded. 'Yes. So, will you take me?'

She held her breath.

CHAPTER SIX

CONNOR GLANCED OVER at Rina, sleeping peacefully in the passenger seat. Although he should be annoyed, he couldn't help smiling. He wasn't surprised that she'd got her own way and they were now driving together to Munich on his visit there before they flew to India.

His company had been more than happy to make arrangements to accommodate her when he'd told them Rina was interested in inspecting some of Newmans' sites to make sure the company was a good fit for Essence. They understood her interest to be a positive and encouraging sign, since no other company had received that. The board had indicated his promotion was pretty much in the bag but would only be announced once Lachance Boutique signed on the dotted line.

He pressed his lips together. This promotion had been his goal pretty much since he'd been promoted to his current position. And now it was in his grasp thanks to Rina.

He didn't flatter himself Rina wanted to travel with him for the pleasure of his company—India held the true allure for her. If he hadn't been travelling to Mysuru would she still have been interested in persuading her aunt to grant the licence for Essence to his company? He didn't usually doubt his skills and abilities, but if his promotion was dependent on finalising the deal with Lachance Boutique, he wanted to be absolutely certain he'd earned it.

Rina mumbled something in her sleep, then turned to her other side so she was facing away from him. Although she'd been bright when he'd collected her, she'd fallen asleep within half an hour. He'd expected her to be tired, since they'd set off quite early that morning. It would take around four hours to drive to Munich, and he wanted to arrive before eleven. But he was still disappointed not to be listening to her chatter away.

Rina's aunt hadn't come out to say *bon voyage*. He wondered whether that was because of their early start time or whether her aunt was unhappy with Rina's insistence on entertaining Newmans' proposal. Or was it something else? He grimaced. Hopefully Rina's desire to travel hadn't caused too much conflict with her aunt. But ultimately, as long as the deal went through, it was none of his business.

Whatever he and Rina had been to each other when she'd been showing him around Thun, now there was only a business relationship between them—and he would maintain a professional attitude. He had to take all personal talk off the table.

It was actually a good thing Rina was sleeping so he didn't have to indulge in any small talk.

After driving for a couple of hours, he pulled into a restaurant. He reached over to wake Rina. He said her name quietly, causing her to turn her head towards him. The shadows on her face emphasised her high cheekbones and her straight, dainty nose. There was no denying she was gorgeous. But he wasn't supposed to have those thoughts about her.

He gently shook her shoulder.

'Rina,' he said quietly. 'Rina, wake up. We've stopped to have some breakfast.'

She came awake with a jolt, automatically putting her hand up to wipe over and around her mouth. He grinned. He could reassure her that she hadn't drooled while she was asleep.

'We still have a few hours' drive. Time for a coffee. Come on.'

He got out of the car and walked round to hold her door open for her.

She took a couple of moments to orientate herself, then reached under the glove box to grab her bag.

As soon as she got out of the car she stretched and yawned, not bothering to cover her mouth. He couldn't help laughing as he watched her rub her eyes.

'What?' she asked, mid-rub.

'You remind me of a raccoon?'

'A raccoon? Has my make-up smudged?' she muttered, reaching into her bag, 'No, wait, I'm not wearing make-up. Did you say raccoon?' she asked, as if unsure she had the correct translation. 'The animal?'

He nodded, trying to hide his smile.

'You think I look like a raccoon?' She huffed.

'A very cute raccoon.'

She quirked an eyebrow.

'The cutest raccoon I've ever seen,' he added for good measure, pleased to hear her chuckle.

'You need to work on your compliments,' she said wryly.

'Being compared to a raccoon is possibly the highest praise I can give.'

'Hmm, sure.' She rolled her eyes.

He needed to stop the flirtatious banter, but it would take a while to adjust to their new solely business relationship.

They walked into the restaurant and were led to a table. After they'd ordered, he deliberately took out his phone and scrolled through messages and emails while they waited for their food.

Without batting an eyelid, Rina took a notebook out of her bag and started jotting down notes and making sketches. He found it hard to concentrate on his phone, curious to know what she was writing.

They both put the items away when the food came.

'Are you sure I can't drive part of the way?' Rina asked after they'd taken a few bites. 'I have a driving licence.'

'I'm fine. Anyway, it's a hire car and I didn't add you.'

'Okay. Stop as often as you need.'

'I plan on driving straight through now. Unless you're going to need bathroom breaks?'

Rina shrugged. 'Who knows? Are you going straight into a meeting once we get to Munich?'

'Pretty much—but it will depend on what time we finally arrive. Newmans has arranged for someone to show you round the office while I'm busy, then we'll both go to the distribution centre. After that we can check in to the hotel. I have a dinner meeting, which will probably last most of the night, so you'll have the evening to yourself.'

She nodded slowly. 'Sounds good. It's a shame we're too late for Oktoberfest. I would love to go to that. How weird that it mostly happens in September. Have you ever been?'

'No. I've been to Munich when it's on, but never had time to take part. I'm there for work.'

She pushed out her bottom lip. 'Seems a waste. But I suppose that's what happens with business travel. You've never wanted to go there for pleasure?'

'No.'

His abrupt response made it clear he didn't want to discuss the topic further. Why was that? Was there something he didn't want her to know? Some kind of secret he was hiding? Perhaps it was something personal to him and he didn't feel close enough to tell her yet—although that idea made her sad, she respected his privacy and wasn't going to press the issue.

They carried on eating for a few more minutes before Rina asked whether she'd be able to access the internet in his office.

'I want to send the notes I just made to my colleague,' she explained.

'I'm sure someone can arrange that for you,' Connor replied.

'Actually, that's okay. I don't know whether I can encrypt it properly.'

'Encrypt?'

Rina gave an embarrassed laugh and shrugged. 'I don't really know what I mean... It's not usually an issue, since we all work off the same system in the tower. But I had a great idea when I saw those dewberries outside and I want to share it as soon as I can. But I can almost hear my aunt warning me it could turn out to be a trade secret so I have to be careful. There's so much to think about when you travel for work…' She exhaled forcefully.

Connor blinked. 'You had an idea based on a plant you saw outside for a second?' He hadn't noticed any of the scenery.

'Yes, I recognised its fruit immediately and it occurred to me…' She trailed off. 'It's not important.' She turned to look out of the window. 'It's so picturesque. I'm going to try to stay awake for the rest of the drive.'

Connor didn't say anything. His company employed some excellent scientists, but he wondered whether any of them would come up with an idea worth sharing based on a brief glimpse of a flower or anything else. Of course he didn't know for sure whether Rina's idea had any merit, but he got the impression, from everything he'd heard about Lachance's product designer, that she was incredibly skilful and professional. He doubted she would share any idea with her colleagues unless it had real potential.

Rina was quiet in the car for the rest of the drive. She spent the time looking at the scenery and writing in her notebook, nodding often.

He wished he could ask more about what she was working on. But whereas before they had constructed an artificial barrier to take work off the table, now there was a real barrier preventing them from talking about work. She would probably assume any curiosity on his part was because of his company rather than out of a desire to understand more of her thought processes, because she, quite simply, intrigued him.

He had anticipated he would regret Rina accompanying him on these visits. So far everything was confirming his view.

* * *

Apart from a couple of occasions when he stopped to take some calls in private, they made good time to Munich.

'I have around forty-five minutes before my meeting,' Connor said. 'Why don't we find a café nearby and have a coffee?'

He would enjoy some more time with Rina before heading into the bustle of work.

'Can't we go to your office early?' Rina replied, surprising him.

'I'm sure we can. The person who's going to give you the tour may not be free, though.'

'That's fine. If you can find me somewhere to sit, and a desk, I'll be fine.'

He could tell her mind was elsewhere—possibly on the idea she'd had over breakfast.

This focus was an interesting aspect of her personality he might never have discovered if she hadn't joined him. If he'd based his opinion of her on the two days they'd spent together touring around Lake Thun he would have described her as someone who enjoyed life, looked for the fun in it and didn't take anything too seriously. Discovering she had created Essence had got him reassessing his initial opinion.

He wondered what else he would learn about her as they spent more time together. Despite his determined efforts not to get closer to her, he was looking forward to discovering more facets of Rina.

Rina's first few hours in Munich had passed by in a whirl of activity. Initially the people she'd seen at the Newmans office and at its distribution facility were understandably curious about her presence, but once she'd been introduced and they heard her surname their attitudes changed.

Rina supposed it was gratifying that so many people knew about her product—particularly when they couldn't yet afford to advertise widely. Essence had become known through word of mouth and beauty influencers. Sometimes, stuck in her small lab in her small tower, she had no idea exactly how popular her products were on a human level—sales sheets and profit and loss accounts were a dry metric.

They'd finally checked into their hotel just after five p.m. After a wash, Rina sat on the bed in her room, looking through the room service menu. Connor had his business dinner so she would be eating alone.

She pursed her lips. This was the first time she had been outside Switzerland—she didn't want to spend the night cooped up inside, eating in her hotel room. Perhaps she could get a recommendation from Reception about a good place to eat that was easy to get to on foot.

If only Connor were free to go out with her. Not because she didn't want to eat alone, but because she enjoyed things more when she was with him. Although he had been strange with her that day—different from usual. She guessed he might still be annoyed that she'd managed to get him to take her with him—or maybe it was just all the driving he'd done.

She grimaced. She could understand why he didn't enjoy travelling for work so much if a hotel room was all he got to see of the places he went to. Perhaps if she had to travel for work she would also find it annoying. But she found that hard to believe. So far her time in Munich had been all about business, but she still thrived on the knowledge she was in a different country, even if in many respects it wasn't that different from her home.

And soon she'd be in India.

Although she'd convinced Connor about her business reasons for travelling with him, he knew her main reason was visiting her mother's homeland. Finally getting a chance to see the place her mother had grown up in, hoping to find a sense of connection with her that she'd missed growing up in Switzerland, where there was nothing to remind her of her mum.

She pulled out the photo she had in her purse. It showed her as a toddler in her mother's arms. Her father had his arms round both of them. It was her favourite family photograph and she always carried it with her.

Aunt Maria had done an incredible job of being a substitute parent figure; Rina had grown up wanting for nothing—it almost made her feel guilty for missing her parents. And now she was missing her aunt. They had never spent much time apart. Even when Rina had gone to university, Aunt Maria moved to the same city, so they could live together. And, although her aunt's overprotectiveness frustrated her on occasion, she understood how her aunt felt—losing nearly everyone she loved in one moment, and almost losing Rina too. Aunt Maria had patiently helped with her rehabilitation and raised her with no thought for herself. Rina owed her so much.

She tried calling her, but there was no answer. Her aunt's lack of response was threatening to dampen the joy of her travelling. She could understand why her aunt was unhappy, but she'd hoped her aunt would be able to understand why she *had* to travel to India. Perhaps Aunt

Maria just needed time. She would still leave messages to let her aunt know she was safe.

In the end, she decided to go down and ask in Reception. The restaurant suggested by one of the receptionists was excellent. She ate a lovely meal and enjoyed chatting to the owners when they weren't busy with other diners. They insisted on someone escorting her back to her hotel.

When she went inside, Connor was pacing in the foyer.

'Where have you been?' he demanded, stalking up to her.

She frowned. Why did he sound angry and as if he'd been scared? 'I went out for dinner. Is something wrong?'

'I tried calling you and went to your room. There was no answer. I had no idea where you were.'

'I was at dinner,' she repeated, wondering why he was making such a fuss. 'I had my phone in my bag…on silent.' She pulled out her phone and noticed a number of missed calls. He couldn't have been that worried about her, could he? She'd been perfectly safe.

'Why didn't you tell me?' he demanded. 'Or leave me a message.'

She felt as if she was being scolded by the school principal.

'What's wrong with you, Connor? You told me you'd be busy all evening. I didn't think my whereabouts would concern you.'

'You're alone in a strange city—for the first time, I might add—and you didn't think I would care where you were?' There was no mistaking the incredulity in his tone.

She rolled her eyes. She already had an overprotective aunt; she didn't need an overprotective travel companion too.

'I may not have travelled much before, but I assure you I'm perfectly capable of navigating a new place on my own. I didn't take unnecessary risks. I wouldn't do that. I was perfectly safe. In fact, I met a lovely family. They own the restaurant I ate at and they've invited me back for lunch tomorrow. But I may try somewhere new. I don't know.' She pasted on a smile. 'Anyway, it's been a long day. I think I'll go up to my room.'

'This conversation isn't finished.'

Well, he would have to continue it with himself, because Rina was already summoning the lift.

He got in beside her, staring straight ahead. Their rooms were on different floors, but he made no move to exit when the lift passed his. Perhaps he had misunderstood her move towards the lifts as a suggestion that they should continue discussing the matter in her room, rather than a declaration that she wasn't listening to him anymore.

Accepting the inevitable, she exited the lift and walked to her room, aware that Connor was following her. She hoped she'd left the room in a suitable state for company, but she'd pulled things out of her case in a hurry. She couldn't guarantee there wasn't underwear on the floor.

She scratched her head. What were the chances Connor would agree to wait outside while she quickly picked things up? She glanced behind her. He was still looking grim. He wasn't going to let her out of his sight before he'd had his say.

The door had barely closed before Connor said, 'In future I would appreciate it if you would let me know where you're going.'

'Pardon?' Rina asked, raising her eyebrows.

'While you're travelling with me, I'm responsible for your safety. I would appreciate you letting me know your whereabouts.'

He spoke calmly. He almost sounded reasonable. But…

'You're not responsible for me, Connor. I'm an adult. I'm responsible for myself. I don't take unnecessary risks.'

'You don't think it was a risk going out alone in a country you've never been to before? At night? In the dark?'

'I went to a place that was recommended to me by someone at this hotel. They told me there would be lighting the whole way and it was barely more than five minutes' walk.' She spoke extra-slowly, enunciating every word. 'And one of the owners even walked me back to the hotel. I was perfectly safe.'

'You walked back with a stranger and you talk about not being reckless?' he scoffed.

Rina tightened her jaw. 'I got to know the family during dinner. By the time I'd finished he was less a stranger to me than you were when I offered to be your guide. That was probably more reckless than going out to dinner tonight,' she said.

Or was that the problem? Had her behaviour with him on their first meeting given him cause for concern?

Connor pinched the bridge of his nose. She could tell he was reaching the limits of his patience with her.

'Rina, I didn't know where you were. Anything could have happened. You were alone in a strange city. I was worried about you.'

Hearing the concern in his tone, all the antagonism left her.

'I'm sorry. I didn't think you'd notice my absence. I

promise you don't have to worry about me. I'm not going to take risks with my safety. But you aren't responsible for me. Any more than you'd be responsible for another work colleague.' Rina's mouth fell open. 'Oh! You probably *do* think you're responsible for your colleagues when you travel.'

Connor turned away from her, confirming her suspicions. She didn't know why, perversely, knowing he would worry about anyone made her more annoyed. Had she hoped she was special to him in some way? That there was a personal concern for her?

She closed her eyes. It didn't matter how attractive he was, or how much she enjoyed his company, nothing could happen between them. No romance, a tentative friendship at most. She should be *pleased* she wasn't special to Connor, not disappointed.

'It's been a long day. I'm tired. I think I'll go to bed now, Connor.'

Heat rose in her cheeks. It was a bad idea to think of Connor and bed in the same sentence.

She turned her thoughts to more boring matters. 'Will you be going downstairs for breakfast?'

They agreed on a time to meet the next morning.

'Have you decided what you're going to do tomorrow?' he asked.

'Not yet,' she replied, walking to the door and holding it open. 'Once I do, I'll make sure to send you a detailed itinerary.'

Connor's jaw tightened. As he walked past her to leave, he paused and opened his mouth—then he must have changed his mind, because he simply nodded and left.

Rina expelled a breath as she let the door close. Dealing with Connor was as bad as dealing with her aunt.

That reminded her that she still hadn't had a chance to speak to Aunt Maria. There was still no answer when she called—it was beginning to look like her aunt was avoiding her.

Her aunt hadn't been pleased when Rina had told her she was going to travel with Connor. At first she'd tried to change her mind. Rina could easily recall the look of disappointment and unhappiness on her aunt's face when she'd refused to back down.

Rina felt she'd betrayed her only family.

She left a perky voicemail message, knowing her aunt would want to be reassured she was all right, even if she was currently unhappy with Rina.

Rina walked over to the window. It was her first time in a different country and she could explore to her heart's content the following day. But instead of feeling excitement or anticipation, she felt frustrated and stressed.

She could only hope a good night's sleep would put her in a better frame of mind.

CHAPTER SEVEN

CONNOR'S GAZE KEPT going to Rina, who was standing by a large window, looking at the planes take off and land. She'd been jittery ever since they got to the airport.

He could understand she must be very excited to be travelling to India—something she'd wanted to do all her life—but he couldn't help feeling there was something underneath all that excitement.

He recalled her setting off the security scanner earlier. It had been due to a metal zip, but she'd joked to him afterwards that for a moment she'd worried that the implants she'd had as a child had set it off. He'd assumed she was referring to her injuries from the accident which had killed her parents.

He couldn't help admiring this woman, who could find the humour in such a situation. At the same time he wanted to take her in his arms and offer her comfort she hadn't asked for and probably didn't need.

She had such a positive outlook and cheery disposition—in some ways the complete opposite personality to his—it would be easy to believe there were no long-lasting effects from the devastating loss she'd suffered as a young child. But her determination to go to Mysuru with him showed clearly how much she must miss her mother.

In that respect, it was hard to stay annoyed with her for effectively bribing him to bring her along with him. He still should be. But she was completely unapologetic about what she'd done. As far as she was concerned, theirs was a mutually beneficial arrangement. And, seeing how excited she'd been when she'd heard he was going to Mysuru, and knowing how much visiting her mother's birthplace meant to her, he doubted he would ever have had the heart to turn her down.

He narrowed his eyes with concern as he continued to look at her. Although she was still smiling, there was a tension in her shoulders he'd never seen before.

He walked over to her. 'Everything all right?' he asked.

She looked up at him, her smile brightening, causing his breath to catch. 'Yes, it's surprisingly addictive watching all the planes,' she replied, pointing to one getting ready to taxi.

'You haven't had anything to eat or drink. Are sure you don't want something? It could be a while before we get any food on the plane.'

She patted her stomach, drawing his attention to its flatness and the trim waist beneath it. He forced himself to look away before he embarrassed himself by being caught admiring her figure.

'I don't think I could eat anything at the moment,' Rina replied. 'Maybe I'll grab some fruit.'

'Good idea. We should probably head down to the gate in fifteen minutes.'

She nodded, but was already turning back to the window.

When their flight was called he noticed Rina looking around her, taking in everything as they boarded the plane, soaking it all up.

'This is something special, isn't it?' she commented, looking around the business class cabin. 'I suppose it's more comfortable for you with the extra leg room.'

She stretched her legs out in front of her, wiggling them to show how much space she had.

She was probably shorter than average for a woman, but since he was over six foot two, he never paid much attention to people's heights—they were all usually shorter than him. Although now he couldn't help imagining enfolding her in his arms and resting his chin on the top of her head, the memory came to him of how he had lowered his head as she'd reached up to him before their mouths met for their first kiss.

He cleared his throat, trying to remember what Rina had said. Something about her legs...no, leg room.

'I usually work on the flight, so additional room is helpful. Why don't you give the flight attendant your coat? Make yourself comfortable.'

He grinned a few moments later as he heard Rina's squeal as she inspected the contents of her amenity bag. She sounded the way as other people did when they received expensive gifts.

'What was that?' Rina asked, suddenly clutching his arm at a noise.

'The engines.' He furrowed his brow. 'Are you nervous about flying?'

'A little bit...'

His eyes widened with concern when he saw Rina's stiff, pale face. It suddenly dawned on him that if she hadn't travelled outside Switzerland before, this would be her first time flying.

He reached across and gently took her hand in his, giving it a squeeze. 'Okay?' he asked.

She gave him a small, excited smile which couldn't quite hide her nerves. She leaned forward to try and catch a glimpse outside.

'I'm sorry,' Connor said. 'I should have thought to arrange a seat by the window for you.'

Rina cast a glance around the cabin. 'It's fine. All the window seats are singles. Sitting in the middle like this, I get to hold your hand.'

She closed her eyes and squeezed his hand tighter as they felt the plane begin to move.

'Would it make you feel better if I explain the physics behind how flight is possible?' he asked.

She laughed, as he'd hoped she would. 'That's okay, thanks. It's odd, feeling this excitement, but slight anxiety as well.'

'I understand. In less than twenty hours you're going to be in India. Have you made any plans for your free time?'

'Nothing specific yet. I have guidebooks in my cabin luggage. I'll look through them when we're in the air. I guess I haven't really thought further than getting to the country. Of course I want to see my mum's old home, but that won't be until we get to Mysuru.'

'What do you know about Bengaluru and Mysuru already, then?' he asked, trying to keep her talking.

He managed to distract her with small talk until the plane had taken off and they were free to move around the cabin.

She released his hand. He almost tried to grab hers again, seeking its warmth and pressure.

'Why don't you try to get some sleep?' he suggested. 'We're at the beginning of a long journey.'

'I'm not going to sleep yet. That would be such a waste of my first experience on a plane. I'm going to choose a couple of movies…maybe try out the games.'

She laughed, the sound bright and joyful, as if her happiness and excitement had to bubble out of her.

She was completely absorbed during the flight, restful, enabling him to make good progress on his work. He noticed her tension return when the captain announced the plane was ready to land.

As soon as she'd returned her seat to the correct position, he reached over and took hold of her hand again.

'First leg of our journey almost over. How was it?' he asked.

'Wonderful. Truly wonderful. But I don't think flying business has given me the real experience of a long-haul flight. I'd like to know what it's like flying in the other class.'

By 'other class', Connor knew she didn't mean first. It was typical of the Rina he'd come to know that the only thing she'd said that might remotely be construed as a complaint was that she'd travelled in relative comfort.

He considered whether they could change one of the remaining legs of their journey to 'the other class'—he wanted to give her the chance to experience everything she wanted to.

If it was possible, he would also see whether they could have a day's layover in Doha on their return leg, or maybe add other stops to their trip.

Why was he spending time thinking about how he could help Rina have some more of the adventure she craved? They were business colleagues now. If there had ever been a possibility they could be something else before he'd known she was a Lachance, then it had been slim and in the past.

Getting the licence, and potentially his promotion, was too important to jeopardise with a brief flirtation. And that was all it could ever be. He wasn't good at making commitments to women, and he'd learnt from experience that it was better not to pretend it could happen. And Rina wasn't like his previous partners—in many ways she was still innocent.

How innocent was she? She spoke about how protective her aunt was, which must make having a boyfriend difficult.

He immediately shut off that train of thought. They'd already had their brief flirtation, when he hadn't known she was part of Lachance Boutique. They couldn't go back to that time, and there was nothing in the future for them but a business relationship.

By the time they were off the plane and resting in the airport lounge in Doha, Rina was back to her usual self. There were no signs that she was nervous about their flight to Bengaluru, but he managed to persuade her to have a massage treatment in the airport spa, to ease out any tension so she could relax fully before the final leg of their journey.

Rina was busy scribbling in her notebook for most of their layover. Her passion as she worked was evident. Connor pressed his lips together. He enjoyed his work, but it had been a long time since he'd felt that kind of passion for what he did. Hopefully, if he got the promotion, some of that would return.

When they were on board the next plane, there were still no signs of anxiety from Rina as they got ready for take-off. She was talking animatedly to some of the flight attendants while the passengers in the other cabin boarded.

Rina flipped through a magazine as the flight took off. He flexed his hand, as if it missed the chance of holding on to Rina's again.

She was a little more restless on this flight, fidgeting next to him. He could have ignored her and concentrated on his work. Instead he put his laptop and papers away and offered to play a game or watch a film with her.

She turned down his suggestions, telling him she was too excited to focus.

'Can I just ask you questions instead?' she asked.

'About work? Sure.' Connor suspected that was the only safe topic of conversation for them.

Rina pouted, showing that wasn't her original intention, but she asked, 'Does your company have offices in any other parts of India?'

'We do. I'm the director of European Operations so I don't usually visit the Indian offices, they're not in my remit but the director of South Asian operations, Nihal Murty, is new to the post. He used to work with me and I recommended him for the position, so I'm going out to discuss any issues he has as kind of a favour.'

If Connor received his promotion he would have many meetings, with directors of all the different sectors, but in future they would travel to him rather than the other way round.

'He knows I'm coming?' asked Rina.

'Yes. He's a trained scientist too, so he's looking forward to discussing your work.'

'Oh, I'm not trained as a scientist,' Rina said with a sombre expression. 'My aunt just knows I like playing with chemicals, so she lets me experiment with them. It seems to work.'

'Pardon?' Connor said, his eyebrows flying to his hairline.

Laughter pealed from Rina. 'If only you could see your face right now,' she managed to gasp out, pointing at him. 'Of *course* I'm trained! In fact I was offered the chance to do a PhD, but I went into the family business instead.'

Connor sighed, as if pained by her joke. If only she could see how stunning her face was when she laughed. Breathtaking. Adorable. He didn't know the right description for her beauty.

He looked away quickly. Maintaining a businesslike, professional distance was becoming harder with every second he spent in her company. He could be in real trouble.

CHAPTER EIGHT

SHE WAS REALLY in India. Her mother's homeland. She was finally here. She experienced a whole gamut of emotions in a matter of seconds. It still felt surreal, unbelievable. She pressed her hand against her chest, trying to ease the choked sensation, as if she wanted to cry and to laugh and to twirl all at the same time.

From Connor's warm expression, she could tell he could empathise with what she was experiencing, but she was grateful he knew to leave her the space to give in to her feelings.

The heat as they left the airport was the first sign she was in a completely different country. Ayun, the man who'd been sent by Connor's friend to meet them at Arrivals, ushered them towards a waiting car and they were soon on their way to their hotel. It was before sunrise, so the roads were clear.

Rina leaned forward to look out of the window, hoping for her first glimpse of India, but it was too dark to see anything beyond flickering lights.

'Try to stay awake until we get to the hotel,' Connor said. 'Then sleep as soon as you can. It will help you get adjusted to the time difference. Set your alarm for around nine-thirty a.m. You don't want to oversleep. It'll make the jetlag worse.'

Rina nodded. It all sounded like sensible advice. Apart from staying awake until they got to the hotel, she wasn't sure she would be able to follow any of it.

Part of her was desperate to wait and watch the sun rise over her first day in India. It was a romantic notion, but now that she'd got it into her head she couldn't let the idea go. She glanced over at Connor. After what he'd just suggested, it was unlikely he would agree to stay up with her.

For a moment she wished Aunt Maria was with her. She tried to work out what time it would be in Switzerland but, regardless of the hour, her aunt probably wouldn't answer her call anyway.

Rina sat down by the window in her hotel room. She hadn't spoken to her aunt since she left Switzerland. It was the longest they'd ever gone without speaking to each other. Surely Aunt Maria couldn't still be angry with her? Usually any disagreements between them were resolved within a couple of days. Rina could understand if her aunt was disappointed in her, but all her life she'd done as her aunt wanted—stayed out of harm's way, stuck in her fairy tale tower.

Rina even understood why her aunt was so overprotective—she was all Aunt Maria had left in the world. But Rina didn't need or want to be sheltered all her life. Even at university her aunt had been there, and now, at the age of twenty-six, Rina needed this tiny taste of freedom. She craved the chance to do something for herself. Did that make her selfish? If so she would be selfish for a few more days. Then, afterwards, Rina would return to the tower and accept her daily life.

Her phone beeped. She hurried over, hoping it was her aunt, but was surprised and delighted to see the message was from Connor.

I know you're not sleeping. Why don't you come to my room? You'll be able to watch the sunrise much better from up here.

She laughed as she typed a reply, telling him she was on her way. It certainly didn't seem to her like an invitation from someone who only thought of her as a business colleague—he knew her well enough to work out exactly what she'd planned.

Connor didn't speak as he opened the door to his room. The silence was almost reverential as they walked over to the large window. It was five a.m. and the sun was slowly beginning to rise.

She watched, breathless, as the golden rays slowly brought the awe and beauty of the Indian city of Bengaluru to light. She gave a quick glance to Connor. Seconds later he stood closer to her, placing a comforting arm around her, allowing her to lean back and rest her head against his shoulder as they both concentrated on the dawn.

She didn't know how long they stood there, silently seeing the city wake up, but the long journey was finally beginning to take its toll on her and she yawned. She felt the ghost of Connor's lips against her forehead.

'Come on,' he said. 'There's still time for you to get some rest before we start the day. I'll see you at breakfast.'

He went to hold the door open for her—an effective way to break whatever spell she'd been under, watching India come to life.

Back in her own room, as she braided her hair, she grimaced. It had been hot even when they'd arrived. If it was that hot now, before the day began, it was only going to get hotter as the day went on.

She didn't love the idea of the heavy weight of her hair plastered to her head in the heat. If only she didn't have to deal with it. She'd kept it long out of an unspoken love for her aunt. After her accident Rina had had to have her head shaved for surgeries. It had taken a while for her hair to grow back, and one of her earliest post-accident memories was of Aunt Maria gently brushing it and tying it into different styles. As she'd grown up, it had become a daily ritual for her aunt to brush her hair, and her aunt often used the time to tell Rina stories about her father and Lachance. Her aunt had told her often how much she loved the length and thickness of Rina's hair, and had always sounded upset if Rina even hinted at getting it cut.

But it had been a long time since her aunt had brushed her hair for her.

At breakfast, Connor outlined what he had planned for her for the day. They were staying two nights in Bengaluru before driving to Mysuru, where they would spend another three days before returning to Bengaluru for the first leg of their journey back to Switzerland.

Rina's mouth turned down. He was making it sound as if their time in India was almost over rather than just beginning. It was such a contrast to the warm man who'd stood with her as she'd watched the sun rise. Now he was all about work, emphasising how business travel was a whirlwind trip without much free time. Although that wasn't going to be the case for her.

'I've been doing some more research on the area,' she began, 'and I have a list of restaurants to visit and food I want to try. Ma used to make idli and dosas when I was younger, but I haven't had a good one in years so that's on my must-do list.'

Connor frowned. 'I'm not sure I'll have much time to take you.'

'That's okay. You don't have to take me.'

He closed his eyes. 'Are we going to have this argument again?'

Rina rolled her eyes. 'No argument. These places are for breakfast. I won't be going out at night.'

'You shouldn't go out alone in a place you don't know.'

She didn't know whether his concern was heart-warming or whether he was irritating in his over-protectiveness. She smiled, deciding to interpret it as a sign that he cared for her a little.

'I spoke to Ayun before I came down for breakfast. He called to check everything was okay with the room and said he's been told to make himself available for my convenience by your colleague. That's kind of them, isn't it? Anyway, he said he can take me to a restaurant tomorrow morning.'

Connor pressed his lips together.

'Oh, come on, Connor. You can't still be worried.'

'I don't know Ayun.'

'But your colleague does. He wouldn't arrange for someone untrustworthy to be responsible for me.'

Why was he being so difficult? If he hadn't drummed it into her that there could only be a business relationship between them she might almost believe he cared about her on a personal level.

She narrowed her eyes. 'Or is it me you don't trust?'

His lips quirked. 'You can be quite the handful.'

Rina huffed in mock offence. 'Nobody has ever said that about me before. I guess you bring out the worst in me. The question is, what do I bring out in you?' she asked, batting her eyelashes.

Connor splashed coffee on his hand. He blinked a couple of times. 'My sense of self-preservation,' he muttered under his breath.

She gave him a cheeky grin, then got up to return to her room and get ready to go into the office with him.

As she was twisting her hair up into a bun she thought again about how much it was getting in her way, with the humidity making it harder to deal with. Luckily, she had some Essence with her, but she still wanted to do something about the sheer weight of her hair. There was no reason for her to keep it that length any more. She loved her aunt, but she wasn't a young girl who needed to be controlled by her any more. Coming to India despite Aunt Maria's objections proved she was independent, and she could make her own decisions—particularly about her hair.

Before she met Connor she wandered along the hotel concourse to see what shops and services they had available, smiling when she saw a small hair salon. She walked in to see if there were any appointments available later that day.

The drive to the office was much slower than that from

the airport. The sounds of horns and bicycle bells competed with loud voices.

Rina sat back in her seat with a huge smile.

'Has it sunk in yet?' Connor asked her with an indulgent grin.

How could he tell exactly what she was thinking?

'It's beginning to feel real. The sounds and smells are so unique.' She had the windows open and sniffed at the air. As she pulled her head back inside she plucked at her top. 'I may need to add buying some cotton clothes to my list, because otherwise I'm going melt into a puddle of sweat by mid-afternoon. Please tell me the office is air conditioned.'

'You'll be relieved to hear it is.'

'You know, my mum went to university in Switzerland, but she worked in IT. I think if she hadn't met my father she might have come back to India and settled in Bengaluru. It's strange to think she could have driven down these roads as a child.' Almost to herself, she added, 'I'm already starting to feel closer to her, just being in the same country.'

Connor covered her hand. He looked over at the driver and at Ayun before giving her hand a quick squeeze and letting go.

Before coming to India, Rina had wondered whether some of her old grief would return. She'd never got the chance to visit these places with her parents. Rina was sure her mother had planned to take her often, since she'd organised her entry card. But instead of grief, Rina felt a quiet sense of connection and belonging.

In some ways it was similar to the connection she'd felt with Connor the first time she'd met him. There'd been a sense of familiarity and recognition with him. It was completely separate to the physical attraction she'd also experienced, although that had been startling in its intensity.

She took a quick glance at Connor. Apart from brief moments when his natural empathy came through, he was trying hard to keep things between them business-like. She didn't fully understand why. They had been developing a friendship—more than a friendship if she thought about their kiss, which she did far too often. But that was before he'd found out she was Maria Lachance's niece and before he found out the company he wanted to do business with was partly hers.

She had to find a way to bring them back to that easy-going relationship. That was all that was possible. At one point she had hoped there could be something more be-tween them, but she wasn't being realistic. Not only did they live in different countries, but they also wanted dif-ferent things from life. She wanted to explore the world, while Connor made it clear he viewed travel as a neces-sary evil.

A few hours later, Rina was beginning to feel that fa-miliar sense of frustration. Connor seemed to be follow-ing her around as she toured the facilities and met the staff. Was he worried about what she would ask them or what they might tell her about working for Newmans? Or was he being protective? She didn't need someone looking out for her when she was inside the company buildings. He wasn't quite as bad as her aunt, but he was becoming close.

'Connor,' she said finally, after he'd moved her away from a large group of people who had surrounded her, interested to meet the lady from Lachance. 'Don't you have meetings to go to?'

He shook his head.

'Isn't Nihal waiting for you?' she asked.

'Not at the moment,' he replied.

'Well, don't you have some work waiting for you? Don't let me keep you from it.'

'You're not.'

She expelled an exasperated breath. 'If you want me to get a real view of Newmans, so I can use my influence on my aunt, then you need to let me go around on my own.'

He pressed his lips together. Then briefly inclined his head. 'Fine. Why don't you message me when you've finished your tour?'

'Oh, that's not necessary. I'm going back to the hotel in half an hour. I'll see you there for dinner.'

'I can come back with you.'

She narrowed her eyes, tempted to tell him he was almost as stifling as her aunt when he was acting like her keeper rather than a business colleague.

'It's fine, Connor,' she said, tersely. 'I'll see you at dinner.'

She was nervous enough about what she had planned. She didn't need Connor questioning her further. If there was the remotest chance he would try to talk her out of it she wasn't going to risk him finding out beforehand. It would be too easy for him to make her second-guess her decision, and this was something she needed to do for herself—a small but obvious sign of her growing independence.

After she'd spoken to some more of the workers at

Newmans she went back to the hotel, heading straight for the hair salon.

'Are you sure you want to cut so much off?' the stylist asked, running the full length of Rina's wet hair through her fingers. 'You can do it in degrees. Perhaps just a couple of inches now? Are you sure you want it to the nape?'

Rina took a deep breath. 'Yes—cut it all off and donate it, as we talked about earlier.'

'All right.'

Rina shut her eyes tight as she felt the scissors touch her hair and, hearing the sound of the first snip, she felt a sense of loss. Her hair wasn't her identity, but it had been like a comfort blanket for so long. But she was committed now. She had to see this through.

Slowly she opened her eyes and watched as the stylist continued cutting, the long tresses piling at her feet.

It was done.

After a quick shower, Rina rushed down to the foyer, eager to meet Connor for dinner.

'Hello,' she greeted him, as she saw him waiting by the reception desk.

'Your hair!'

She started at Connor's exclamation.

'Oh, yes.'

She ran her hand across her nape. It felt bare, and slightly cold. She was used to it being covered by her hair, but she didn't miss the weight that had fallen with each snip of the hairdresser's scissors.

'I had it all cut off. Do you like it?' She performed a slow turn.

Her smile fell at Connor's frozen expression.

'What's wrong? Why are you looking like that? Does

it look really bad. I've never had my hair this short before, but I thought it suited me. Doesn't it?'

'You look fine,' he answered curtly. 'Let's go. The car's waiting.'

Rina's eyes smarted. Why had his reaction hurt so much? His opinion of her hairstyle didn't matter as long as she liked it. And she did.

She ran her hand across the back of her neck again. The short length would take some getting used to, but taking such a simple and yet big step such as having her hair cut made her feel independent, empowered, invincible. Ready to take on the world.

But first she had to face a meal with Connor.

Connor knew he was staring, but he couldn't get over the way Rina looked. All that beautiful hair—gone. It would take some getting used to. Of course she was still Rina. Still beautiful. But now she looked more delicate.

During dinner he'd been staring, but that was partly because they were sitting opposite each other and it would have been rude and awkward if he'd avoided looking at her. Now, after their meal, they'd decided to take a walk in the grounds of the hotel and, despite a Herculean effort on his part, he still wasn't able to keep his eyes off her.

'I'm still me, Connor,' she said, unconsciously echoing his thoughts.

'You, but different.'

'A new me, then.'

'What made you decide to have it cut? I know you're impulsive, but I have to admit I am a little shocked.'

'It wasn't really impulsive. My hair has been weighing me down for a while.' She paused, and with a giggle added, 'Physically and metaphorically. It was time to do something about it.'

'When was the last time you cut your hair?'

'I've never really had it cut before, just trimmed the ends to keep them tidy.'

'That's a drastic change, then.'

'Hmm, I'm not sure about *drastic*. I think the correct word is necessary.'

She sounded happy, and free, as if the loss of her hair really had lightened her. He hoped she wouldn't regret it and become upset later.

'Don't worry, I'm not going to lie awake crying about how I've lost my beautiful hair.'

How was she reading his mind?

'Was it really that much of a nuisance?' he asked.

'When you're trying to stand but your head gets wrenched back because you've accidentally sat on your own hair, even once, is one time too many.'

He couldn't help laughing at the image her rueful confession conjured.

'How do you think your aunt's going to react?' he asked.

'Surprised, I guess.'

She sounded blasé, but he already knew how much she loved her aunt and cared about her opinion.

'It's going to be strange for you now, working on hair products. You were a walking advert for Essence before.'

Rina gave him a cheeky smirk. 'Everybody who uses Essence is a walking advert for it.'

He inclined his head, captivated by her easy wit.

'Anyway,' she continued, 'Essence works on short hair just as well as long—as you should know.'

He inhaled sharply when she touched his own wavy strands.

'How did you know I use Essence?' he asked.

'I can always tell. Like I said, it shows.'

'Ah, so you judge people on their hair?'

Her laughter trilled out. 'No, only people from companies that want to buy Essence. It's an easy way to weed only those who are only interested in the money they can make from the product but don't care about Essence itself, or the ethos of Lachance.'

It was the perfect segue into a conversation about business, but Connor was reluctant to follow that path. In fact, he was finding that Rina was distracting him from business. He had spent most of the day accompanying her while she toured the company's facilities, which had been completely unnecessary. He could have come up with a million reasons for his actions, but the simple truth was that he had wanted to see the company through her eyes—see her face light up when she met people or learned something new, listen to her perceptive observations, hear her tinkling laugh and feel it cheering his soul.

He stiffened. They were business colleagues. Regardless of how enticing she was, he had to forget the first couple of days they had spent together and flirtatiously got to know each other and maintain a professional distance.

'Time to head inside,' he said abruptly, and slightly more harshly than he'd intended, judging from her expression. 'There's lots to do tomorrow.'

He walked her to the lifts in the foyer, but couldn't risk being in a small, enclosed space with her so told he needed to speak to someone at Reception and walked away, knowing she was looking after him until the lift doors closed.

He knew he was sending mixed messages, but despite his best efforts he couldn't maintain the necessary distance between them.

The next morning, Connor positioned himself near the reception desk in the hotel foyer. From his vantage point he could see the lifts and the stairs, so there was no possibility he would miss Rina when she came down.

He glanced at his watch. She was ten minutes late. She couldn't have already left, could she? She'd promised she wouldn't go out on her own. She was impulsive, but not reckless. He looked at the door. Should he call Ayun to make sure he hadn't met Rina?

'Connor! Morning. I didn't expect to see you down here. Is your driver late?'

As he turned towards Rina's voice he was again taken aback by her changed appearance—and by the realisation the urge to run his fingers through her hair hadn't gone away.

'Connor, are you okay?' Rina asked, with a look of concern.

'I'm fine.'

She gave him a relieved smile. 'That's good.' She looked towards the door. 'Have you seen Ayun? I'm running a little late, so I thought he'd be here by now.'

'I asked him not to come.'

'Why would you do that, Connor? Do you still think I'm being reckless?'

'No!' He hurried to reassure her. 'I mean *I'm* going to take you to breakfast.'

Her mouth dropped open. 'I thought you had back-to-back visits and meetings today.'

'And it's good to start a busy day with a big breakfast.'

Rina's grin was worth the adjustment to his schedule—although he still didn't fully understand his urge to change his plans. He'd felt guilty that he had spoilt their evening by being abrupt with her. Although there couldn't be a romantic relationship between them, there was no reason their business relationship couldn't be on cordially friendly terms. He hadn't have to treat her as a stranger. He certainly didn't see her that way.

'Shall we go?' he asked, putting a gently guiding hand to the small of her back.

The breakfast café was busy, but the owner quickly cleared a table for them inside, under a ceiling fan.

Rina waved a hand in front of her face. 'Wow, I can't believe it's so hot so early. Thank goodness we've got the breeze.'

Connor nodded. 'Are you sure you want something hot to eat?' he asked.

'I definitely need to try the dosas, and I doubt it will be any cooler another day while we're in India, so now's as good a time as any.' She turned the menu over, looking through the options. 'Have you eaten here before?'

'Not at this restaurant. I eat idli and dosa fairly regularly, though. There's a really good takeaway restaurant near where I live in London.'

Rina raised her eyebrows. What had he said that surprised her?

In an effort to avoid getting caught up in her penetrating gaze, he stared at his menu.

'If you haven't tried dosa before I would recommend

getting a plain one, or maybe a masala dosa,' he said. 'If you like cheese, then the cheese masala dosas are usually good.'

'What about idli? Do you have a recommendation?'

'I like sambar idli—but again, if you haven't tried them before, then perhaps plain idli would be the safest option.'

'I'm not sure I like taking the safest option...'

This time it was Connor who raised his eyebrows and released a sigh of resignation.

'I mean in my food choices,' Rina explained with a small laugh. 'I promise you I'm not going to take risks with my safety while I'm here.'

He wondered if she was beginning to regret coming with him on his business trip. She was seeing more of his offices than of the city.

A waiter came over to take their order, asking them about where they came from and what they were doing in the area. When he heard it was Rina's first time in Bengaluru, he offered suggestions for places she had to visit.

'Everyone is so friendly here,' Rina commented.

Connor looked at the other patrons. 'I would guess we're the only tourists they've had here for some time.'

Rina followed his gaze. 'Well, if they're mostly locals here, that's a good sign the food is tasty.'

They didn't have long to wait for their food. This time it was the owner who stopped to chat with them.

Connor observed the interaction between him and Rina. She was probably completely unaware how much her bubbly and engaging personality contributed to the friendliness she received from the people around her.

Now Rina leaned over her plate and inhaled deeply. She gave a small moan which caused an immediate reaction in his body. Would she moan like that in bed with their bodies joined? Or would her moans be breathy, sultry or piercing?

He cleared his throat.

She looked up at him. 'Am I drooling?' she asked, wiping her hand across her mouth and picking up her first dosa.

'I can ask for cutlery if you prefer,' he offered.

Rina's mouth opened in mock horror. 'Not at all! I wouldn't think of using cutlery. Please tell me you're not the kind of person who uses a fork and knife to eat their pizza.'

He lifted his hand up. 'I wouldn't think of it.'

He felt as if he'd smiled more in the few days he'd known Rina than he had in the rest of his life.

He picked up his dosa and then, apart from some appreciative noises from Rina as she dug into her food, they ate in relative silence.

'Oh, that was so good,' Rina said when they'd finished. She sat back in her chair and patted her stomach. 'I don't think I'll need to eat for the rest of the day.'

Her action brought his attention to her flat stomach and curvy hips. He turned to signal for the bill before his eyes were tempted to linger on her too long.

'Are you going to the office now?' she asked once they had left the café. 'I don't know what you arranged with Ayun. Is he meeting me back at the hotel or should I go with you?'

'Weren't you planning to come to the office today?'

'I thought I'd do a bit of sightseeing before our appointment at the distribution centre. Ayun was going to accompany me, but I don't know if he's returned to work. I don't want to disrupt him unnecessarily.'

Rina chewed on her bottom lip, a habit he'd noticed she had whenever she was weighing up her options, particularly those which might impose on other people. He could tell she really wanted to explore the city but, maybe partly because of his concerns, she didn't want to go on her own.

'Why don't we both go to the office now?' he said. 'I'll speak to Nihal about bringing the visit forward and then I can sort out a tour of Bengaluru for you.'

She bit her bottom lip again.

'Don't worry—it won't inconvenience anyone. The meeting I had with the London office immediately before our scheduled visit has been postponed, so I would be twiddling my thumbs during that time anyway.'

Rina smiled with relief. 'Oh, that's good. If you're sure?'

Connor gave a brisk nod. He *was* sure—at least he would be once he'd contacted the London office to excuse himself from that meeting. It was a regular weekly meeting with his core team and, since they were expecting him to be on leave this week anyway, they could hold it without him.

When they got to the office building, one of the people Rina had met the previous day came to greet her and lead her away. He called after her to remind her of the time they would have to meet to leave for the distribution centre visit, her thumbs up being all he got in acknowledgement.

Later that evening, Connor and Rina went to Nihal's home for dinner with him and his wife Mausami, but it was ridiculous how much Connor wanted to talk to Rina alone. He'd almost been tempted to get out of this dinner, so he could spend some time with her, but that would have been even more ridiculous.

'It's a shame you had to reschedule your holiday,' Nihal said. 'Rohan mentioned you were planning to visit him.'

'Yes, I thought I'd spend a few days with him before I came to see you, but plans changed.'

Connor gave a meaningful glance in Rina's direction. She had been chatting away to Mausami, but now she turned to him and gave him a quizzical look. He shrugged and shook his head briefly, and she turned back to her conversation. Had she sensed he was looking in her direction? Or had she been tuning into his conversation? He had to admit he'd kept one ear on what she was saying.

He noticed Nihal's small smile as he followed the direction of Connor's gaze. It wasn't the first time that evening his friend had caught him looking at Rina.

'I haven't seen Rohan since his wedding,' Connor continued.

'Really? So you didn't go to the—?'

'No, I was in Australia on business and couldn't get away.'

'Well, you missed an extravaganza.'

'Hey, guys,' Mausami said, coming to stand next to her husband. 'Do you want to play a board game. Rina said she hasn't played one since she was a child.'

Connor agreed immediately, although board games weren't usually his thing. If Rina hadn't played a board game for years it was probably because she didn't have any people her age to play with, stuck in Lachance tower with her aunt.

The four of them were soon laughing and bantering over the game until it was time to return to their hotel.

'I've had a lovely evening,' Rina said when she was in the car next to him. 'Your friends are wonderful. I like them so much. Thank you for inviting me along.'

'It's my pleasure. And they really liked you too.'

In fact he'd been shocked at how easily she'd got along with Nihal and Mausami. Although she had been friendly with the people she'd met at Newmans, she'd maintained a slight professional distance, maybe even some reserve, since she clearly wasn't used to meeting so many people. But with Mausami and Nihal she'd been engaging and witty and vivacious, and she'd won them over as quickly as she had him.

'You never mentioned you knew Nihal before. You made it sound like you met him through work.'

'Nihal is one of my closest friends. I've known him for years. We met at university.'

'Hmm…'

'What's that sound for?'

'I don't know. I guess for some reason I thought you didn't have any close relationships.'

Connor pressed his lips together. 'I have a few close friendships that I've had for years. But I don't have long-lasting relationships with women, if that's what you're referring to.'

'Why not?'

Connor was silent for a moment. The topic was completely unsuitable for people with a business relationship, but that evening the four of them had been a group of young people relaxing and having fun together, so perhaps it was natural for Rina to treat him accordingly.

And perhaps it wasn't a bad thing to make it clear to Rina that any romantic relationship with him was impossible.

'I met Nihal through Rohan. Rohan was in my tutor group at uni. I was never close to anyone before then, apart from my brother and sister. We moved around too much when I was a child. It was better not to get close to anyone.'

Rina's forehead wrinkled. 'I don't understand. What do you mean, you moved around too much?'

Connor sighed. 'My dad found it difficult to hold a down a job, so we had to move around the country a lot to wherever he could find work. When I was a teenager there was one time I found myself getting close to a girl, and we tried to date. But then my family had to move suddenly. She wanted to stay in touch, but I couldn't see the point. We would be living miles away, I wouldn't have the money to go back to see her, and my family wouldn't have the space for her to visit me. So it ended. Since then I've kept any relationship very short term.'

'Because you travel for work a lot.'

Connor wasn't sure whether it was a question or a statement. 'Partly,' he said, although that wasn't the reason at all.

All the women he'd dated previously had been interested only in their career, and hadn't been looking for a long-term relationship, just occasional companionship— which was exactly what he wanted too. He'd never met anyone who'd made him believe commitment was something he could do.

'What about you?' he asked. 'Have you had any long-term relationships?'

Rena giggled. 'No. It's a bit tricky when you have an

overprotective aunt. I've been on some dates, but nothing really developed. I've never met anyone I wanted to introduce to my aunt—it didn't seem fair to put anybody under such scrutiny. But I do hope to meet someone and get married someday, to somebody who understands that I need to stay with my aunt. Although that's probably unrealistic.'

Even in the darkness he could tell her face had fallen. He wished she would find a man who could make her dreams come true. But that man wasn't him.

CHAPTER NINE

RINA TRIED TO act nonchalant as the car approached Mysuru. With every mile they covered, they were a mile closer to the place her mother had lived for the first ten years of her life. Perhaps Rina would finally find the connection to her mother she had longed for.

She glanced over at Connor. As usual, he was scrolling through his tablet, writing notes. His face when he was concentrating was now so familiar and endearing to her. She wanted to reach out and run her finger along the furrows on his forehead.

If she was thinking about connections, she'd also like to rediscover the connection she'd felt with Connor when they first met. She still loved spending time with him, sharing her thoughts, hearing his opinions. But there was a distance between them now. He was sticking to his plan to maintain a business relationship—for the most part.

Occasionally the Connor from the rampion field reappeared. And she adored it. Because she knew without any shred of doubt *that* was the natural Connor. He was forcing himself to be aloof and maintain a professional distance. If only she could convince him it wasn't necessary.

'Are you sure you don't want to come to the office with me?' Connor asked.

'I'm sure, thanks. Unless you think I need to go?'

He pressed his lips together. 'It was your suggestion to see Newmans' facilities, not mine.'

Rina bit the inside of her cheek. She supposed she shouldn't be surprised he was still irritated that she'd forced him to accompany her to India.

She beamed at him, as if she hadn't noticed his grumpy attitude. 'I think I've got a good idea of how your company functions by now. Thanks. I'm very impressed.'

Even if she hadn't already promised him, she would have definitely tried to convince her aunt they should accept his company's proposal based on what she'd seen. Regardless of how much she liked Connor on a personal level, she would encourage her aunt because she was convinced, with everything she'd seen so far, that it would be the best business decision for Essence.

That was if Aunt Maria ever spoke to her again. She hadn't returned any of her messages. It was the only low point of the entire trip, but Rina still couldn't regret her decision to seize what might be her only opportunity to visit Mysuru.

'I'll be fine with Ayun. If you're sure you won't need him?'

Newmans had assigned Ayun to stay with them until they left Karnataka. Although technically he was supposed to be available for Connor's needs, they all knew Newmans would agree to anything Rina requested, so Ayun had said he would accompany her while she explored Mysuru.

Rina did feel a slight twinge of guilt that the company was going out of its way to make sure she was happy.

It had come as a surprise when Connor hadn't protested at her plans to go around without him. Perhaps she had misjudged him as being overprotective when he really wasn't.

Besides, Ayun was only going to be with her for the day. The following day she was hoping that Mausami would be able to come up to spend some time with her. They'd got on like a house on fire during dinner the previous evening, and had made plans to see each other again. Mausami worked for an IT company and was able to set her own hours, so she'd told Rina she was going to take the day off.

After having so few friendships while she was growing up, it was a blessing for Rina to find someone she got on so well with. But it made Rina realise how different her instantaneous connection with Connor had been. She couldn't pretend that she hadn't found him incredibly attractive from the moment he'd turned round in the rampion field. And while their friendship developed, her attraction to him kept on growing.

She hadn't wanted to say goodbye to him after showing him around Lake Thun. It had seemed as if all the pieces were falling into place when he'd told he was travelling to India.

But since then she'd felt like a yo-yo—bouncing back and forth between wanting to explore having something more with Connor or maintaining a friendship.

In a way, Connor had taken some of the decision away from her, by trying to adopt a business-only attitude. It was almost as though he'd drawn an indelible line between the couple who'd shared a passionate goodbye kiss and the couple they were now. But there were times when he looked at her with such intensity, he still had to feel something more than business.

She liked him. A lot. But she knew as well as Connor did that there was no future for them. She could never leave her aunt for good and she doubted Connor would leave England for Switzerland. It was clear to her they wanted different things out of life; their dreams were not the same. She wasn't so naive as not to realise that.

Calls and car horns broke her out of her introspection and she realised they were already in Mysuru. She laughed to herself. She had almost expected a huge sign welcoming her—some kind of fanfare heralding this actualisation of a dream. But visiting the place where her mum had been born and raised wasn't a big deal to anyone but her. No need for fanfares.

After dropping Connor off at the Newmans office, Rina went with Ayun to look at some temples. But although on any other day the unique structures stretching to the sky would have had her brimming full of ideas, it didn't take her long to realise it wasn't what she really wanted to do. She was desperate to see the house her mother had grown up in. Perhaps even go to the park where her grandfather had pushed her mother on the swings.

Sometimes the stories her mother had told her—as few as they'd been—seemed like something from a dream. Rina wasn't sure how much she could rely on her memories from sixteen years ago.

Rina's mood deflated further when Mausami called to let her know she hadn't been able to get time off work because an emergency had cropped up, but she tried to keep the disappointment out of her voice as they made arrangements to meet up when Rina returned to Bengaluru before she took her flight back home.

After she left the temple Ayun recommended a nearby

public garden which had beautiful flower beds and said there would be benches. She wasn't sure whether or not that was his subtle way of indicating he needed a rest, but she agreed.

Once she found a free bench, Ayun handed her a drink and then moved away to speak on his phone.

She tried to concentrate on the beauty of her surroundings, but she was thinking about how her plans for the following day would need to change now Mausami wouldn't be there. Although she was sure Nihal would agree to Ayun accompanying her again, she was also sure he wasn't excited about playing chaperone to a tourist. But from what she now knew she doubted Connor would be happy with her going out alone.

She had wanted someone with her for moral support when she visited her mum's childhood places. She didn't want to put Ayun, lovely as he was, in an awkward position if she happened to get emotional.

'What's wrong?' a familiar voice called out.

She looked up in shock as Connor walked towards her with a concerned expression. He was so perceptive…always surprisingly attuned to her feelings. There was no point pretending everything was okay.

'Mausami can't come up. Didn't Nihal tell you?'

'Yes, that's why I came. I wanted to see how you were, since I knew you'd be upset once you heard the news.'

Rina pouted. Why did he have to be so kind? Every time she'd convinced herself there was no future for her and Connor, he did something to show he must care about her and started her hoping all over again.

She reminded herself of all the reasons they couldn't be together. They were on different paths in life. He lived in

England. She couldn't move away from her aunt. He wanted to stay grounded and she wanted to explore the world. He couldn't make a commitment. At least, he'd convinced himself he couldn't—and who was she to say he was wrong?

Although in so many ways she felt as though Connor knew her better than almost anyone else, and she wanted to believe he'd let her get to know him on a profound level, the reality was they'd only known each other a week. And she wasn't ready to move her world to his— not that he'd ever indicated he wanted her to.

Connor couldn't quite interpret Rina's expression. Surprise, naturally. Pleasure? He hoped so. But there was something else too.

'You came here because you thought I'd be upset? What about your meeting?' she asked.

'It finished quicker than I expected, so I decided to leave work early and join you on your tour. I've managed to get everything I needed done today, so now I'm at your disposal.'

She didn't know he'd condensed everything into one meeting as soon as he'd found out Mausami wasn't able to come and spend time with Rina.

'What?'

This time her expression made him laugh. 'I'm going to be your guide. I took the rest of today and tomorrow off. I was supposed to be on holiday this week, so it wasn't a problem.'

'Didn't you have plans to go somewhere? I thought I heard you were hoping to meet your friend? Rohan I think you called him.'

Connor realised that although she'd been chatting with

Mausami, Rina had clearly had one ear on Connor's conversation with Nihal.

'There isn't enough time for me to fly to Rohan's island. I can visit him another time.'

'Rohan's island? Your friend has his own *island*?' Rina asked with a laugh.

'Not technically. But he is the King.'

Rina blinked. She stared at him, furrowing her brow, as if she was trying to work out if he was serious.

'Your friend Rohan, the man you were swapping stories with Nihal about, is a king?'

'That's right. I was invited to his coronation, but I couldn't make it.' His lips quirked. 'What's was on your list of places to visit?'

'The palace, of course—I still haven't done that. And tomorrow I planned to see the sculpture museum. Mausami also suggested I go to one of the silk markets.'

'Are you ready to leave? The car's waiting.'

She grabbed her handbag and cotton covering, but didn't say anything else until they were in the car.

'I'm not sure which is harder to believe, that your friend is a king or that you've taken time off.'

He rolled his eyes. 'I do have a life outside work.'

She quirked an eyebrow. 'Really? Do you? Not from what you've told me. It's movies, books and cooking—no socialising.'

'Perhaps I haven't told you everything I do in my spare time.' He waggled his eyebrows suggestively.

She made a spluttering sound. 'But would you be doing this if not for me?'

He grimaced. If Mausami had been able to come he probably wouldn't have taken the time off. But Rina would feel guilty if he admitted that. And, if he was being strictly truthful with himself, a part of him had been pleased when he heard Mausami couldn't make it. He enjoyed spending time with Rina and there wouldn't be many opportunities to do so going forward.

He'd already decided it would be a bad idea to keep in touch with Rina after she'd returned to Switzerland. If she kept her promise and managed to persuade her aunt to go into business with Newmans he would still be involved with Lachance Boutique in obtaining the licence for Essence. But Rina was the product developer—there would be no reason for her to be involved with those details.

But that would be after they'd returned to Switzerland. They still had a few days in India and then the long journey back. After that they wouldn't be in each other's futures—it wouldn't be fair of him to keep in contact with her when he couldn't offer her any kind of permanence. But as long as he was honest with her why shouldn't he enjoy the time he had with her in the present?

Connor was content to follow Rina round as she toured Mysuru Palace. She barely spent seconds viewing some of the architecture, but then spent long minutes with her notebook out, looking at pieces that seemed to him exactly the same as the ones that hadn't held her interest.

Looking inside her notebook would be a fascinating insight into Rina's mind, Connor felt a strange pang in his chest—a pervading sense of loss that he would never be the one she shared her notebook with.

The next day they went to Brindavan Garden, followed by the Mysuru Sand Sculpture Museum, before driving to a street bazaar.

Rina rushed from stall to stall, reaching out to run an admiring hand along the bales of silk, lifting some towards the sun, laughing as she chatted to the stallholders.

He walked over to her. 'Please, let me try bargaining for anything you want to buy.'

She shook her head. 'It seems wrong. Putting it in perspective, it's not as if they're charging outrageous starting prices. I know they expect bargaining when they name their price, but it seems unnecessary to me.'

He laughed ruefully. Why had he expected anything different?

'Oh, that's the place Mausami mentioned. Let's go,' she said, grabbing his forearm.

Inside the stall Rina looked over the ready-made salwar and kurtas. She reached up to touch the occasional sleeve or hem of an outfit worn by the mannequins, then looked at the clothes on the shelves to see if she could find the same garment.

It wasn't like a department store, where you could find the same outfit in different sizes. It was rare that the same material would have been used more than once, let alone in a variety of sizes.

She made a beeline for the sarees. 'How gorgeous is this colour?' she asked him.

She held it against her arm, where the pink hues of the material brought out the peach tones of her skin. She would look absolutely stunning in any outfit in that colour. He wanted to rush over and buy huge quantities.

'And it feels so wonderful,' she said, as she ran her fingers over the material. 'I would love to somehow recreate this sensation in a Lachance product.'

Connor gave her a confused look. 'How would you do that?'

'Here—feel this.' She grabbed his hand and ran it with hers over the silk. 'This is how your hair should feel after washing and using a treatment,' she continued. 'I want to capture the same rich, luxurious experience when people use a product.'

He became conscious they were still holding hands and released her reluctantly. 'It sounds like India is inspiring you—as you hoped.'

She nodded, her eyes bright. 'It's amazing. I've been under such a dry spell recently, but now I feel like I'm in a monsoon of ideas. I've made so many notes! Not only ideas for products but for new containers, and there's even a new method I want to experiment with.'

'A new method?'

She pressed her lips together. 'Lots of ideas.' Then, clearly changing the subject, she said, 'There are so many beautiful sarees. I wish I had the chance to wear them. But maybe more opportunities will come if I buy the sarees first.'

'I don't think that's how it works,' he said, with a dry tone.

'Yes, I know... I know. You don't believe in fate or destiny—you think it's coincidence. And I'm sure you don't believe in manifesting. But "there are more things in Heaven and Earth, Connor, than are dreamt of in your philosophy."'

'Pardon?'

'*Hamlet.*'

'Okay...'

Her mind was an enigma—one he wanted to unravel

almost as much as he would love to unravel Rina wearing a saree...

He blinked at the direction of his thoughts. He might have decided to enjoy his time in her company but he still needed to maintain a distance. 'Perhaps you can buy a few sarees for inspiration at Lachance.'

'That's a brilliant idea!'

The smile she gave him took his breath away.

'Perhaps we should carry on looking at the other stalls?' he suggested, deliberately walking away from her.

She was far too fetching, and if he didn't move he would give in to the temptation to gather her to him and press his lips to hers, regardless of how public the setting was. But he wouldn't move too fast—he didn't want to lose track of her in the crowd.

After they'd finished at the bazaar they stopped at a café for a cold drink and some snacks.

'Where's next on your list?' Connor asked.

Rina bit her lip. Why was she looking nervous?

'What's up?' he asked.

'I told you my mum lived in Mysuru until she was ten, didn't I?' she asked. When he nodded, she continued, 'I'd like to go to the area she lived in. Perhaps even find the house. But it won't be interesting for you.'

'I would enjoy going with you, if you don't mind,' he replied softly. Although she hadn't mentioned it yesterday, he knew she wanted to visit her mother's former home.

'Are you sure?' she asked, her relief visible.

'Yes.'

She smiled, but there was a small, almost imperceptible tension in her mouth. She was worried about the visit. He imagined it would be overwhelming to finally have the chance to go somewhere your heart had longed to see. A place that had great significance for her mother—a chance for a connection with the person Rina had missed since she was young girl.

He probably would have gone with her for support even if Mausami had come up. He wanted to be there for her, even though he would never tell her his reasoning—she might be able to work out that he cared about her if he told her.

'Let's go back to the car and we can head there now,' he said, instinctively holding out his hand.

She grabbed it with a grateful smile, then she took a deep breath and they walked to the car.

'Can I help you?'

Rina turned from the gate enclosing what had once been her mother's home to see a woman, perhaps the age her parents would have been, speaking to her.

Since she'd asked in English, Rina replied in the same language, rather than attempting to speak in Kannada.

'Oh, I'm just looking at the house here. My mother grew up on this road, but I don't know if the houses have been rebuilt since she was here.'

'No, I grew up here too, and my mother still lives next door. The houses are exactly the same.'

Rina turned to Connor with a huge smile. 'So my mother did live in that exact house. She went through that door and looked out of those windows.'

'What was your mother's name? Maybe I remember her,' the woman said.

When Rina told her, the woman smiled warmly. 'I *do* remember her. Your mother was the same age as me. We played together all the time and walked to school together. I was sad when she left. I think when we were nine or ten?'

Rina nodded. Meeting someone who'd spent time with her mother, perhaps shared stories and secrets and wishes for the future, was surreal. She wanted to ask the woman to tell her everything.

'I can't believe I'm seeing her daughter,' the woman continued. 'How is she?'

Rina's sorrow was echoed in the woman's face when she heard about Rina's mother's passing.

'My name is Urmi. If you have time, why don't you come inside? I know there will be some photos of me playing with Riya. And my mother is always telling me about what the two of us used to get up to, if you want to hear her stories.'

Rina blinked back the sudden rush of moisture in her eyes as she tried to absorb this offer to see childhood photos of her mum and hear what she'd been like when she was younger. Even hearing her mother's name, Riya, spoken so easily.

She sensed Connor coming to stand next to her, offering silent comfort and support. She swallowed. 'I would love to do that, if you're sure we won't be disturbing you.'

'Not at all. Unfortunately, the people who live in Riya's old house aren't here for a few days, otherwise I'm sure they would have showed you around. You don't live in India do you?'

'No, I live in Switzerland.'

Urmi's eyebrows rose. 'I see. And is this your husband?' she asked, looking at Connor.

'No, Connor's a work colleague. We actually came to Mysuru on business.'

'Well, please, both of you, come inside.'

Rina took a step forward, then halted. She looked through the bags Connor was carrying for her and pulled out a box of mithai. She couldn't go into the lady's house empty-handed.

Before long they were sitting with Urmi and her mother, enjoying tea and snacks. And hours later Rina walked back out onto her mother's childhood street in a daze, still trying to process everything she'd been told and store it in her memory for ever.

'Are you okay?' Connor asked, resting his hand on her arm.

She nodded, unable to speak.

He gathered her into his arms, holding her tight. She leaned into him, soaking up his wordless support. He made her feel safe and protected, secure and brave enough to process how she was feeling. She only wished he could always be there for her in situations like this, and she also wished she could be the one to offer *him* strength and support whenever he needed it.

She'd been without her parents for sixteen years. She'd had to get used to a new normal at an early age, leaving the home she'd grown up in and moving to a different country. Just as her mother had left India, at a similar age, to move to England.

She slowly became aware of looks from passers-by.

'I'm okay. Thank you. Thanks for coming with me,' she said.

'Of course.'

He reached out to hold her hand as they walked back to the car, where Connor gave the instruction to head back to the hotel.

Part of her felt bad that she was cutting the day short, but she knew Connor wouldn't mind, because he was accompanying her rather than visiting somewhere on his own accord. She needed to take some time to recalibrate. She had never expected to meet anyone who had actually known her mother. When it came to her father, Aunt Maria was able to share many stories of him growing up, but there had been nobody to tell her stories about her mum until today.

When they reached the hotel, Connor turned to her. 'Do you want to have a cup of tea or something to eat?' he asked.

She shook her head. 'I think I want to take a rest.'

They walked to the lifts. To her surprise, Connor got out on her floor and walked with her to her room.

He didn't follow her inside, but remained in the doorway.

She tried to smile, but knew her effort was weak from the concern in his eyes.

'I'm okay, Connor. You don't have to worry about me. I'm actually really happy.' She reached out to squeeze his hand and reassure him.

He leant forward to press a kiss against her forehead. 'Do you want to be alone, or can I stay here with you?'

Suddenly being alone was the last thing she wanted. She knew Connor wouldn't pester her with questions or even force a conversation. He was exactly who she needed to be with at that moment.

She nodded for him to come in. 'Why don't I order some tea and food to my room?'

At his nod, she went to the phone to place her order, then went to stand in front of the window while they waited for their food to arrive. As she'd expected, Connor came over to stand next to her. She put her hand in his. Then she made some small talk about the view until there was the knock at the door.

'Do your parents live near you, Connor?' she asked once they'd started eating.

She noticed his grip tighten on the cup handle and wondered whether she'd upset him with her question. He'd mentioned his brother and sister, and how his father hadn't kept a job for long so they'd always moved around, but she couldn't recall him saying much else about his parents. Were they still around?

'I keep a home for my parents in England. Norfolk. Do you know it?'

'The bump on the east coast?'

He smiled. 'That's right. It's in a place called Cromer, near the beach.'

'Is that where you grew up?'

His mouth tightened. 'As I told you, I grew up all over the place. We rarely stayed anywhere for long. Even now, my parents are travelling round the world. They don't even tell us where they are. But I bought them a base where they can stay if they are ever in the country.'

'And where do your brother and sister live?'

'Both of them live in London. North of the river.'

'The River Thames?'

He smiled again. 'That's right. Sometimes I forget you don't live in England.'

'Well, I did live there until I was ten.'

The stories she'd heard of her mother came rushing back to her mind. Rina had grown up with a loving aunt, and would describe her youth as happy. But she had never admitted how much she missed her parents...missed her mother. More now than ever.

She shut her eyes tight, overwhelmed and exhausted by the intensity of her emotions.

'I think I'm going to lie down for a bit,' she said, standing up and heading to the bed.

'Good idea,' Connor replied, standing up too.

'Would you...?' Rina began, before tailing off.

'Would I what?' Connor asked in a gentle tone.

'Would you stay and lie next to me for a little bit?'

She needed the comfort of Connor's presence. Wanted the strength of his arms.

He paused for a moment, then with a slight inclination of his head, he walked to the side of the bed and took off his shoes.

They both lay on the bed, facing each other. Connor traced the contours of her face with his fingertip. He leaned over to gently press his lips against hers, then turned onto his back and held out his arms. Rina lay against him and closed her eyes.

He heard her breathing change and saw the gentle rise and fall of her chest, relieved that she'd finally fallen asleep in his arms. He fought the temptation to stay next to her, perhaps even join her for a short nap. Carefully, he drew his arms away, anxious not to wake her. He looked down at her, desperate to press his lips against hers but knowing it was a bad idea. Instead, he rose off the bed.

He'd never felt this way before. Their closeness went beyond a physical attraction. It made him wary, made him want to put up his defence shield.

Should he return to his own room? He looked over at

her sleeping figure. After the day she'd had he didn't want her to be alone when she woke up. He briefly went to his room to fetch his laptop and then returned to hers. He wanted to be there in case she needed him—for anything.

When Rina finally woke up it was already dark outside. She looked peaceful, but drained. He suggested they order a meal from Room Service. While they ate he kept the conversation neutral, not wanting to talk about Lachance Boutique or Newmans but letting her know she could talk to him about her mother, her family, if she wanted.

CHAPTER TEN

RINA WAS SILENT on the car ride back to Bengaluru. She had chatted with Connor over breakfast that morning, but there was something forced in her smile. Was she as confused as he was about their closeness the previous evening? Or was she thinking about her mum?

The previous day had clearly taken an emotional toll on Rina. He tried to empathise with what she must be going through. Rina's mother sounded so much like her. He might not have the best or even a good relationship with his parents, especially with his father, but he couldn't imagine growing up without them.

The original plan had been to spend a few days in Mysuru and then a few more in Bengaluru before flying home to Europe. But he'd decided to take some more leave for the rest of his time in India, rearranged some things, and added a stop in Mumbai to their plans.

Rina's face when he'd told her had held the first genuine smile he'd seen.

They'd decided to head back to Bengaluru after breakfast, since Rina hadn't done much sightseeing on their previous visit.

When they got there their first stop was Tipu Sultan's Summer Palace. At first he wasn't sure whether that was a wise decision. Would it bring back memories of Tipu Sultan's Mysuru Palace, which they'd visited just before going to her mother's place the previous day? But the building seemed to help Rina's high spirits return. She was back to being curious about everything, with endless questions and insightful observations.

As they wandered around Rina would occasionally stop and take out her notebook, making a quick note or sketching some of the shapes she was looking at. He couldn't imagine how she found new things to add to her notebook after they'd already visited the other palace. But then, he didn't have the same kind of creative mind as Rina.

In some ways they had their devotion to work in common. Rina was always thinking about Lachance Boutique—the products she could develop and the improvements she could make. Perhaps it was because it was her family's company. Connor hoped her aunt would come to understand Rina's need to leave her everyday surroundings once in a while. He was sure she would—this inspired Rina was something to behold.

Passion for work. Passion for life. He couldn't stop his mind from wondering what her passion in bed would be like. Based on their kisses, she would be dynamite. He wished he could blame the sultry heat for the nature of his thoughts. But it wasn't to blame.

Rina was superlative—that was the only way he could think to describe her. And he wanted her. Wanted her in his arms, in his bed, underneath him.

But that was impossible. Apart from the fact she wanted to experience more than her hometown, and he wanted to travel as little as possible, his experience showed him he wasn't good at making commitments. The nomadic nature of his upbringing made him incapable of forming long-term attachments. Or perhaps he wouldn't have been a relationship kind of person regardless of his childhood. No one he'd previously dated had managed to keep his attention, and he always began to get bored quickly and want to move on—possibly the way his parents did. Only for him it was women rather than places.

He couldn't imagine getting bored with Rina—she was too engaging, too interesting. But that didn't change his intrinsic nature. His itchy feet could start up at any time. If he couldn't offer commitment then it wouldn't be fair to start anything with Rina. She deserved more than a brief affair. He wished things could be different—that *he* could be different—but he was too much of a realist to believe they could.

He needed to keep a physical distance from her. He made a quick decision to suggest a number of temples as their next stops. As always, Rina's notebook was out almost immediately. She lost herself in her drawings, ignoring all the noise and bustle around them.

When the heat of the day became a little too much for them, they managed to catch the late-afternoon show at Jawaharlal Nehru Planetarium.

Being pressed close to Rina in the darkness, under a vast, brightly lit sky, was like being alone in their own universe. He glanced over at Rina to see whether she was feeling the same intimacy, but she was watching the presentation in fascination. He laughed at himself, slightly put out that she didn't seem affected.

When they came out, Rina was buzzing. 'That was incredible!' she said.

He nodded.

'At first I wasn't sure, you know,' she continued. 'I never thought space and the solar system would be that interesting, to be honest. But those images. The lights. I wish there was a way I could incorporate some of that into our products.'

Connor's lips turned up at the corners. 'I'm sure you'll find a way,' he said, with absolute conviction. 'I think your problem is more likely to be how to narrow down which ideas you start working on first.'

'You've got that right,' Rina said. 'There are so many bubbling in my mind. I want to try everything immediately. But I'll need to get my aunt to approve any new work.'

'You still haven't heard from her?' he asked, almost wishing he hadn't when her shoulders slumped and she shook her head.

It was clear Rina loved her aunt. It must have been hard for her to leave against her wishes.

'Your aunt will come around,' he said. 'And maybe this experience, and seeing how happy you are after travelling, will help her realise you needed to get away and how good it's been for you.'

'Maybe.' She didn't sound as if she believed it.

'You mentioned her concern is a result of your accident? Now your aunt will know that you can travel alone without anything bad happening.'

'I guess… I just wish she would take some counselling to help her manage her anxiety. I would love to travel *with* her.'

'Did you have counselling?'

'Yes, for years after the accident. Have you ever spoken to a therapist about your childhood?'

'No, but I've encouraged my brother and sister to take therapy when they feel they need it. Our childhood was far from ideal and they suffered a lot.'

'It sounds like you suffered as well. Perhaps you should consider counselling too.'

He nodded. It seemed natural for Connor to discuss personal, intimate topics with Rina. He'd shared more details of his childhood with her than her had with anyone—even Nihal or Rohan. And he'd shared his feelings about it. Something he never did.

The following day they went out to KR Market. Rina seemed to be in her element among the different flowers and plants, taking photos and making more notes.

'This is so wonderful! This place! This whole visit! I'm almost tempted to take Nihal up on his offer,' she said.

'What offer?'

'Nihal said if I was ever interested in working on product development in one of the Newmans labs he would make it happen.'

'And are you interested?'

Rina laughed. 'I could never leave my aunt or my lab at Lachance Boutique. It's my baby.'

Connor laughed too, but he was reminded again of why they could never act on the attraction that had been between them since that first day. Rina might want to leave her own backyard occasionally, but at the end of the day her home was with her aunt in Switzerland. His home was in England. And if he got the promotion to Global CEO he could choose to remain in London. He had no intention of moving—even the idea of it brought up childhood memories of packing his suitcase every few months.

'Are you okay, Connor?'

His brow creased. 'I'm fine—why do you ask?'

'I thought you shuddered? Are you cold?'

He shook his head. He hadn't realised his body had reacted physically to the idea of moving—proof that it wasn't in his future.

After they'd left the market, Connor noticed Rina's gaze following the autorickshaws as they passed by.

'Do you want to ride a tuk-tuk?' he asked.

Her eyes became bright with excitement at the possibility. How did she find such joy in the little things?

'But what about the car?' she asked.

'We can either ask the driver to meet us somewhere, or send him home for the day.'

'Oh, let's send him home for the day. He's been more than patient with us. But will we see him again before we leave?'

'Yes, he'll be taking us to the airport.'

'Okay. That's good. Because I wanted to give him a small gift along with his tip.'

Although the tipping culture was common, Connor was touched by how Rina wanted to go that extra step and give him a thank-you gift too. And if he knew Rina the way he was sure he did, the gift would be personal. She'd chatted enough to their driver during their trips to have an idea of what he and his family needed.

They used a tuk-tuk for the rest of their visits.

Already having to sit close to each other because of the narrowness of the vehicles, they found the unsteady surfaces jostled them together constantly. Feeling Rina pressed up against him wasn't helping Connor in his resolve to ignore his attraction to her and remain detached. Was she feeling the same desire, the same need to press even closer together? He could hear her breathing accelerate and deepen with every contact.

Back at the hotel, he walked her to her room. She inserted her key card, but before she unlocked the door she turned round to face him.

'Thank you. For today. And for yesterday.'

'You don't have to thank me. I was happy to go with you.'

'That's not what I meant.'

He bent his head, but said nothing.

She reached up and placed a gentle kiss on his cheek. He reached out his finger to trace it across her hairline, as if moving an imaginary stray strand. Bending down slightly, he pressed his lips to her cheek, then slowly moved across, pressing another kiss to the corner of her mouth. Neither of them seemed to breathe as their heads turned and their mouths met, slowly and gently at first, then becoming harder, hungrier, as they were both swept up by the smouldering heat.

He was in danger. In danger of giving in to this desire and taking everything she was offering—taking their physical attraction to the next level. In danger of wanting more from her than the physical—of wanting everything.

He dragged his mouth away before it was too late.

CHAPTER ELEVEN

RINA WAS RELIEVED when she found out she wasn't sitting next to Connor on the plane to Mumbai. Having a single seat next to the window was a luxury she hadn't expected. The only downside was that it gave her time alone with her thoughts. Still, it was better than sitting in close proximity to the very subject of those thoughts.

When they had finally broken apart after their kiss Connor had blinked rapidly, looking startled. He'd mouthed goodnight and then walked away. She'd watched him, her heart leaping when he'd turned around to look at her before quickly turning back when he caught her gaze.

But this morning he'd acted as if nothing had happened. As if they hadn't shared the most amazing kiss ever. Yet again.

They wouldn't get a chance to speak to each other during this short flight from Bengaluru to Mumbai. Although she didn't suppose that either of them would have brought up the subject of the kiss even if they had talked. But she replayed it constantly in her mind.

Had it really been that amazing, or was her memory hyping up something fairly normal?

At the end of the day, it was only a kiss. It didn't mean anything. It couldn't mean anything.

They only had a few days in Mumbai before they flew to Frankfurt, and then a night in Frankfurt before they drove to Lake Thun. After that there was a good chance she wouldn't see him again, depending on whether she was able to influence Aunt Maria to accept Newmans' proposal on her own or whether she would need to liaise with Connor to convince her.

From the moment she'd first seen Connor she had been confused about what kind of relationship she wanted with him. Initially, she'd thought it could be a friendship, but her physical attraction to him hadn't decreased and she'd started hoping they could have a romantic relationship too. All that had changed when she'd found out he was Newmans' representative—but that was before she'd come up with the deal to convince Connor to take her to India with him.

And Connor hadn't always been able to maintain that professional difference. He'd shown her in the way he looked out for her, in the way he always thought about what she would find interesting, even though he gruffly pretended they were only in India to visit the company offices. He'd even arranged this detour to Mumbai, and taken more leave. Was it any wonder she liked him so much?

The problem was she could easily feel so much more for him, but it would be futile when they wanted different things. She *had* to push away any inkling that she was falling deeper. She already knew she cared—a lot—but she had to protect herself from passing a point where her heart would be too far gone.

Newmans had arranged for a car and driver to be at their disposal in Mumbai, even though they wouldn't be in the city for business. Rina knew they were pulling out all the stops to encourage Lachance to licence Essence, but it still made her feel like a princess, with all her whims catered to.

At her request, their first stop was at the Gateway of India.

'Why did you choose to come here first?' Connor asked as they stood in front of the basalt memorial arch.

'I don't know,' she answered honestly. But Connor's kind and caring but curious expression encouraged her to try to articulate her thoughts. 'I guess I've been thinking about identity a lot recently. And this symbolises an important part of India's history. I haven't learnt much about it and I want to start changing that. Particularly since I'm actually British but I don't feel at all British. I've lived in Switzerland the majority of my life, but I'm not sure how Swiss I feel either. I've felt closer to my mum since I've been here. Would I have felt closer to her if I'd stayed in England?' She shrugged. 'I don't know. I'm just rambling now.'

'Not rambling at all—processing. It's a complicated issue. I understand something about the need to feel a sense of belonging.'

'You do?'

He nodded. 'Not about family or nationality. But, growing up, I didn't ever make any attachments to people because we moved so often. London's my home now, and it's the first time I've felt settled.'

Rina's widened her eyes at hearing him share such vulnerabilities with her. 'You mentioned before that your family moved a lot because of your father...'

Connor's smile was grim. 'As I told you, my dad never

stayed in one job for long, so we had to move wherever he could get work. To be honest, I don't think he tried. Dad would get bored if we stayed in one place for more than a few months. We could always tell when he was beginning to get restless and a move was imminent.'

After hearing about his family life she could understand why he wanted to be settled in one place. She reflected again on how different they were in what they wanted for the future. She wanted to explore more of the world, but now it made sense why travel was only a necessary evil for Connor.

'Sounds like your dad has a wandering spirit—like me,' she added after a pause.

He glanced at her sharply. 'Wanting to see the world isn't a bad thing. Particularly when you're young and don't have any commitments. But it's a different story when you have a wife and three children you're dragging around with you.'

'Didn't your mother try to give you a stable home base?'

His laugh was humourless. 'My mother is perfect for my father in that respect. She loves moving around… never putting down roots.'

'Roots are important.'

It was strange how close she felt to him in that moment. Was it odd that in some ways she envied Connor's parents? They'd each found a partner who shared the same vision. She and Connor might not have a future together, yet they shared a need for belonging that had been shaped by their childhoods.

Automatically she put her hand in his, and then suggested they continue walking along Marine Drive. She considered taking a ferry to Elephanta Island, to look at the caves, but when Connor told her he had something planned for after lunch she decided she didn't want to risk running late for whatever it was.

Despite her constant questions, he refused to tell her where they would be going, not giving her any details. She could barely sit still during lunch as he teased her, by pretending to drop hints about the activity, making her guess random places, and laughing at her face when she got it wrong.

'It's probably going to be a big let-down,' she said finally, sitting with her arms folded and her jaw jutting out.

'Probably,' Connor agreed placidly. 'But if you don't like it's only a couple of hours out of our lives.'

'But you *do* think it's something I'll like?'

She sighed with frustration at his enigmatic smile.

'It can't be somewhere I've mentioned I'd like to visit because I didn't know we'd be coming to Mumbai until the last minute.'

'You really are impatient.'

'I've decided I don't like surprises.'

He laughed. 'You would hate it if I told you now—especially now that I've built up all this anticipation.'

She grinned, acknowledging the truth in what he said.

'Come on,' he said, once they'd finished eating and paid for their meal. 'We should head back to the car. It's quite a distance.'

'Is it?' she said, her ears perking up. 'So are we going outside Mumbai, then?'

He tapped her nose affectionately. 'It won't be long until you find out. Let's go.'

Rina remained silent, smiling to herself, not only because of this surprise trip Connor had planned for her, but because after they'd left the restaurant he'd voluntarily reached for her hand and held it as they walked to the car.

She loved these small indications from Connor that he cared about her—not as a business partner, but as someone he could be fond of if he allowed himself.

Her head drooped. How often did she have to remind herself it didn't matter whether Connor opened himself up to the possibility of something developing between them—*she* couldn't allow it. She might be having a taste of independence and exploration, but after this was over she would return to Lachance tower and stay there with her aunt.

As the car arrived at their destination, Rina read the large words on a sign.

'Bollywood?' she asked.

'That's right. We have a tour of Bollywood Park and Mumbai Film City.'

'You're kidding? That's incredible! Is it a real set?'

'As far as I'm aware. We'll find out on the tour,' he said.

But Rina was already looking things up.

'It says there are permanent sets of a temple, a prison, a court and even an artificial waterfall. And they're used by a lot of the Bollywood films. Wouldn't it be great if we got to see someone filming using one of the sets?'

She'd mentioned that she enjoyed watching Bollywood movies in passing, in a general conversation about films, and yet—as she'd come to learn was typical of Connor—he'd remembered that detail and organised a visit he thought she'd enjoy.

She couldn't believe her luck in meeting such an incredible man. She would be foolish to let these few days be all the time she ever spent with him. She resolved to do everything she could to convince Connor to stay in contact with her once he was back in England and she was back in Switzerland. She might be a naïve optimist, but perhaps if they stayed in contact they could at least be friends. And maybe one day the stars would align and they could find a way to have something more.

She didn't want their inevitable goodbye in a few days to be final.

After they'd finished their tour, they went out for dinner and then walked along Marina Drive, which looked vibrant and magical in the night-time lights, before returning to the hotel.

Outside her room, Rina paused to thank Connor again. They stared at each other intently, their breathing becoming shallow. She wasn't sure who made the first move before they were devouring each other. He pressed kisses across her cheekbones, then along her jawline, before she impatiently brought his mouth back to hers.

She was about to invite him into her room when he broke away and hurried off down the corridor. She tutted in frustration. Each time they were affectionate he bolted, as if he was…

She paused, trying to analyse Connor's behaviour. He ran away as if he was scared of what had happened. He couldn't be scared that she didn't want their kisses—she'd obviously been a willing and eager partner. So what was he so afraid of? Could it be that he was frightened of his feelings for her? Was he beginning to drop his guard? And did that mean she had a chance to break down his remaining barriers?

She would just have to try harder.

She couldn't help chuckling as she walked over to the windows of her hotel room. She felt as if she was reliving her teenage years, being walked home after a date and sharing a goodnight kiss, counting down the minutes until they could see each other again and kiss once more.

Of all the places Rina could have suggested they visit in Mumbai, why had she chosen to come to the Dhobi Ghat first thing in the morning?

Connor watched as Rina scribbled away in her notebook, wondering what could have inspired her just by watching linen being washed. Was it the sounds or the colours? Since Rina was a scientist, creating hair products, perhaps it was the soap.

He would love to talk to her more about her work and her ideas. She was so passionate about everything. It was a shame she couldn't share such an important part of her life with him. But he completely understood about her concerns over proprietary information, so he'd avoided asking her anything at all.

He was unsure why he kept forcing himself to draw boundaries around his interactions with Rina. It didn't seem to do any good anyway. They'd kissed a few times now. And every time it became harder to walk away. He wanted to indulge their passion. But he had to leave.

Suddenly Rina snapped her notebook shut and walked over to him.

'All done?' he asked.

She nodded.

He no longer wanted to pretend he had to interest in

what she was working on. It was her choice how much she shared.

'Were you thinking about soap?'

'Hmm...?' Her attention had been taken now by the linen being hung out on the lines to dry. 'Soap? No—why?'

He shrugged. 'I was trying to work out what caught your interest.'

'Oh, I was watching the dhotis work. The different techniques they use.'

He grinned. 'Did it inspire you to come up with an alternative to the lather, rinse, repeat process?'

She giggled. 'Some things are too perfect to change. It wasn't the process itself I was thinking about. It just gave me some ideas about something we're working on back in the lab. I can't wait to share it with my colleagues.'

'It won't be long now.'

Rina grimaced. 'I'm looking forward to seeing Aunt Maria and getting back to work, and I haven't felt that way in a long time. But I'm sad we're leaving India. There are so many places I haven't been yet.'

'Now you've come away for the first time, perhaps your aunt will be more open to you travelling in the future.'

'I truly hope so,' Rina replied with a sombre tone. 'In my ideal world I would travel abroad at least twice a year, so I can come back to India annually and then for the other time I would pick a different country each time.'

'What's stopping you?'

'Apart from my aunt? Work... Finances...'

'You do realise if you manage to influence your aunt

to accept Newmans' proposal then once the deal is finalised you're going to be very wealthy, don't you?'

He almost burst out laughing when her jaw dropped.

'I never even thought about it.'

'Well, start thinking about it—and all the potential travelling you'll get to do.'

'I don't think so,' Rina replied with a sad shake of her head. 'Aunt Maria hasn't replied to any of my messages. She's really upset. I can't imagine she would be happy with me travelling again, and I don't want to disappoint her.'

Connor squeezed her shoulder, then couldn't resist running his hand down her arm to join their fingers.

Rina shrugged. 'I guess the memories of this visit will have to be enough to last me a lifetime.'

Connor's eyes widened. Memories would have to be enough to last him too. If he got the promotion this would be the last time he travelled for business, and travelling for pleasure wasn't likely for him.

Now the prospect was in front of him, he wasn't as pleased as he probably would have been before meeting Rina. Seeing the sights with her had been fun. This time around, travelling hadn't brought that clenched feeling to his stomach at the notion of living out of a suitcase. In fact, he was the one who'd brought up his childhood, almost wielding it like a shield against falling for Rina.

But in the end how he felt about travelling didn't matter. He was still the same man who was incapable of making a commitment—he still couldn't offer her anything approaching a relationship. Hurting Rina was the last thing he wanted to do. He wished he could be a better man than he knew he was, but pretending he could change would inevitably lead to disappointment.

'Where do you want to go next?' he asked as they walked back to the car.

'I'd like to go shopping.'

'To a street bazaar?'

'No. Can we go to a mall? I don't mind which one.'

Connor raised his eyebrows. 'A mall?'

'Why do you sound so surprised?'

He shook his head. 'No reason.' He gave the driver their destination. 'Is there something specific you want to buy?'

'No.'

'Are you researching which hair products are stocked there?'

Rina furrowed her brow. 'I hadn't thought of doing that. I just want to do some window shopping.'

'I see...'

Why was he so surprised by her choice? It wasn't because she wanted to shop—there was nothing unusual in that. And it had been surprising when she'd suggested Dhobi Ghat in the morning. Maybe because they were both public places?

After their kiss the previous night, Connor would have chosen to go somewhere peaceful, where they could talk easily. Or he would have chosen to stay in his hotel room with her.

On second thoughts, a public place like a busy shopping centre sounded like the perfect choice.

They held hands as they walked around the mall, as if they were the same as countless other couples there.

But they weren't a couple.

He didn't know what they were.

He didn't know what he was doing.

If he were sensible, he would release her hand and keep some distance between them. Even though his gaze went to their joined hands, the instruction from his brain didn't make it to his hand, as if it had been interrupted on the way. Perhaps by his heart.

He stopped suddenly. Rina gave him a questioning look, glancing at the store they were passing, which happened to be selling luggage.

'Do you need to replace your suitcase?' she asked.

'No. I need the restroom,' he replied—untruthfully, but he needed some space to get his thoughts in order, and that excuse was the best he could come up with at the time.

He stood at the washbasin, running some water over his face.

Why was he thinking about his heart? His heart knew as well as his head that there was only goodbye in their future.

So why was he holding her hand? Why was he kissing her?

What impression was he giving her? Did she think they were starting something?

He had to let her know the reality of the situation. He wasn't going to lead her on or make promises he couldn't keep.

There was never any point in his forming an attachment because he never wanted to make a commitment when he knew he couldn't maintain it. And even if he were foolish enough to ignore his previous experience and try a relationship, Rina would be the wrong person.

155

It wasn't even about the travel, per se. It was the fact that she'd been sheltered most of her life and she needed to be free to live a little—just as she'd said when they'd first met.

He couldn't restrict her, and he'd already seen how much it had irritated her when he'd worried about where she was going and whether she was alone. Once, she'd described herself as a wandering spirit, and that was how he saw her—a free spirit, full of optimism, looking for the best in the world, the best in people.

He was too cynical to believe the best of people. He never wanted to be the cause of Rina's spirit being trapped and creating her disillusionment because some-times—more often than not—things didn't work out sim-ply because you wanted them to.

They needed to have a serious conversation. He would have to apologise if he'd given her the wrong idea.

He debated suggesting they return to the hotel, but decided it would be better to have this conversation in a public place. Not because he didn't feel it deserved pri-vacy, but because he couldn't trust himself if they were alone in a hotel room together—not when there was a bed in the room, and not when the sensation of holding her in his arms, pressed tight to her, was almost physical rather than a memory.

'Why don't we get a drink and maybe some kulfi?' he asked. 'I think we should talk?'

Rina furrowed her brows, then shrugged. 'Sure. Let's find somewhere we can sit down.'

Once they were seated, he fiddled with a sugar packet.

'What's wrong, Connor?' she asked.

He took a deep breath. 'I think we need to talk about our kiss last night.'

'And the other nights?' Rina added, with raised eyebrows.

'They were very pleasant,' he said, with considerable understatement. 'But I don't want you getting the wrong idea. We can't start anything.'

'Why not?'

Staring into her deep, dark brown eyes, he wasn't sure of the answer. 'Geography,' he finally managed to say.

He saw the look of determination in Rina's eyes and knew their conversation was far from over.

'We live in different countries,' he added.

Rina quirked an eyebrow. 'And no couple has ever tried to make it work long distance?'

He snorted. 'I've never made a *close*-distance relationship work,' he told her honestly. 'I wouldn't have high hopes of making a long-distance one work. I didn't see the point of them when I was growing up and I don't see the point of them now.'

He knew he should say something callous, almost deliberately mean, to convince her there was no future for them, but he couldn't bring himself to do it. He never wanted to see that kind of pain in her eyes—it was the reason he wasn't prepared to encourage whatever was happening between them. He couldn't hurt Rina.

But if she was upset now, because of their conversation, it was better than the potentially greater hurt a little further down the line, when he lived up to his nature and was unable to make a commitment to her.

'It's not just the distance,' he went on. 'You want to explore the world and I don't enjoy travelling.'

'I understand that. But I don't know how much travelling I'd get to do, and you wouldn't have to come with me.'

'I don't want to hold you back from your dreams of seeing the world.'

'I can have new, different dreams.'

'I would never want that. It wouldn't work out between us. You told me you want to get married some day, and I never want to settle down.'

'I also said I thought it was unlikely that I would find someone.'

'Because of your aunt. Because of geography. It all comes back to that.'

She furrowed her brow. 'You're not prepared to hear anything I have to say about this?'

'I'll hear you. I'll listen to your opinions. But they're not going to change my mind, no.'

CHAPTER TWELVE

THE FOLLOWING DAY Rina stared out of her hotel window at the view of the River Main. She was in Frankfurt, but somehow the excitement of being in a new city was missing,

She wasn't sure whether it was because it was the last day before they headed home to Lake Thun, or because of her sobering conversation with Connor at the shopping mall.

They hadn't spoken much on the flight from Mumbai. She'd still been feeling emotionally fraught, and had decided to escape into the colourful and joyful world of one of the Bollywood inflight movies, enjoying it even more after their visit to Film City.

Connor had his laptop out, so she presumed he'd been working—as usual.

Perhaps he was tweaking his proposal for Lachance. She was mindful that if Connor had his way, the only reason she would have anything to do with him in future would be if she persuaded her aunt to accept Newmans' deal—an added incentive for her to work her influence, even if she wasn't already convinced it was the best path for Essence.

It was frustrating, how he'd couched all those reasons

why they couldn't be together as if they were for her benefit. Although she accepted there was a lot of truth in what he said, she didn't agree that it had to be an all-ornothing situation. There had to be room for compromise. But she didn't have long to find one.

She headed down to Reception to meet Connor, as they'd agreed. Part of her didn't want to go sightseeing with him—not after their conversation. But if she refused to go out or went alone she'd be doubly spiting herself, not only missing out on exploring a new city, but also missing out on spending time with Connor. And the more time she spent with Connor, the more likely she would be able to find that compromise solution.

Why couldn't it be like in novels, where all the rooms in a hotel were booked for a convention, or something, which meant she would be forced to share with Connor. Although in that scenario Connor would probably hire a car and drive them straight back to Switzerland, so on reflection she decided it was better the way it was.

As they walked along the river, Rina's hand almost instinctively sought out Connor's, but at the slightest brush of her fingers he moved away. She shoved her hands into her jacket pockets to stop her reaching out to him again.

She tried to convince herself that was a good sign. If he really had drawn a line under their relationship he wouldn't have any problems with the occasional touch. But it was awkward. She couldn't even find something to chatter about, small talk seemed futile.

Connor didn't say anything either. She would hate it if having that frank discussion had ruined the core connection she'd always felt between them. She didn't want potentially their last moments together to be spent in silence.

To ease the tension, she paused along the way to take some photos, smiling ruefully when a man offered to take their photo together. Connor met her smile, as if he too remembered their day on the Sigriswil Panoramic Bridge. Had it really only been two weeks ago?

As they posed, Connor put his arm across her shoulder, as he had before. This time Rina wasn't going to miss out on the opportunity, and she put her arm around his waist.

It felt so right to her, standing so close to Connor. Couldn't he feel that too?

She raised her head and met Connor's stare. He turned towards her slightly and reached out to run a finger along her cheek. She leaned in towards him…

She didn't know whether he would have leant down to her, because they were interrupted by their amateur photographer, returning Rina's phone to her.

Her heart did somersaults. He wasn't indifferent to her. He might be giving mixed signals, and his body was probably acting against his will, but she would take that as a sign that he instinctively wanted to be with her.

'Do you want to visit the shops or a museum while we're here?' Connor asked, moving ahead.

She wasn't surprised. Connor was an intelligent man. He would have realised what his action meant. Her positivity went up a notch or two.

'I don't, really. I'm happy just walking around and seeing what there is. Is there somewhere you want to go?'

Connor shook his head. 'I'm happy to walk around too.'

They moved on. Rina almost stumbled when she felt Connor's hand against hers. She tried not to grab it too enthusiastically, or clasp it too hard, but she wasn't going to give him a chance to let go.

After a leisurely walk, they reached Main Tower.

'You know, this is one of the stops for the hop-on, hop-off bus tour of Frankfurt,' Connor said.

'Is it?'

'I happen to have tickets for the tour bus, if you want to go on it?'

Rina smiled. 'You do?'

Connor gave an embarrassed shrug. 'I arranged them at the hotel. I thought it would be an easy way of getting around the city. I don't think we have too long to wait for a bus, if you're interested.'

'Sure—why not?' Rina replied.

They chose to sit on the top deck of the open-top bus. The weather was comfortable for mid-October, but a stark contrast to the heat and humidity of India.

Rina snuggled up to Connor, pretending she wanted him to keep her warm. He moved his arm around her, hugging her close to him.

She grinned. Intellectually, he might not think their relationship was a good idea, but instinctively he wanted to be with her as much as she wanted to be with him. There *had* to be a way to get him to change his mind about them.

If he'd made it clear that he wasn't interested in her, she would never have considered pursuing him. But he'd admitted he was attracted to her and enjoyed her company. He was letting geography and a belief that he didn't 'do' commitment keep them apart. And that didn't make any sense. If Connor was always there for his siblings, and had maintained long friendships with Nihal and Rohan, then he *could* do commitment.

But there was no point saying that to him—she had to make him see it and believe it.

After a full day of sightseeing, Connor and Rina returned to their hotel to freshen up before dinner.

They'd had such a lovely time together, but now it was coming to an end. She didn't want to say goodbye, although she accepted it was inevitable. It broke her a little that she hadn't found a way to convince Connor.

She'd never felt this way before.

She loved him.

She wasn't going to deny it to herself. Her feelings for Connor had always been strong, because she'd been falling a little more in love with him every moment since they'd met.

He was and would always be the love of her life. Maybe her dream of marrying one day would never come true, but there was still one dream she could make happen— there was still one memory she wanted to make.

Nodding her head with determination, she left her room and walked along the corridor to Connor's.

His eyes widened with surprise when he answered her knock, but he gestured for her to come inside.

Barely waiting for the door to close, she took a deep breath. 'Connor, I have something I need to say to you.'

'Go on...' he replied.

She couldn't work out whether his expression was curiosity or wariness.

This was it. Her last chance.

'I know everything you're saying is right, Connor. I know we don't make sense together in the long term. I know you think what I want is completely the opposite of what you want. I know you don't see me as part of your future. And I accept that. But I don't care.'

Connor blinked a couple of times and shook his head, as if trying to clear it of what he'd heard. 'I… I don't know what you're saying.'

Rina swallowed, then she clenched her fists, gathering her strength. 'I know you don't think we have a future together. I'm not asking for that. I'm not asking you to make any commitment, or any promises to me. I'm asking you for one night. Just tonight.'

Just tonight.

Connor kept repeating the words in his head.

Could she really be offering him a one-night stand.

Could he refuse her if she was?

'Rina…' he began, trying to be sensible.

'Don't say no, Connor.'

Rina shook her head and walked closer to him. He took a few steps backwards until the side of the bed hit his legs, causing him to sit down.

'Rina…' he said again, with a quiver in his voice as she put her arms around his neck and pressed her lips against his. 'Rina, we can't do this.'

He felt bereft when she moved away.

'Why not, Connor? Why can't we have tonight? One perfect night and then we'll say goodbye.'

'Do you think you could say goodbye easily afterwards?'

She laughed—a low, sultry sound that speared right to his groin.

'You seem very confident about your abilities, Mr Portland. Now I definitely need to see if you're right.'

He couldn't help laughing. 'Rina…' he said, holding her against him and then pulling her onto his lap.

The sensible voice inside his head was telling him to move away. But when she looked at him through half-closed lids and smiled, before brushing her lips along his jawline, he found it hard to pay any attention to that voice.

Just one night, he thought, before laying Rina down on the bed and covering his body with hers.

Hours later, Rina cuddled into Connor's side. He couldn't resist bending his head to taste her lips again, and both of them were quickly swept up by passion once more.

Then Rina's stomach rumbled.

They both laughed at the sound, finally breaking their kiss.

'We should get something to eat. What time is it?' Connor said, reaching for his phone. 'It's after nine-thirty. We could get Room Service, or take a walk by the river and see if anything's open.'

Rina stretched, and at that moment all thought of leaving the bed fled his mind.

Until Rina's stomach rumbled again.

'Come on. Why don't we have a quick shower and then go out.'

Rina raised her eyebrows. 'You want us to shower?'

Connor bit his lip at the image that formed in his mind. 'Not together. We'll never leave the room if that happens.'

'I'm not sure that's the punishment you think it would be…'

'Come on, Miss Lachance. Go to your own room and get ready.'

'Okay,' Rina agreed putting her clothes back on. 'But this,' she said, pointing at his bed, 'is to be continued.'

She wasn't going to get any argument from him about that.

They walked hand in hand along the river, tracing the same path they had taken that morning. But it felt different now. Now he was feeling relaxed. Happy. He couldn't remember the last time he'd felt this level of happiness—if he ever had before. When was the last time he'd felt so at peace?

Rina was a special woman. A spark of light that he hadn't realised he needed in his life. But she needed more than him. He couldn't change who he was for her, and he would never ask her to change for him. Which left them at the same impasse as before.

He'd learnt when he was young that goodbye was an inevitable part of life. And if you didn't get too attached, it wasn't even difficult to say.

If tonight was all they would have together as a couple, then he would enjoy every moment of it.

Rina had taught him to make the most of any situation, and that was exactly what he was going to do.

CHAPTER THIRTEEN

RINA WASN'T SURE why she was so reluctant to return to the tower. Was it worry about her reception from her aunt? Or was it the inevitable moment when she would have to say goodbye to Connor?

They had spent one perfect night making love. Rina had hoped that would be enough—that the memories of their intimacy would be enough to last the rest of her life. But now she couldn't deceive herself. They would never be enough.

The drive to Lake Thun seemed to go too quickly. By unspoken agreement they talked about a variety of topics, but nothing too personal—nothing about the future.

She was grateful Connor had insisted he drive her back. He could easily have taken a flight to London directly from Frankfurt. Instead, he would be staying overnight in the same hotel he had on his previous visit, before driving to Geneva and taking his flight home.

She'd asked for one night. But had she truly meant that? Or did she want more?

She wasn't sure if spending another night with Connor later would help, or make it even harder to say goodbye.

She turned her head to drink in Connor's profile. He

must have sensed her looking at him, because he turned and smiled.

'Are you ready to go home?' he asked, reaching out to squeeze her hand.

'Quite honestly, no,' she admitted. 'Once I go home my adventure comes to an end. And I still don't know what kind of reception I'll get from my aunt.'

'Do you want me to stay around for a while?'

She shook her head. 'I think it's better if I see her alone.'

They completed the drive in silence, with Rina still worrying about how her aunt was going to react.

Connor dropped her off outside Lachance tower, then drove off to check in to his hotel.

Rina took a long breath, squared her shoulders and prepared to see her aunt.

Her aunt completely ignored her. All Rina's attempts to start a conversation were futile.

After a couple of hours, Rina followed her aunt into the lounge, then barred the door to prevent her aunt from leaving the room.

'Aunt Maria, please talk to me,' she pleaded.

'Why do you want me to talk to you? You didn't care about my opinion before you left. I don't understand why you came back. Why didn't you keep travelling?'

'I'm ready to work again. I just took a short holiday. I needed inspiration. I was stagnating. My work was stagnating.'

'Well, I wouldn't want that to happen again.'

Rina closed her eyes, desperately hoping the words to appease her aunt would come to her.

'I have so many new ideas to share with you. Why

don't I take my bags to my room and then, when I come back down, I'll make us something to eat and I can tell you all about them.'

'Why are you telling me? I have no say over what you do, apparently.'

Rina huffed, but decided there was no point replying to her aunt when she was in that mood. It wasn't the first time her aunt had been like this, but it had never lasted for so long before.

She went to the room that had been hers since she was ten years old. Although she loved the circular tower room, even one wall could be constricting if it was all she could see.

Now she'd had her first adventure, and although she hated being on poor terms with her aunt, Rina couldn't regret making the decision to go.

Not only had it been the correct decision for her, she was also convinced that accepting Newmans' proposal was the best decision for Essence.

She had a large arsenal in her power, to use to convince her aunt to make the deal—assuming her aunt was ever ready to listen to her. Essence actually belonged to her. As she'd told Connor, when she'd been trying to convince him to take her to India with him, she didn't fully understand the legalities, but she had created the formula for Essence, and the method of extraction, so she'd have a large input into the final decisions concerning the future of Essence in particular.

What had happened between them didn't change their business relationship—particularly since he had made it clear he wasn't interested in any other kind of relationship with her.

She went into the kitchen to start preparing dinner. She didn't really expect her aunt to come and chat with her, as she usually did, but she couldn't help being upset.

Then she received a text from Connor, telling her he was waiting in the field where they'd first met.

She rushed out. His broad smile when he saw her momentarily lifted her spirits and she ran into his open arms.

'What's wrong?' he asked as she held tighter to him.

She looked up at him without releasing her hold. 'Nothing. Don't worry.'

She felt his chest heave underneath her cheek.

'Is your aunt upset with you?' he asked.

'You could say that.' She gave him the gist of what had happened.

He took a sharp intake of breath as he held her closer. 'Is it because of Essence? She doesn't want to sell?'

'It's not about that at all. It's because I left. She didn't say it explicitly, but I know she was worried the entire time I was away—even though I left her messages and she could have spoken to me at any point if she'd wanted to. I've always understood she lost everything in that one accident, but is it really so selfish that I grabbed a once-in-a-lifetime opportunity?'

'You're the least selfish person I know.'

Her lips quirked. 'You're a little bit biased.'

'Do you want me to speak to her?'

Rina was confused. 'What good do you think that's going to do?'

Connor shook his head ruefully. 'I don't know, but I feel helpless seeing you so upset when I can't do anything.'

'You're doing everything I need just by listening to

me. It means a lot to have someone to share my thoughts with.'

Rina frowned as Connor took a step away.

'You should think about *all* your alternatives,' he said, staring at the view of the mountains rather than at her.

'I don't understand what you mean?'

'I'm sure you and your aunt will fix things, and you'll go back to your former relationship. But working at Lachance Boutique isn't your only career option. I know many companies would snap you up. Nihal wasn't joking when he offered you a job. And you would get to live in a different country.'

Rina swallowed the lump in her throat. 'I could never leave my aunt—you know that.'

'Your aunt will always be your family. But she doesn't have to be your employer too.'

'Despite how things are between us at the moment, with my holiday and my preference to accept Newmans' offer, I know it would break Aunt Maria's heart if I went to work for a different company. I couldn't betray her by leaving for good.'

Connor inclined his head to acknowledge what she'd said. Then he spoke. 'I'm just saying you shouldn't let anyone tie you down and force you to settle down before you're ready. Not your aunt...' his voice trailed away but she knew what he was going to add '...and not me.'

He had physically distanced himself. Was he worried that she was hoping their relationship would continue? She couldn't pretend she wasn't holding on to that hope.

She walked over to the fence and looked out at the view of fields and peaks in the distance. She understood the parameters Connor had set, and she accepted them, but it wasn't wrong to be hopeful, was it?

Perhaps a tiny part of her had hoped Connor would ask her to go to London and stay with him—but she knew that wasn't really ever going to happen. Although a woman could always dream…

She still didn't even know whether he intended to keep in touch with her outside of business. He'd initially been clear that there couldn't be anything more between them.

And then they'd kissed.

And then they'd made love.

But in the end, despite their current frosty relationship, Rina needed to stay with her aunt. She owed her everything. And Connor wouldn't move from England.

It didn't matter how much she cared about him, or how much he cared for her, there could never be anything lasting between them.

These two weeks were all there would be, and the memories would have to be enough for her.

But she still had a few hours before Connor was leaving Switzerland. And her problems with her aunt would still be there after he'd gone.

She didn't want to waste a single minute.

She led out her hand to Connor. 'Come on,' she said. 'Let's go back to your hotel.'

CHAPTER FOURTEEN

CONNOR WOKE EARLY the next morning and lay on his side, watching Rina as she slept. For a moment he imagined what it would be like if he could wake up to the same view every morning. But he knew it was impossible.

Nothing had changed—not materially. Their relationship might have developed into a physical one, and he was no longer going to deny he cared about Rina—a lot. But the fact remained that they wanted different things out of life. And there wasn't any space for compromise—not that he could see anyway.

He knew she would never leave her aunt permanently, but he'd watched her revel in the taste of freedom she'd had the chance to experience. Her relationship with Maria would soon settle back into its loving nature, but she had grown—he'd observed that himself in the time he'd spent with her. Soon her wings would take her to so many new places, and she would meet so many new people that she would grow beyond him.

So today they would say goodbye.

He sighed and lay back on the bed with his arm bent beneath his head.

He was used to saying goodbye. This shouldn't be any different.

But he knew it was. They weren't saying goodbye because they didn't like each other. If they had been any other two people they could probably have tried to find a way to make things work. But she was Rina Lachance, genius inventor, the wunderkind with wanderlust—someone who shouldn't be held back in any way. And he was Connor Portland, product of a nomadic childhood, a loner outside his family and a few friends—people who'd refused to accept his determination not to form attachments.

In a way, Rina was similar to those friends. She'd listened when he'd explained why they couldn't be together. She hadn't tried to persuade him to try having a relationship. But she'd also refused to accept that meant there couldn't be anything between them, and she had claimed one night with him.

And then another night.

What would he do if she wanted more? Would he be able to refuse? He hadn't stopped desiring her. He hadn't stopped wanting her. He hadn't stopped caring about her.

But it would be kinder in the long run if he broke off all contact with her now.

How long would they really be able to maintain any sort of relationship? Hopefully, she would be travelling, and if she wasn't travelling she would be here with her aunt in Switzerland. They would hardly get a chance to meet up since he was also likely to be busy.

He really hoped Rina would be able to influence her aunt to make the decision to agree to Newmans' proposal. And if Lachance did sell the licence for Essence, the role of Global CEO was his. The promotion he'd been working towards for ages. The culmination of years of hard work. He should be excited that it was almost his. Instead, he had a sense of regret…

When he dropped her outside Lachance tower later that morning, she lifted her head and opened her mouth. He shook his head before she could say anything, and bent forward to kiss her on the cheek. Then he got straight back into his car and drove away.

This time he couldn't even say goodbye—it was too hard to speak.

It felt like a physical pain, watching as her figure grew smaller in the rear-view mirror.

It didn't take long for Connor to realise he'd made the biggest mistake of his life. It had only been a few weeks since he'd left Rina at Lachance tower, but he missed her.

Of course he missed her kisses, and the feel of her in his arms, but he'd expected that. What he hadn't expected was how much he missed seeing her bright eyes and the huge smile he couldn't help responding to. He missed her laugh. He missed making her laugh. He missed talking with her, hearing her thoughts. He even missed sharing his own thoughts.

He hadn't made any attempt to contact her since he'd left. But then she'd made no effort to contact him either. Would it be strange if he messaged her out of the blue? What would she think? Would she be pleased?

He knew there was only one way to find out, so he sent her a text. Almost immediately he received a response. They exchanged a few more messages, but it wasn't enough for him. He video-called her.

Her smiling face coming into focus warmed his heart. It was exactly what he needed to see.

'Hey, congratulations, Mr CEO,' she said, in greeting.

'The promotion hasn't formally taken place yet.'

'But that's all it is? A formality.'

'How are things with your aunt?' he asked.

Rina grimaced. 'Still not good. She speaks to me about work matters, but she always makes these snide comments about when I'm planning to leave the tower. You know, if I hadn't inherited half of the tower from my dad, I think she would ask me to leave.'

He furrowed his brow. 'I'm sure it wouldn't really come to that.'

'She said she doesn't want to hear my ideas at all. And she's said I'm not needed in the lab for a while. Almost like I'm replaceable.'

'Perhaps she needs more time. Why don't you go travelling again?'

'Not sure it's a good idea to leave her again when that's what's annoyed her.'

'She might need to be reassured that you'll always come back to her and that you'll be safe.'

Rina nibbled her bottom lip, making him groan inwardly—he knew she didn't intend it as a provocative gesture.

'Do you really think so?' she asked.

'I do. She's worried about you.'

'I know. And I don't like worrying her. But one positive thing from all this is that Aunt Maria mentioned she's finally started seeing a counsellor.'

'I'm pleased.'

He was telling the truth. Rina's openness about her own therapy had made him think about whether speaking to someone would help him.

'I hope it helps her,' he said. 'But you can't wait until she's ready. Do you really want to stay stuck in your tower?'

She shook her head. 'Actually, Mausami has contacted me, asking if I want to meet her in Japan in a couple of weeks.'

'You should go.'

For the first time in his life, Connor wished he could travel…with her. It didn't feel as if he was living out of a suitcase when he was travelling with her.

'I don't know…'

'Go. Your aunt will be fine. She'll miss you a lot, though.'

'Will she?'

'Of course. *I* miss you.'

Her face brightened at his words. 'I miss you too.'

'Do you want to video call again, later in the week?'

She nodded vigorously.

For the next few months Connor and Rina had regular video calls. She often showed him the view from her hotel rooms as she travelled, even showed him some of the sketches she'd made in her notebook.

He looked forward to the nights when he would get to see her beautiful face appear on his screen. But it wasn't enough. He needed to be in the same country—he needed to be in the same room.

And *he* was the only reason he wasn't with her. *He* was the obstacle to his own happiness.

He'd taken the plunge and started meeting regularly with a counsellor to help him process things from his childhood. There was still a lot of work to do, but he'd already seen how he'd let his fear of forming attachments, of making commitments, stop him trying to make it work with the woman he loved.

He'd known on a subconscious level for months that he'd fallen in love with Rina—perhaps even at first sight, even though that still sounded unbelievable. Definitely he had by the time they'd got to Mysuru.

And that was what made it different from the past. He'd never loved any of the women he'd dated before, so of course he hadn't wanted to commit to them. With Rina he wanted attachment, he wanted commitment... he wanted for ever.

He wanted to spend a few more months working with his counsellor, but he was already starting to make plans for a future with Rina.

And one of the first people he needed to speak to was her aunt.

CHAPTER FIFTEEN

RINA WALKED THROUGH the old town towards Charles Bridge. It was her last day in Prague. She was flying back to Switzerland the following day, and was more than ready to be back home with Aunt Maria.

The last six months had been wonderful. After meeting up with Mausami in Japan she'd visited Singapore, and then returned to Switzerland where she remained, determined to stay at Lachance tower and wait until her frosty relationship with her aunt melted.

It didn't take long. She'd proved to her aunt that she could travel safely and that she would always return home. And, on top of that, some of the ideas she'd been inspired with on her travels were shaping up to develop into exciting new products.

After Rina had been a month at home, her aunt had actually suggested she travel to Italy to inspect some potential suppliers.

Rina understood what a big step that had been for her. She'd never forgotten why her aunt was so protective of her. She was her aunt's world, and Rina would never downplay the love Aunt Maria had surrounded her with. And it was a testament to that love that Aunt Maria was now accepting Rina's need to spread her wings.

For the past six months Rina had travelled on business every couple of weeks. She suspected her aunt was going a little overboard in accommodating Rina's wanderlust. But now she was itching to spend a long time in her laboratory, testing out her theories and refining new products.

She still wanted to travel in future, but she didn't have the same sense of longing to get away she'd used to have. And she could definitely appreciate why Connor hadn't enjoyed all his business travel.

There was a pang in her chest when she thought of Connor—as she did constantly.

She'd been over the moon when she'd received his first message, two weeks after they'd said goodbye. Although she'd been the only one who'd actually *said* goodbye. Connor had left without even a wave.

Since then they'd kept in touch, and video called at least once a week. He seemed to enjoy hearing about her travels, but he had never invited her to visit him in London. She didn't really know what to make of that. Only last month she'd brought up the suggestion herself, but he hadn't sounded keen, mentioning something about him being very busy for a while.

She'd had to take that at face value—she had no reason to doubt what he said. But although she often mentioned how he might join her, he hadn't taken her up on her offer—which she understood, knowing how he felt about moving from place to place.

But surely he couldn't still think geography was a barrier against them continuing their relationship?

Trying to sort things out over a video call or a message was never going to work. Once she'd settled back home she would book a ticket to London for a weekend. She had to see Connor. She missed being next to him, touching him, kissing him. She missed everything about him.

She'd fallen in love with him so quickly, part of her had wondered whether it was their proximity that had fed her emotions. It hadn't taken long after he'd left for her to recognise that her feelings for him were deep and strong and unwavering.

She loved him. But she'd never told him. She'd been too scared. And he probably hadn't been ready to hear any declaration earlier. But she could tell from their conversations that something was different about his views of the future.

She wanted to see Connor when she told him she loved him for the first time. Even though she had no expectation that he would reciprocate, she didn't want to deny her feelings.

But if he cared about her at all—as she was sure he had started to—then she wanted to discuss how they could work on a long-distance relationship. She was ready to do all the travelling, so he never had to move or feel as though he was living out of a suitcase.

And although, for now, she still couldn't leave her aunt permanently, she could fly to London to spend weekends with him, if he agreed.

She couldn't wait to finish this next appointment so she could go back to her hotel and call Connor. She wanted to hear his voice and see his smile.

She checked her watch. She was still early for her appointment with a potential supplier of glass containers for their products. For some reason he'd suggested through his correspondence with her aunt that they meet at the Charles Bridge, although she'd told her aunt to tell him she was happy to find his shop. Apparently he'd been insistent.

She shrugged. Perhaps his goods were as quirky as he sounded.

She hoped the meeting would go quickly. Another reason Rina wanted to get back to Switzerland was because she was sure something was happening with the Essence deal. Her aunt had been in negotiation with Newmans, but neither she nor Connor had spoken about the deal. All Connor had told her was that he'd stepped away from the deal, feeling he now had a conflict of interest.

And here she was, back to thinking about Connor again. She needed to put him out of her mind and concentrate on Lachance Boutique—for the next couple of hours at least.

But first she needed to find this person she was supposed to be meeting next to the statue of St Christopher. Rina wondered whether Aunt Maria had deliberately chosen the patron saint of travellers for their meeting spot.

She was staring at the statue when she heard a familiar voice behind her, calling her name.

She turned towards the sound, wondering whether her longing had conjured the voice. She blinked a couple of times to make sure she really was seeing the man she loved most in the world right in front of her.

'Connor!' she cried, almost running in her hurry to get to him, to hold him in her arms and reassure herself that he wasn't a figment of her imagination.

'Rina…' Connor said, as he pulled her to him and swept her off her feet. 'Rina, I've missed you.'

'I've missed you too. I've missed you so much. I can't believe you're here,' she said, cupping his face in her hands and then lowering her head to plant hundreds of kisses on it. 'This is the most wonderful surprise,' she said when they finally broke apart. 'I can't believe Aunt Maria helped you.'

'Maria thinks I'm great.'

Rina raised her eyebrows at Connor's use of her aunt's name. In the past he'd referred to her formally as Miss Lachance.

'Shall we walk along the bridge?' he suggested before she could ask him any more about her aunt.

'Okay… We can head to my hotel, if you want?' she said shyly, biting her lip while she waited for his response.

'Sounds good,' he said, holding out his hand.

She turned to him as soon as they were in the lift going up to her room. 'I was going to fly to London to see you,' she said.

'That would have been a waste of time,' Connor replied.

'What?'

She took a step back. What did he mean by that? Didn't he want her to visit? To spend time with her?

The lift came to a stop. Once they were inside her room she moved slightly away from Connor.

'Why would me coming to London be a waste of time, Connor?'

He shrugged with one shoulder. 'Because I won't be there.'

She raised her brows. 'How do you know? I didn't tell you when I was planning to go.'

'That's not the point.'

She sniffed. He was hiding something from her, and it was aggravating the way he was stringing out the conversation.

'Why don't you want me to come to London, Connor? Just tell me the truth.'

'Because I don't live there any more.'

'You've moved?' That was the last thing she'd expected to hear.

'Yes, I moved to a town near Lake Thun a few weeks ago.'

Rina's mouth dropped open and she fell into a nearby armchair.

Connor laughed at Rina's shocked expression. Her surprise at seeing him on Charles Bridge was nothing compared to her reaction at this news.

'Are you serious, Connor?'

'I wouldn't joke about it. I moved to be closer to my girlfriend?'

'Me?' Rina asked, somewhat foolishly, pointing to herself.

'Of course you,' he replied, rolling his eyes.

'But why? Why would you move for me?'

'I love you,' he answered, as if it were the most obvious thing in the world.

She drew in a sharp breath. 'I love you. I have for a long time—although I only realised the truth in Frankfurt.'

Connor felt the warmth of true happiness spread throughout his body. It had been enough for him to know he loved Rina. He had hoped over time her feelings for him would become stronger and she would come to love him too. He had never dared to hope she already did.

And her revelation that she had known in Frankfurt

made her actions in coming to him and asking for that one night even more special.

'Come here,' he said, pulling her up and into his arms.

They kissed deeply. He desperately wanted to make love to her, but they still had lots to talk about first.

He sat down, drawing her onto his lap. 'You can't leave your aunt,' he said, 'and I can't be without you. So the simple solution was for me to move.'

'Connor, I can't ask you to give up your need for stability.'

'You're not.'

'You can't know that!'

'Rina,' he said, holding her face in his hands. 'You don't need to worry. Actually, I took your advice and started seeing a counsellor. I'm going to continue, but it's already helped a lot. He's helped me understand how all my life I've thought that belonging meant to a place. That moving constantly meant I never really had a home. You made me realise home isn't a place—it's a person. Wherever you are is my home. And although I can't promise I'll always travel with you, I will go occasionally. And when you go without me I'll always be at home, waiting for you.'

He noticed Rina blink rapidly, but she couldn't stop the tears falling.

'Don't cry, my darling,' he said softly, wiping the tears with his thumbs.

'I'm just so happy. It doesn't feel real.'

'Should I pinch you?' he offered, smiling.

She nodded.

'I think I'll kiss you instead,' he said.

When they finally came up for air, his ever-practical

Rina asked, 'But what about your job? What about New-mans?'

'I resigned.'

'What? Aren't you the Global CEO?'

'They offered the promotion to me. I turned it down. I'm after a new challenge.'

'What kind of challenge?'

'I've found a small company with an amazing product developed by an intelligent, beautiful woman. It needs some help with growing the business, and I have some expertise in that. So I've accepted a job with Lachance Boutique.'

'My aunt offered you a job without telling me?'

'She told me she's in charge of recruitment.'

'She is, but…'

Connor grinned. He'd finally seen Rina at a loss for words.

'Are you pleased?' he asked.

'I think so… There's a lot to process. So we'll be working together?'

'That's right. Although I'll have nothing to do with the product development side.'

'Don't you think you might get bored with me?'

Connor laughed. Didn't she know every day with her was a new delight? 'Impossible!' He kissed her again.

'I love you, Connor Portland.'

'And I love you, Rina Lahiri Lachance.'

EPILOGUE

RINA SIGHED DEEPLY as she lay in the field of rampion and gazed up at the cloudless sky. She'd had another frustrating day in the lab, and Lachance Boutique hadn't launched a new product in almost a year.

The products they had developed since her trip to India had gone on to be extremely successful globally, with Connor's expertise at the helm. And Essence was performing wonderfully with the new distribution agreement Connor had negotiated with Newmans, which had brought the product to a wider market at a lower cost, leaving strategic control to Lachance—everything she'd wanted for her miracle product.

But although she could rest on her laurels, she had no intention of doing so. Not now Lachance Boutique was hers completely.

Less than two years after Connor had joined the company, her aunt had surprised them all by announcing her plans to retire and cruise around the world. She'd transferred ownership of the boutique to Rina, but wanted to keep her share of the tower—which Rina had been happy to agree to.

At the time, Connor and Rina had been planning their wedding. Rina had known that although Connor was happy to live in Switzerland, he missed his family and England. So, since Aunt Maria was the only reason Rina stayed in Switzerland, she'd suggested they move to England.

They'd appointed an operations manager to look after the company in Lachance tower, then bought a home outside London and set up an office for Lachance Boutique nearby.

Their visits to Switzerland coincided with Aunt Maria's trips back—which was the reason they were staying at Lachance tower now. Rina had hoped working in the tower would bring her some much-needed inspiration. But it hadn't happened so far. Perhaps it was time for her to go on her travels again. She hadn't been for a long time...

'Ma! Ma!'

Two young voices called out for her—the reason she hadn't gone off on any inspiration trips.

She sat up to watch her three-year-old son and daughter running towards her, gathering them in her arms as their momentum pushed them all backwards. She gave them a quick tickle, enjoying their high-pitched squeals. Having twins was rewarding, but it was also exhausting.

Rina couldn't pull her eyes away from her husband, now walking towards them. Her heart still flipped at the sight of him, the same way it had when she'd first seen him six years before.

She and Connor had only been married for a few months when they'd found out about her pregnancy. Rina had initially worried that the news, coming so soon after settling into a new job and getting married, would be too much for Connor. He'd had to go from being a man who avoided attachments and commitments to having the biggest commitments of all thrust upon him. But it turned out she'd had nothing to worry about—he cherished fatherhood as much as being a husband.

'Ma, will you read this story, please?' her son asked, resting his head against her legs.

'Please, Ma,' her daughter echoed, right on cue.

She looked at the book, which contained their favourite story, *Rapunzel*. She raised her eyebrows at Connor.

He put both hands up. 'Don't blame me. I've already read it to them three times today.'

'Yes, but Daddy's not good at being the witch like you are,' her daughter explained.

'I'm not sure if that's a compliment,' Rina said, laughing.

Connor sat behind her, drawing her to him. 'Well, I did tell them you cast spells in your magical tower,' he said, against her ear, pressing a kiss to her temple before sitting back.

Rina rested against Connor, with her children resting against her. Could anything be more perfect?

She opened the book and started to read.

'Daddy said there's a plant called Rapunzel,' her daughter said when she'd finished.

'That's right. It's also called rampion.'

'Is it really what Rapunzel's mother wanted to eat?' her daughter asked.

She nodded.

'That's funny...naming your baby after some food,' her son remarked.

'If we'd named the two of you after what your mother ate when she was pregnant you'd be called idli,' Connor said, poking his son's belly gently. 'And you'd be called dosa,' he continued, poking his daughter in the same way.

Aunt Maria called the children to her, leaving Rina and Connor alone in the field.

'So, will you be eating authentic idli and dosa soon?' he asked, lifting her hair, which she hadn't cut since India, and kissing the back of her neck.

'What do you mean?'

'You're planning your next trip.'

'How could you tell?'

'The look on your face before the children came to you.'

She pulled his arms tighter around her, covering his hands with hers. 'I was thinking about it.'

'We can find a good time for you to go. I'll take care of the kids. And perhaps later in the year we can all go on holiday as a family.'

Rina closed her eyes and lay back, basking in the sun and in the comfort of Connor's arms.

* * * * *

PART OF HIS
ROYAL WORLD

NINA SINGH

MILLS & BOON

To RJ, a true prince of a man.

CHAPTER ONE

PRINCE ERIKO RAFAEL SUAREZ had to get away. He couldn't stand one more minute under the same roof as his family. He loved them, he really did. But sometimes they could be a bit...well, much. Especially about his need to eventually succeed his father on the throne. Recently, it seemed his ascension was all the king wanted to talk about. The conversation at breakfast this morning had Riko approaching his breaking point. So he'd made his excuses and left before the second serving of coffee.

Now, he made his way down the sandy beach toward the dock. He was breaking all sorts of protocol. He'd slipped his bodyguards' attention and hadn't told anyone where he was going. Doing so would have only invited argument and the insistence that someone else join him. When all he wanted was solitude and a few moments of peace, sailing on the wide-open sea.

Still, maybe he should have notified Manny of his intentions. His twin could often be the proverbial thorn in Riko's hindquarters, but he'd always been trustworthy.

Too late now. Riko had no intention of going back to the castle and in his haste to get away, he'd left his cell behind. Besides, there was no need to tell anyone what he was up to. He was an experienced sailor, having manned boats since he'd been a preschooler. He even raced competitively once or twice a year. Plus he'd be back in no time.

The sky above was clear and sunny, the wind a gentle breeze and the waves of the water lapped gently on the beach. It was the perfect time for a quick sail. It would be a sin to waste such an opportunity.

Within minutes, he was off, guiding the cruiser smoothly over the water, the shore growing distant behind him. Right away he felt the tension slowly leaving his tight shoulders, the knot of frustration in his gut gradually loosening. Being on the water always had this effect on him. Nature's therapy.

The enormous responsibility of the future that awaited him wasn't lost on Riko. Did his father, the king, really not see that? Of course, Riko knew all that responsibility would land on his shoulders within a few short years. He knew he would have to get married and start a family. His people expected it of him. They expected a royal family to replace the current one on the throne. It was essential for the stability of the kingdom. A smooth transition to the throne was an absolute, following centuries of history.

Not for the first time in his life, Riko had to marvel at the utter randomness of it all. The slight twist of fate that had him being born mere minutes before his twin brother. A humorously short period of merely 120 seconds that settled the very history of Versuvia and made him the firstborn son of the king and hence the heir. In her usual manner of efficiency and competence, the queen had delivered both the heir and the spare within the same small window of time.

Riko gave his head a shake and inhaled the salty sea air deeply. Later. He would worry about all of that later. Heaven knew, he'd be back at the palace soon enough to face his responsibilities. Right now, he just wanted to enjoy these precious moments of solitude.

But Mother Nature apparently had other ideas.

If Riko was a superstitious man, he might have figured some cursed form of magic had brought about what happened next. A thick gray cloud appeared in the sky not far from where he'd anchored, seemingly out of nowhere. After drifting like a stealth plane across the sky for several minutes, it dropped like a rock directly over the boat. Riko could only stand frozen to the spot, watching helplessly. Then the heavens opened up. Torrents of rain dropped like mini golf balls, pounding against his cheeks and forehead. His hair plastered against his scalp. A claw-shaped bolt of lightning lit up the now darkened sky, followed moments later by a sudden crack of thunder that split the air.

The shock of it had him stunned.

But only for a moment. Riko's expertise and training finally kicked in. With the waves growing larger by the second, he knew he couldn't stay anchored much longer. He was bound to take on water. Or worse.

Fighting against the wind and the punishing rain, Riko pushed his way across the deck. Wasting no time, he lifted anchor and ran across the deck to the wheel. It was like wrestling with a sea monster. Riko exerted every bit of strength he could muster to try and turn the wheel to give the sailboat a chance against the blustering wind and violent waves attacking the craft. He knew there was no way to steady her. He just had to keep her afloat and try to take on as little water as possible.

Streams of sweat ran down his face, mixing with the wetness from the pounding rain. The muscles in his shoulders and upper back cried out in protest at the strain. As an ardent gym enthusiast who made sure to put in regular punishing workouts, the strain of effort surprised him. He didn't have time to dwell on it. The next instant, a powerful wave surged toward the boat. Riko gritted his teeth and braced his feet on the deck preparing for impact. The boat was almost completely on its side. Nothing to do now but pray to the gods above that somehow it righted itself.

How stupid of him not to have worn a life jacket. But it had been such a clear day with the water so smooth. And he hadn't intended to be out here long. None of those were excuses for how unprepared he was. And how foolhardy of him not to have told anyone where he'd be or what he'd be doing.

For one spirit lifting moment, the boat appeared to be righting its position. It didn't last. Another massive wave rose out of the water, and Riko knew there would be no escaping this one. He managed to reach for the flotation ring hanging by the wheel just as the monstrosity of water came crashing down.

What came next felt as if it were happening in slow motion. The primitive part of his brain suddenly went on high alert, trying to process exactly how much danger he was in. All in all, he was a fairly competent swimmer, but he'd never swum in weather even remotely this dangerous. As far as visibility went, he couldn't see past the bridge of his nose. His only hope was to swim to the nearest shore, which he would guess was Majorca at this point. Whatever he did, he absolutely couldn't let go of the ring. He knew that much. He gripped the hard plastic and shoved it under his arms.

Then the world went black.

* * *

This had to be the strangest weather she'd ever experienced. Such volatile shifts certainly didn't happen where she came from. Chicago certainly had its share of windy days and dramatic dips in temperature from one day to the next, but nothing like this.

Elle promptly gathered all the children out of the ocean and then back onto the beach to the water sports cabana several feet away. No easy feat given her costume of the day. The chosen book today happened to be *The Little Mermaid*. As a result, she was clad in a shell-covered halter and a lengthy silicone fish tail with the narrowest slit at the bottom. Thanks to the storm, character-led story time had just been cut short.

With the seven toddlers under her care in tow, she led them to the shelter just in the nick of time. The lightning and thunder that immediately followed made her jump in her tail. More than a couple of the children began to sniffle in fear. She felt a gentle tug on one of her scales.

As best as the costume allowed, she crouched to a lower position so that she was at face level with the child, one she recognized as belonging to the American family who was staying at the resort.

Large, brown eyes full of anxiety met hers. "Miss Elle, is the lightning gonna hit us?"

Elle pulled the child closer and gave her a reassuring squeeze around her shoulders. "No, sweetie," Elle answered, making sure to keep her voice calm and steady. "As long as we stay put right here, we should be just fine."

The little girl gave her a skeptical look, clearly not convinced. The other children looked equally as apprehensive. Elle gave a silent prayer that the unexpected storm wouldn't last much longer. The children appeared ready to start crying at any moment. She could hardly blame them. One moment they were enjoying story time in the water, and the next they had found themselves in a scene straight out of a disaster film.

"Que es eso?" The question came from a small boy, spoken in his native Spanish. He thrust a pudgy, sand-covered finger in the direction of the water. Elle saw immediately what the little boy was referring to. She had to blink to make sure she was seeing it too.

What in the world?

In the distance, a few yards from the shoreline, an orange-and-white object was bobbing in the water. To her former high school lifeguard's eye, there was no mistaking what it was. Someone was in trouble out in the ocean, apparently floating on a safety rescue ring.

Elle glanced around in desperation. Aside from Señora Rita, the sweet little old lady who sold custom jewelry out of a kiosk on the beach, Elle and the kids were the only ones remaining in the immediate area. No one else was there to help the stranded swimmer. She didn't have her cell phone. There was nowhere to carry it in her shell-covered halter or her mermaid tail.

Elle's breath caught in her throat as a wave rose in front of the person floating in the water, blocking her view. Had he or she just gone under? A surge of relief ran through her when the person reappeared a second later. But it was tempered by the fact that there was still someone in trouble in the ocean.

"Is dat a person?" Chloe, the American child, asked.

"It certainly is." And what was she going to do about it? There hardly seemed to be much of a choice. She couldn't just leave the poor soul out there to drown. How would she ever live with herself?

Frantically, she began waving in Señora Rita's direction, several feet away. The woman was crouched under the roof of her kiosk, doing her best to stay dry. A futile attempt. The wind was blowing the rain in all manner of directions.

Finally, Señora Rita looked her way. Elle made the universal motion of "come here" by scooping her hand back and forth. The older woman appeared confused but finally stepped around the kiosk and began the perilous journey toward the cabana. It took so painfully long that Elle began to grow nauseous with concern for the stranded swimmer.

At last, Señora Rita made it into the cabana. The poor woman was soaking wet. In broken Spanish, Elle explained that she needed her to stay with the children for a few moments. Thank heavens Señora Rita seemed to understand and nodded her head.

Crouching again to the children's level, she gave them all a serious glare. "I'm going to go try and help that person. I need you all to promise me that you'll stay right here with Señora Rita. Understood?"

She repeated it all in Spanish. Several tiny heads bobbed up and down seemingly in agreement. Still, not terribly reassuring. More than a couple of them looked confused and, heaven help her, more than a little anxious. But it would have to do. Elle didn't want to risk wasting any more time.

"I'll be back in no time," she reassured them, hoping fervently that it wasn't a lie. "Promise."

She was met with another round of nods that didn't do much to ease her discomfort. Again, she would have to believe that they understood. Bracing herself against the wind and rain, Elle hurried out of the small hut as best she could and made her way toward the water, discarding the cumbersome lower part of her costume along the way. Expertly, she dove into the waves. Childhood swim lessons and her several medal-winning years on the school dive team made the motions second nature. Nevertheless, her heart pounded in her chest with fear and doubt. Despite her one-year stint as a lifeguard at the country club pool, she'd never actually had to rescue anyone before.

The current was surprisingly strong. But Elle hardly noticed, her sole focus on making it to the person in trouble out there. Keeping her strokes smooth and long, she opened her eyes long enough to locate her target. To her horror, they seemed to be drifting farther from the shoreline. Taking a deep breath, she ramped up her speed. Several agonizing moments later, she finally found herself within a few feet of the drifter.

Even with the terrible visibility, two things struck her at once. The person on the life ring was a man. One with ebony dark hair. Even with the slight tinge of purple shadowing his face, she could tell he was sporting a glowing tan.

Something tugged in the vicinity of her chest. A weird attraction that came out of nowhere and took her by surprise.

So not the time.

Focus!

Elle forced her attention back to the task at hand. Whoever he was, she'd reached him just in time. He seemed to be drifting in and out of consciousness. One moment, he appeared to be giving her a grateful smile, the next his eyes drew shut and his features grew slack.

Elle wrapped her arm around the rim of the rescue ring. Thrusting her legs as hard as she could, she did her best to propel them both toward the shore. Lord, it was strenuous work. He was heavier than she would have imagined. Between his weight and the strength of the oncoming waves, she had her work cut out for her. Luckily for both of them, she had well developed lungs given the years of swimming. Her parents and sisters often referred to her as a fish. If they could see her now.

Elle lost any sense of time as she made her way to the shore. Her chest was on fire and her limbs were on the verge of cramping. But she somehow managed to hang on and keep going.

By the time she finally reached the sand, every muscle in her body was screaming. Still, she wasted no time getting the man on his back and beginning chest compressions and alternately breathing into his mouth. One… two…three…

Please let him be okay.

Elle couldn't even be sure how much time had gone by before she felt a hand on her shoulder pushing her aside none too gently.

Help had finally arrived. A couple of EMTs began working on the stranger. Several agonizing seconds passed as she watched them resume what she'd begun. Finally, the man gave a wet sounding cough and began to heave. Moments later, he was loaded onto a stretcher and taken away.

Elle dropped to her bottom onto the sand, adrenaline still surging through her blood.

It took a while to get her breathing back to normal but when it finally did, she turned back to face the children and Señora Rita. Thank heavens, they all remained exactly where she'd left them, watching her with a combination of awe and horror. She hadn't even noticed until that moment that the storm had ended as quickly as it had begun. The sun shone bright once again in a clear and cloudless sky. As if none of it had happened.

"Well, look who's finally up and about."

Riko didn't bother to stifle a weary sigh as his brother approached him from the other side of the terrace. For a set of identical twins, they were different in as many ways as they were similar. Whereas Manny kept his dark hair straight with the use of two different products, Riko preferred his natural waves. Manny's style of dress was completely different also: he preferred casual shorts and T-shirts even in cool weather whereas Riko made sure he was dressed appropriately in the way the occasion called for.

Now, Manny was no doubt about to pepper him with the same questions about what had happened to him the other day. He appreciated everyone's concern, he really did.

But he was getting a little tired of the attention and the constant concern for his well-being. Mama in particular was bordering on obsessive, checking on him constantly, trying to pamper him like a toddler. It was bad enough she'd had the family physician move into Riko's personal wing in the palace. And everyone had so many questions, lobbed at him from every direction.

It wasn't as if he could remember the details clearly. Aside from a pair of haunting bluish-green eyes and fiery red hair in his mind's eye, he couldn't recall a thing about the accident. It was a blurry vision, dreamlike. A vision everyone assured him he must have imagined.

"How're ya feeling?" Manny asked, pulling out a metal wire chair and sitting across from him. A server immediately appeared with a steaming pot of coffee and a fresh mug.

"I'm fine," Riko answered. "No different than last night when you asked."

Manny grinned, taking a large swallow from his cup. "And we're gonna keep asking you until all of this becomes a distant memory." He set his beverage down. "Speaking of memory…"

Riko shook his head. "Nope, all I remember about the accident is what I already told you and everyone else."

Manny lifted an eyebrow. "Still sticking to that story, huh?"

"I know what I saw."

"Except you don't, big bro." Riko hated when Manny called him that. They were identical twins, for heaven's sake. Just because he happened to be delivered first hardly made him Manny's big bro.

His brother knew exactly how much it perturbed Riko to be referred to that way. Which was why Manny insisted on doing so.

"Somebody got me out of the water," Riko argued.

Manny nodded once. "Right. We've established that. The palace is trying to locate the person as we speak. The incredulous part is you seem to think your rescuer was a girl wearing seashells with fiery red hair. Who appeared out from the churning waves and swam you back to shore." His brother didn't bother to hide his disbelieving smirk.

"That's right."

Manny gave him a mischievous wink. "You sure you haven't been fantasizing about mermaids, big bro?"

Riko ignored the silly question. But it irked him enough that he wasn't going to let the nickname slide this time. Though he wasn't sure why he even bothered. Not like Manny would be deterred. "Don't call me that."

"You know I will."

Riko groaned out loud but decided to let it go. Again. "What's the latest about finding her?"

"Your mermaid?"

His brother could rile him like no one else on the planet. It was no wonder half the physical scars they both sported were a result of all their fisticuffs as children. The rest were mostly due to the two of them trying to outdo each other with reckless stunts like climbing the highest tree in the royal gardens or riding their bikes too fast downhill in the wooded area behind the palace.

"My rescuer," Riko corrected. "I'd like to make sure she's properly rewarded."

Manny's lips thinned, suddenly growing serious. "As would we all. Mama and Papa are very grateful."

Riko wasn't one to pass an opportunity to tease his brother, even about a matter this serious. "What about you, huh? Are you grateful that your twin brother didn't perish in a tumultuous sea? How badly would you have missed me?"

The mischievous grin immediately reappeared. "As if."

Riko leaned back in his chair, not ready to let his brother off the proverbial hook. "Huh. I seem to recall you arriving at my hospital bed before anyone else and looking rather concerned."

Manny shrugged. "I just knew Ramon and Tatyana would have been upset to lose their only uncle," he answered, referring to his six-year-old son and four-year-old daughter respectively. "I was concerned on their behalf."

"Right."

Manny rubbed his jaw with such exaggerated serious-ness that Riko could tell without a doubt he was about to receive some more ridicule. "You know, it occurs to me that maybe we're looking for this person in the wrong places."

He knew better than to ask but couldn't seem to help himself. "How so?"

"Rather than on land, maybe we should be searching for her under the sea."

He'd been right. "Ha ha. Very funny. Don't you have a pregnant wife to tend to instead of sitting here has-sling me?"

A shadow darkened his brother's eyes. Any hint of humor left his features. "What is it?" Riko asked, alarm churning in his gut.

Manny's lips tightened. "We didn't want to say any-thing so as not to worry anyone. Especially after…" He gestured in Riko's direction. "We swore the obstetrician to secrecy."

His alarm tripled. "Obstetrician? Is Isabel all right?"

Manny rubbed his forehead. "She's been experiencing some pain. Some other symptoms that aren't normal."

"You don't want to tell Mama?"

Manny shook his head. "We don't want to tell anyone." His brother didn't have to say aloud what they were both thinking. Riko was the exception. There'd never been any secrets between them. If it wasn't for his accident, Riko would have known that something wasn't sitting right with his brother.

Manny continued. "Not yet. Not until we know a little more. You know how Mama can get. Look at how she's reacting to your accident."

"Overreacting might be a better term. She needs to stop hovering." Riko took his brother's words as what they were, a desire to change the subject. When Manny was ready to talk more about his worry for his wife, Riko would be there to listen. He just hoped his sister-in-law didn't have anything serious to contend with during her pregnancy.

Manny was a strong man, but the love he had for his wife and children was definitely his soft spot. A weakness Riko understood but couldn't quite relate to himself.

He didn't know if he ever would.

CHAPTER TWO

ELLE WASN'T MUCH for cursing. But she was silently going through every expletive in her vocabulary as she collected her few belongings.

What in the world was she supposed to do now? As of an hour ago, she had no job, no place to stay, and very little money.

Of all the nerve. Diego had been looking for an excuse to get rid of her. And she'd handed him one on a silver platter by leaving the children with Señora Rita. Never mind that she'd done the only thing any sane person would have done in the same situation. What had Diego wanted her to do instead? Let the poor man drown?

Her phone buzzed on the wooden tableau across the room. No doubt her sister Lizzie calling. Again. She ignored it. As much as she loved her three sisters, she wasn't ready to talk to anyone in her family just yet about her latest disappointment. Though the word Mom and Dad would use would run more toward "failure."

Damn it. This last one was not her fault. The buzzing of her phone stopped finally. But it was immediately followed by several texts. Her sisters could be pretty demanding. One could hardly blame them. They didn't have time to waste trying to get hold of their younger sibling.

They all had important careers and big responsibilities. Unlike her.

Striding over to the device to shut it off, Elle glanced at the screen.

Haven't heard from you in two days. If you don't call me back right away I'm sending the Spanish army after you.

Elle sighed. Being a prosecutor, her sister Lizzie saw her fair share of alarming crimes. As a result, she could be a bit overprotective. Annoyed but resigned, Elle plopped onto her stripped mattress and hit the call back button. She'd tell Lizzie just enough to get her off her back. For a while anyway. Her sister wouldn't relent until she knew the whole story.

And when she did, out of her misplaced concern, she would tell their parents. That was the last thing Elle needed.

Lizzie answered before the end of the first ring. She didn't so much as bother with a "hello." "Where have you been? Are you all right?"

Elle rubbed her forehead then mustered the cheeriest voice she could. "I'm great. Everything's great. But I'm a little busy right now. Can I call you back?"

She realized her mistake immediately. How stupid of her. She'd overdone the enthusiasm. Several seconds of silence passed before Lizzie let loose. "Spill it, Arielle." Uh-oh, her sister was even using her full name. "What's the matter?" she demanded to know. Elle tried to hold strong, she really did. But the concern and worry behind her sister's voice had her undone in seconds.

She found herself blurting out the whole story while utterly failing in her attempt not to cry.

This was a disaster. Lizzie was going to go straight to her parents. Then either Mom or Dad, perhaps both, would be on the next flight to Barcelona then onto a ferry straight to Majorca. She wouldn't even get a chance to try and fix her predicament on her own. Never mind that Elle had no idea how exactly she would have done so. That was beside the point.

Surprisingly, Lizzie's next words had no mention of notifying their parents. Instead, her sister did some colorful swearing of her own, outrage on Elle's behalf clear and strong in her voice. "Do you mean to tell me that SOB fired you for saving a man from drowning?"

"I'm afraid so," Elle answered. "He said I should have figured out a way to help the drowning man without leaving the kids with only a little old lady to watch over them."

"Wasn't that the guy who kept asking you out and you kept turning down?"

"One and the same," Elle answered, stifling another sob.

"Of all the... Clearly, he had ulterior motives."

Be that as it may, it still left Elle without a job or a roof over her head until she could think of a solution to her predicament.

"He's lucky I have no jurisdiction overseas," Lizzie added.

A hiccup escaped her throat. "Do you think he was right, Liz? Maybe even a little?" After all, she *had* left the children entrusted to Señora Rita's care. They hadn't been in any kind of danger, but what if one of them had wandered off and Señora Rita hadn't noticed?

"Absolutely not," her sister answered right away. "It was an impossible situation, and you used your best judgment. At the least, your creep of a boss could have given you a verbal warning or some other kind of slap on the wrist. Instead, he fires you."

The tension she hadn't even known she was holding in her center loosened. Up until she'd asked the question aloud, Elle hadn't even realized how much the notion that Diego might have been right had been bothering her. Her sister's reassurance had her feeling better, if only slightly.

"It's okay, Lizzie. I'll figure this out. Just promise me you won't tell Mom and Dad. I don't want them to worry." *Or worse, show up in Majorca*, she added silently.

Another long pause. Elle could practically see her sister debating internally about making such a promise.

"I'll come up with a plan. I just need some time," Elle pressed.

"Elle… I don't know. You don't even have a place to stay. Your room and board were a part of your employment at the resort."

A faint rustling sound from outside her door drew Elle's attention before she could answer. "I'll have to call you back, Lizzie. Just give me some time before you say anything to Mom and Dad."

She hung up the call before her sister could protest.

He could hear the distinct sound of someone crying behind the door. A child? No. It was a most definitely a woman. Riko paused midknock, unsure what to do. This was the correct resort and the correct room number. The palace guard had been very thorough in its investigation. He was here to personally express his gratitude to one Miss Arielle Stanton, American, originally from Chicago, Illinois, for having saved his hide from drowning two days ago. Not that he could remember it all that clearly.

Maybe this wasn't a good time.

Before he could make any kind of decision, the door was suddenly flung open. A startled pair of hazel-green eyes met his over the threshold. Eyes that turned instantly hostile. She looked him up and down then literally huffed before speaking. "If Diego sent you down to accompany me out of here, I assure you there's no need. I'm almost done packing."

Riko took a moment to process her words, trying to make some sense of them. Clearly, she'd mistaken him for someone else. Who was this Diego? A boyfriend perhaps? Had she been crying because of a recent breakup? The thought sent a wave of irritation over him, a feeling he couldn't identify. He was no doubt simply feeling protective of the woman after what she'd done for him the other day.

Though said woman was now shooting daggers at him.

Then she gave an exaggerated eye roll. "Look, I'll be out of here in no time. Tell Diego he didn't need to send a goon to try and intimidate me."

A goon? Intimidate her?

What kind of relationship had she been in anyway?

"I beg your pardon?" he asked for lack of anything else to say.

She began to shut the door. Reflexively, Riko stuck his foot out to stop her from closing it all the way. The action earned him a withering look. Somehow this interaction was escalating into some kind of strange confrontation.

"Who are you?" she demanded to know. "I haven't seen you on the grounds as part of the security detail."

Riko cleared his throat. "Señorita Stanton. Clearly, you have mistaken me for someone else. Allow me to introduce myself."

Her eyebrows furrowed with curiosity.

"My name is Eriko Rafael Suarez. I'm the man you rescued from nearly drowning the other day."

Her hand flew to her mouth. "Oh! I didn't recognize you! You're so…" She trailed off.

He nodded. "Yes, I imagine I looked quite different. For one, I'm a bit less unconscious now."

As far as jokes went, it was a rather bad one. Still, the corners of her mouth lifted ever so slightly. His attention fell to her lips, full and rose pink. Her hair was a shade of red he'd be hard-pressed to describe. Arielle Stanton was a looker by half. Riko didn't know what he'd been expecting, but he hadn't been prepared for the jolt of awareness coursing through his core that hadn't relented since she'd opened her door.

"Also, drier," she said. "You were much wetter when we first met."

He rubbed his chin. "Apologies. I should have thought to use a spray bottle on myself before approaching your door." Another terrible one. He so wasn't one to quip and joke with women he'd just met. What had gotten into him?

The slight smile turned to an all-out grin, and Riko wanted to pat himself on the back for putting it there. But it was short-lived. Any hint of humor suddenly left her eyes and the grin turned to a frown the next instant.

"So, I don't mean to be rude. But why are you here? This is not really a great time for me."

"I'm here to personally thank you. For myself and also on behalf of the king and queen."

She gave her head a shake. "The king and queen?"

"Of the kingdom of Versuvia. It's a small island nation a few nautical miles from Majorca to the east and the Spanish coast to the west. We're known as the Monaco of the Spanish world."

Her brows furrowed once more. Again, she eyed him up and down. "Right." She dragged out the word, pronouncing it as if it were three syllables. "Listen, I don't know how to break this to you, but I think you might have suffered some type of head injury during your accident. Probably wanna get that checked out." She began to shut the door again.

"Please wait. I know it might be hard to believe, but it's the truth. I'm Eriko Rafael Suarez, heir to the Versuvian throne. Firstborn son of King Guillermo and Queen Raina. My friends call me Riko." He tilted his head, waiting for her reaction.

She stuck her hand out. "Pleased to meet you. I'm Arielle Trina Stanton, the duchess of Schaumburgia. Daughter of King Alfred III and Queen Tammi, MD."

He simply stared at her, completely at a loss for words.

"See how that sounds?" she asked with a kind smile, humoring him apparently.

For the life of him, he couldn't figure out why he was still standing there. He'd felt obliged to thank her in person, and he'd done so. Anything else could be handled through his advisers. But something kept him planted in place where he stood, unable to walk away just yet.

So he decided to play along. "What a surprising coincidence, Your Highness." He performed an exaggerated bow slash curtsy.

The performance earned him a small chuckle. She crossed her arms in front of her chest. "Look, this has been entertaining and all. And I really am glad you're doing okay. But, like I said, I'm kind of in the middle of something. Packing up my apartment that I have to leave. And besides, I've run out of the Earl Grey I usu-ally serve to other royalty."

Definitely his cue to depart. So why exactly did he say what he did next? "Perhaps I can buy you a cup then? If you can step away from your current task. I can even send a couple of men who are waiting outside to finish your packing for you."

Her jaw fell. "Wow. That's some real commitment to the bit. You're really still going with whole prince thing, huh?"

"I don't really have a choice. Birthright being what it is and all. I'll wait here in the hall while you go google me."

He should probably have just led with that option. Not that he hadn't enjoyed the little exchange.

She threw up her hands. "Fine. I'll go do that. If it means I can get on with my day. Versuvia, you said?"

"Yes."

She shut the door before he could thank her for oblig-ing. What a fun errand this had turned out to be. He hap-pened to have a morning meeting on the island with the mayor. Figured he'd take care of this as well. He'd only planned on introducing himself, handing her his card and directing her to call the palace with anything she might want or need as a gesture of gratitude. Instead, here he stood waiting for her do some basic research to confirm he was who he said he was.

The look on her face when she opened the door several minutes later made it all more than worthwhile. Her jaw agape, eyes wide, shaking her head in disbelief.

"Holy sh—" She cupped her hand to her mouth. "Oh! I probably shouldn't swear in front of royalty, huh?"

Joining him in the hall, she began to pace a few feet then back to where he stood. "Wow. Do you mean to tell me that the man I pulled out of the water was a real life, verified, true-blood son of a king and queen?"

"Firstborn. Although, that's something of a fluke. I only beat my twin brother by a matter of minutes."

She stared at him, still stunned. "Where's your entourage? How are you here by yourself?"

He pointed up. "They're waiting for me upstairs in the lobby and along the street. Figured you'd be less startled if I showed up alone rather that with two bodyguards and my personal secretary."

"Huh. Well, consider me startled nevertheless. Wait till the girls hear about this."

"Girls?"

"My sisters. They're not going to believe any of this. I can hardly believe it myself. An honest to goodness prince, here at my door. A prince I dragged ashore."

She really was delightful.

"So about that tea. Or coffee if you prefer?"

Her eyebrows lifted. "Give me a second to grab my bag. What kind of fool woman would turn that offer down?"

Riko chuckled and watched as she reached for a large leather bag hanging off a hook on the wall.

His afternoon had just gotten exponentially more interesting.

This couldn't really be happening. She had to be in the middle of some kind of prank someone was pulling. Elle looked around for any hidden cameras as she followed the man—rather, the prince—upstairs. Maybe she was in the middle of some kind of dream, and she should pinch herself to see if it would wake her. Or she wanted to pinch the man standing next to her in the elevator as they rode up to the lobby floor.

A prince!

How in the world had a prince almost drowned until she'd swum out to get him? Only one of the many burning questions she was yearning to ask. It was why she'd agreed to grab a cup of tea with him, despite all she had to do.

Diego could wait for her apartment key. Right now, she had a much more pressing engagement. To think, she'd almost sent him away this morning. Thank goodness he'd persevered, despite her trying to slam the door in his face.

Now, she watched as he spoke into the smart watch at his wrist in rapid-fire Spanish. Too fast for her to understand.

He clicked off the device then turned to her. "I've asked that arrangements be made to be able to leave the building while drawing as little attention to us as possible. And that a private room be secured for us in the back area of a nearby café."

That seemed like an awful lot of trouble for a measly cup of caffeine. But what did she know? She wasn't of royal blood like her companion here.

"Sounds like a lot of hassle."

He shrugged. "I'm used to it. I don't get recognized that often in Majorca, but it does happen occasionally."

When they reached the lobby doors, a big burly man in a dark suit opened the glass door for them. "It's clear to enter the vehicle, Your Highness."

"*Gracias*, Juan," Riko answered the man, guiding her to a black SUV parked a few feet away, his hand at the small of her back. A puddle of warmth resonated through her where his palm touched.

Just haven't been touched in a while, that's all. And definitely never been touched by a prince.

By the time they'd arrived at the café and were led to a back room, reality still hadn't quite settled in her mind. It had to be one of her earlier theories—dream or prank. She wasn't really sitting down in a chair a real prince had just pulled out for her.

A server appeared immediately with a large tray of pastries and fruit. Another immediately followed him with two steaming carafes of a heavenly scented coffee that filled the air. They hadn't even had to order anything.

"You seem deep in thought," he said, shrugging the jacket off his shoulders to reveal a crisp white shirt over a toned chest and arms. Elle forced herself to avert her gaze from his physique and look straight into his eyes instead. They were an unusual shade of brownish black that a girl could easily get lost in. The man certainly had a lot going for him.

"You have to know I have a lot of questions," she began as the man poured their beverages then left without a word.

"What do you Americans say…? Shoot them my way."

She nodded. "Close enough. First of all, what should I even call you? Like, Your Highness, or something?"

He chuckled softly, took a sip of his drink. "Well, seeing as I owe you such a big debt, I consider us to be something akin to friends."

Right. She wasn't naive enough to believe that was a real possibility. This wasn't her first experience with a celebrity of sorts. She'd sung backup on tour last summer with the latest social media sensation turned pop star. But this experience was something else entirely.

"So, call me Riko like my other friends do," he continued.

That suggestion didn't quite sit right with her. Was it really okay to be so informal with him? Enough to call him by his first name?

"What else?" he prompted.

Elle cleared her throat. "I'm not quite sure where to begin."

"How about I start then? With my own questions."

"You have questions about me?" Elle didn't trust herself to pick up her cup, her hands were shaking with nervous excitement. She knew he was just being polite. Why would a royal have any curiosity about someone like her?

"Certainly. What do you do when you're not saving strangers from a watery death?" he asked.

"Believe it or not, you are my first and only rescue."

"You do realize you didn't actually answer my question."

Elle gave her head a shake. She couldn't recall what he'd asked her. Her mind didn't seem to want to work around this man. "I'm sorry. What was it again?"

Riko chuckled. Somehow, he grew even more handsome every time he laughed. She could really see herself getting used to being around this man.

Like there was any chance of that happening. She had to remember she was only sitting here through a series of very random circumstances.

"How about you just tell me what you're doing here in Majorca?"

Elle ducked her head, embarrassed. It had been hard enough explaining her journey to the Spanish island to her parents and siblings. It would be mortifying explaining it to someone like him.

"I see it's something of a sore spot then," Riko said when she didn't answer for several beats.

Oh, what the hell? She might as well tell him the whole sordid story. Not like she would ever see him again after today. "I was chosen to perform in a traveling vocal band. We were touring Europe. Had just landed for the latest gig in Barcelona."

"You're a singer."

She could only nod. Elle couldn't even justify calling herself that anymore. "We were playing some small venues when the whole thing fell apart."

And once more, she'd found herself without a job or any kind of money. Only this time, she was thousands of miles from home in a foreign country.

"What happened?" Riko asked.

Elle released a deep breath. "Everything came apart when the bassist found the drummer in bed with the keyboardist. Who happened to be his wife."

Riko merely lifted an eyebrow, so she continued. "Anyway, the bassist took pity on me seeing as I was so far from home and recommended me for an entertainer position here at one of the resorts." The woman had neglected to mention that the opening was for a children's entertainer. Basically, a babysitter in costume. Not that it would have mattered; she hadn't exactly been in a position to turn the job down.

The job she no longer even had.

"When are you onstage next?"

Elle huffed out a laugh. "They never had me onstage. Basically I was there to entertain the kids while their parents enjoyed their vacation."

Riko rubbed his chin. "I see."

She reached for a sugary churro, drizzled in chocolate

glaze. "It hardly matters now anyway," she continued, not quite certain why she kept going. It made no sense that she was comfortable sharing so much with this man she'd just met.

"Why's that?" he asked.

"Because I managed to get myself fired. Which means I also need to find a place to stay."

His eyes narrowed with concern and question.

"The room came with the job," she explained, taking a bite of the pastry. It melted in her mouth like some kind of sweet, buttery cloud. It was hard not to groan out loud.

"Maybe I can make a phone call to this boss of yours. Ask him to rethink his decision."

Elle immediately shook her head. "That's very nice of you. But, no thanks. I don't think I want to work for Diego any longer anyway."

"Why were you let go?"

Elle did her best to explain. She didn't want Riko to think she faulted him in any way.

Riko listened intently and silently while she did her best to summarize the events that had led to her pulling him semiconscious out of the water.

She was nearly breathless by the time she finished, finally adding, "I only left the children with Señora Rita for a few short minutes. And they were totally fine."

"So you're saying I'm the reason you're now unemployed. The least I can do is offer you some type of financial gift. Especially given that I'm the cause of your current predicament."

She shook her head once again. "No. I refuse to take your charity for doing what any decent person would have done under the same circumstances. Besides, Diego's been looking for a reason to fire me for weeks now. It was bound to happen sooner or later."

"This wouldn't be charity, Elle. Consider it a reward for your efforts."

"It would still feel like charity to me."

He looked ready to argue, but something in her expression must have made him think better of it.

He leaned back in his chair, rubbed a palm down his face. He studied her for several long moments before saying, "Well, if you don't want me to intervene on your behalf with this Diego, and you refuse to accept any kind of reward, I might have one last idea."

That sounded encouraging. "I'm all ears."

"I don't understand that phrase in the least."

"It's an American idiom. It means I'm open to suggestions. What did you have in mind?"

"Perhaps there's someone else I can call on your behalf."

"So let me get this straight, you want us to hire a nanny who was just let go because she was bad at watching kids?" His brother sounded amused more than annoyed over the phone.

Riko glanced through the doorway where Elle still sat at the small wooden table, sipping her third cup of coffee. "Yes, I know how it sounds. But I explained why she left the children. And they weren't even unattended. We owe her."

"Riko, you told me she was fired."

"That wasn't her fault. She was fired on account of me."

"Why can't you just pay her?"

Riko pinched the bridge of his nose. "I tried that. She refuses. Says it would be accepting our charity."

"So she asked you for a job?"

Riko stepped farther into the hallway, toward the kitchen. "No, in fact, she has no idea I'm doing this. But it's perfect, isn't it? You and Isabel need a nanny while she's on bed rest. And Elle has experience taking care of children."

"I suppose it would be nice to be able to stop searching so that Isabel can focus on healing. The last woman the agency sent was completely unacceptable."

Riko pounced on his brother's hesitation. "Come on, Manny. I feel like I owe it to this woman to help her fix what I had a hand in breaking. Maybe we can just give it a trial run, see how she does. You can keep looking for a permanent replacement in the meantime."

He could hear his brother's long sigh from across several miles of sea. "Let me run it by Isabel. But I warn you, she will have the final say, big bro."

"Fair enough."

Elle greeted him with a shy smile when he reentered the room. "I'm guessing you called a contact at another resort to see about openings."

"Something like that," he answered, pulling out his chair and taking his seat again.

"You didn't need to do that, Your Hi…uh, Riko. But thank you. It's very kind of you."

He waved that away. "Would you like anything else to eat or drink?"

"No, actually I should be getting back. Finish packing." Lifting her cloth napkin off her lap, she dabbed it at the corners of her mouth.

Riko had to look away. It was bad enough when she'd

taken a bite of churro and gotten some of the glaze on her bottom lip. For an insane moment, he'd envisioned himself helping her remove that glaze in all sorts of ways.

Focus.

She started to stand, and Riko felt a surge of sadness. They'd been sitting here for close to two hours. He had things to do, calls to make back at the hotel. Yet he found he didn't want the time to end. He couldn't recall the last time he'd felt that way about time spent with a woman. It didn't help that any woman he'd been with in the past had been handpicked as his date.

"What about after that? Where will you go?"

A shadow crossed her face. "I can find a hostel or something. There has to be an opening somewhere that isn't exorbitantly expensive."

Riko stood as well, shrugged back into his jacket. There was no lodging in this resort town that wasn't exorbitantly expensive. Especially if needed last minute.

He had no intention of letting her find that out the hard way.

She couldn't have heard him right. "I beg your pardon?" Elle asked with a shake of her head. Had Riko really just asked her to spend the night with him?

A surge of anger burned in her chest. Along with a stinging disappointment. She should have known he seemed too good to be true.

He held a hand up. "I can tell you're getting the wrong idea. I assure you it's not what you think."

"I certainly hope not. Because I could have sworn you just made me an offer to spend the night with you at your hotel."

He nodded once. "I did. Technically."

What on earth did that mean? "Technically?"

"I'm staying at the Hotel Galencia. The suite I'm in has two separate bedrooms. It's the same suite they book for me whenever I'm in town. The second room always sits empty. There's no reason it should tonight."

Well, that sounded much more reasonable than what she'd been thinking. A rush of heat flamed her cheeks. She'd insinuated that he'd been coming on to her with a sketchy proposition. How mortifying. As if someone in his position would have any interest in her that way.

Embarrassment aside, did she dare take him up on his offer? She didn't know the man from Adam. "I don't know…"

"If it makes a difference, each door has a lock."

That certainly helped matters. But still. A girl couldn't be too careful.

She supposed it wouldn't hurt to take a look at the place. Not like she had a lot of options to go with here.

An hour later, Elle stepped out of the marble shower stall and glanced at her image in the three-panel mirror on the opposite wall. That had to be the most luxurious bathing she'd ever done. A girl could get used to such plush surroundings.

The suite beat any hostel that might have been her shelter tonight. Elle would have had to use a shared bathroom with only cold, rusty water running through crumbling faucets. Riko's offer had been heaven-sent. All the while, he was also scouting a job for her.

Her phone buzzed on her mattress in the other room. Probably her sister calling for an update. Elle adjusted the thick Turkish towel wrapped around her and made her way slowly to the other room. Her muscles felt loose and languid for the first time in as long as she could remember. Amazing what a strong jet of hot water could do for a person.

The text message on her phone screen was indeed from her sister. Elle's stomach tightened as she read it.

Dad is about to videoconference you. I strongly suggest you answer.

So much for the relaxation the hot shower had afforded. Her shoulders tensed tightly, and she felt the beginnings of a tension headache. Conversations with her father always ramped up her anxiety.

Sure enough, her screen lit up with her father's photo and the icon for an incoming video call. For just a split second, Elle was tempted to ignore it. After all, she could have still been in the shower. But that would just be putting off the inevitable. Her father would simply call back until she answered, and the delay would only serve to make him irate.

Too late. When she clicked to accept the call, it was clear as day that her father was already irate. To make matters worse, he appeared to be in full power attorney mode—his silver-gray hair perfectly coifed, dark navy tie around his neck, collar stiff and straight.

"Hi, Dad."

"Elle, how are you?" He didn't give her a chance to answer. "What's this about you being unemployed?"

How in the world did he know? If Lizzie had told him about her predicament, she was going to throttle her sister as soon as she saw her again. But Elle tossed that assumption aside as soon as it had hit. That didn't sound like Lizzie at all. Her sister had promised.

"Just a temporary setback, Dad. I already have other prospects lined up. But how…?"

"Your former employer called the house. To see if this address was where to send your final paperwork."

Diego strikes again.

"He said you'd neglected your duties."

"That's not what—"

But he cut her off again.

"Are you finally ready to stop gallivanting around the world and come back home?"

"I'm not exactly gallivanting, Dad. I was here on tour," she said, telling him what he already knew but refused to acknowledge.

Her father waved his hand in dismissal. "Just come back. We'll have you reenrolled in your studies in no time."

Elle gripped the phone tightly in her hand. She really didn't have the energy for this same old argument. Simply didn't have it in her. So she remained silent, pacing and nodding until her father was finally done. It took much too long.

"I'll think about it, Dad," she lied when he'd finally finished his rant.

"See that you do." With that, her screen went dark.

The sound of someone clearing their throat behind her startled Elle into dropping her phone. "Oh!"

With no small amount of mortification, Elle realized she'd paced herself right out of her room and into the common lounge area. Riko stood a few feet away by the wet bar, a glass tumbler in his hand. Even at this time of night, he looked like something out of a cologne ad. Polished and handsome and definitely prince material. He'd unbuttoned the top three buttons of his shirt, rolled his sleeves up to the elbow. And here she stood in nothing but a towel, her wet hair a messy nest atop her head.

"You heard all that, huh?"

He nodded once. "Sounded intense."

She rubbed her forehead. "My father is nothing if not intense."

"Want to talk about it?"

"Not particularly." What she wanted was to somehow forget that her father considered her to be flaky and impulsive, with no direction in life.

Riko nodded once and took a sip of his drink. "Well, if it helps, I heard back about the job proposal I had in mind for you. It's a go. You got the job. If you want it." He lifted his glass to her in a mini salute.

Elle had to bite down on her urge to squeal in delight. Finally, some good news. "Thank you! Will I be working at another resort?"

"Not quite. You'll actually be working at the castle. For the royal family."

CHAPTER THREE

Three days later

"Ms. STANTON. On behalf of the royal family, please allow me to welcome you to Versuvia."

Elle walked down the steps of the prop plane and approached the middle-aged smiling gentleman who waited on the tarmac to greet her. A sleek black sedan with shiny silver tire rims idled behind them, the windows tinted dark gray. She glanced around, a tinge of disappointment in the pit of her stomach. What had she expected? That the crown prince himself would be there waiting for her? How silly to think someone that important would run such a common errand. Besides, he'd done more than enough for her already. Plenty in fact.

"I'm Phillipe, Prince Eriko's steward," the man announced, taking her carry-on from her and extending his hand. Silver-haired, tan and wearing a pinstriped gray suit, he looked straight out of central casting for the role of royal assistant.

Elle swallowed a nervous lump in her throat and smoothed the skirt of her muslin dress. Perhaps she should have taken more care with her appearance. She was dressed pretty casually, in a summery sleeveless dress and flat leather sandals. Her chaperone appeared as if he was about to attend a state dinner.

She took the hand he offered and followed him to the vehicle. The driver's window rolled down slowly, and a hatted, mustached younger man gave her a friendly smile and slight nod of greeting before rolling the glass back up.

Phillipe helped her into the car and soon they were driving down the runway, eventually turning onto a lined paved street.

"How was your flight, Ms. Stanton?"

Elle cleared her throat. She fervently hoped this level of formality wasn't going to be the norm during her tenure here. Phillipe and the driver seemed friendly enough, but there was no mistaking the all-business atmosphere.

"Quite lovely, thank you. Ri—" She stopped before completing the word. Even if Riko had explicitly told her over coffee few days ago that she should use his first name, somehow it felt inappropriate under the circumstances. Clearing her throat, she began again. "His Highness was very generous to have arranged the flight for me."

Generous was hardly a sufficient word. He'd given her three extra days' stay in his suite so that she could get her affairs in order and enjoy a little rest.

She'd spent those days on a cloud of relief. Before he'd knocked on her door, she'd had no idea what her future was going to hold. Riko had presented her with a dream job—working in a palace with good pay and an elegant roof over her head. But now, as she sat in the back of a late model SUV in a plush leather seat with a tuxedoed driver and someone who called himself the prince's steward, a blossom of anxiety spread in her chest and spread lower to her stomach.

What exactly had she gotten herself into?

* * *

Riko had no doubt his personal secretary was fed up. He could hardly blame the man. This had to be at least the fourth time he'd had to repeat himself. Riko couldn't recall the last time he'd been this distracted.

Once more, he forced his mind to focus on the numbers before him on the spreadsheet the other man was referring to—something about a discrepancy in reports about an upcoming change to the euro exchange rate and the effect it might have on the kingdom's many casinos.

Had she arrived at the palace yet?

There he went again. Riko puffed out a breath of frustration and flung his handcrafted gold pen on the top of his mahogany desk. The action earned a small gasp of surprise from his exasperated assistant.

"I'm sorry, Marco," he said, running his hand down his face. "I'm a bit out of sorts this morning. Perhaps we can resume this meeting later in the afternoon."

The truth was he'd been out of sorts since he'd left Majorca three days ago. His mind replayed the events of the afternoon repeatedly. His café date with Elle had felt like a breath of fresh air.

Marco didn't need to be told twice. He immediately stood and snapped the cover of his tablet closed. "Of course, sir. Ring me whenever you're ready." In no small amount of haste, he strode to the door and shut it behind him.

Riko stood and paced over to the large bay window across the room. For the first time he could recall, he regretted the fact that his office faced the back gardens and not the mountain road that led to the main entrance of the castle. Usually he loved to be able to gaze out at this view, the myriad colors, the lush greenery of the expertly manicured shrubbery.

Today, he wished he were watching the road instead.

There was nothing for it. Without giving himself time to think any longer, he made his way out of his office and down the circular stairway to the first floor to see if she was here yet.

He might not fully remember the afternoon of the boat accident, but thoughts of Elle Stanton seemed to occupy his mind without end.

Elle wasn't sure what she'd been expecting. But she certainly hadn't been prepared for the breathtaking view that met her as they drove through a tall, automated metal gate and up a circular road meandering around a high stony mountain. Before long, a majestic castle appeared in the distance like something out of a fairy tale movie. Her breath caught in her throat at the scene before her as the car drew closer.

With red stone walls and two towers that reached the clouds, the structure was framed by the ocean on one side and an emerald green field on the other. She still hadn't quite recovered from her awestruck reaction by the time the car came to a stop in front of a grand brick stairwell that led up to a massive pair of wooden doors. A uniformed footman appeared out of nowhere and immediately opened the car door for her. Phillipe spoke to him in Spanish, and he gave a quick nod then made for the doors.

"This way please, Ms. Stanton," Phillipe said, then took her arm and led her up the steps. The doors seemed to magically open on their own, and Elle found herself stepping into a foyer that reminded her of the Art Institute of Chicago, the city's historical art museum. Marble tile floors, high arched ceiling and ionic columns on either side of a wide circular staircase. A chandelier the size of a small car hung glittering high above her head.

No doubt about it, she'd entered an honest to goodness castle.

"I'll show you to your room to give you a chance to freshen up," Phillipe told her, his voice echoing slightly off the massive walls.

"If you would follow me," he added. If he had any indication of just how awestruck Elle was, he showed no sign of it. Though she was certain her wonderment had to be written all over her face. She'd never seen such a magnificent structure in her life, let alone been inside one. To think, she'd be living here. A week ago what she'd been referring to as home was a dark, six by six foot room in the basement of a hotel with one solitary light bulb hanging from the ceiling as her only source of light.

Phillipe cleared his throat, looking at her expectantly. That's right. He'd asked her to follow him. Fully expecting to be led up the staircase, she was surprised when he led her around the sculpted banister instead and through a wide hallway behind the steps. He stopped at a glass panel and pressed a button. The wall slid open to one side to reveal a steel door elevator. He motioned for her to step in then joined her inside. A moment later, the doors opened once more to reveal a wide corridor.

"These are the staff quarters," Phillipe explained, removing a key from his jacket pocket as he led her to a wooden door several feet away. He unlocked it then handed her the key. "This is your personal room, miss. Though I'm certain you will also have lodging in the Granada wing."

She blinked at him. "The Granada wing?"

He nodded. "Where Prince Manuel and Princess Isabel reside with their children."

Right! Her employers. Thanks to them, and Riko, she'd gone from barely having a place of her own to being able to claim two rooms in a castle.

"Maribel, our lead housekeeper," Phillipe continued, "will be by in a few moments to give you a tour and present you with a preliminary schedule." He executed a small bow that Elle mimicked though she had no idea if that was the right protocol. She really was out of her element here. A true fish out of water.

"If you'll excuse me." With that, the man turned and left the room.

Elle clasped a hand to her chest as soon as he was gone. A sliding screen door led to a balcony that overlooked the ocean. The furniture in the room appeared handcrafted and expensive. Again, the feelings of inadequacy she'd managed to brush off during the ride here began to resurface.

Suddenly, she felt completely disoriented and alone. She was in a strange land, where she didn't even really know the language. The resort where she'd worked less than a week ago drew guests and employees from all over the world.

She'd been merely one more visitor there among many. Here, she was a complete outsider. So far, there'd been no sign of the prince who'd invited her here. Now that she thought about it, it had been beyond foolish of her to think that she might have any kind of interaction with him.

No matter. Prince Eriko Rafael Suarez was not the reason she was here. She was here to do a job and nothing more. The sooner she got that into her head, the better off she'd be and the sooner she'd be able to adjust to her new surroundings.

Or so she told herself.

Before she could do any more wallowing, a gentle knock sounded on her door. That must be Maribel, here to show her around. Not a moment too soon.

"Come in."

Elle's breath caught in her throat as the door opened. Then she sighed in relief. Riko had shown up to welcome her, after all.

But her smile froze before it could fully form on her face as she instantly realized her mistake. The gentleman standing before her might have had the same friendly smile and the very same facial features of the man she'd pulled out of the water that day, but there was no question it wasn't him.

Elle's heart sank, but she forced the smile she no longer felt. This had to be Prince Manuel. Riko's twin brother, the man she'd be working for.

The one who had really hired her.

"This is the second time I've seen you in this hallway, big bro. Why don't you just go ahead and ask where she is?" Manny asked with no small amount of glee as Riko rounded the corner and nearly barreled into him.

He adjusted the collar of his shirt and tried to look clueless before he answered. "I have no idea what you might be referring to. I was just on my way to find Marco in order to resume our meeting that was unexpectedly delayed this morning." Never mind that he'd been the reason for that delay.

Manny gave him a knowingly suspicious smile. "Honestly, I have no idea why you bother trying to lie to me. After all these years, you have to know it never works."

Riko shrugged. "It's always worth a try."

"Save it, man. Maribel is taking her around the gardens until Isabel is up to seeing anyone for the day. I already introduced myself. I take it you'd like to find her."

"Fine. You're right," Riko admitted. "Just trying to be polite and cordial." It was the truth. Riko was merely being courteous. It was only polite to welcome Elle to the castle on her first day. He had been the one to hire her, after all. His intentions were completely innocent and honorable. The small voice in his head that wanted to argue that point could easily be ignored. For now.

Riko stepped around his brother to make his way to the back door leading to the royal gardens, but Manny stopped him before he'd gone more than a couple of steps. "Funny thing is," his brother began, "I have no doubt she thought I was you at first."

"That's hardly novel, it happens all the time."

"Sure it does. But you should have seen the look of disappointment on her face when she realized it was me and not you at her door."

Riko decided to ignore that as he resumed his path, as well as the clear tone of mischief in Manny's voice. Though it was much harder to ignore the electricity buzzing along his skin at his brother's words.

...the look of disappointment on her face...

Warmth curled in his core at the thought before he shrugged it off. His brother was probably exaggerating about Elle's disappointment at finding Manny at her door instead of himself. An attempt to try to goad Riko into some kind of response, to see if he reacted at the possibility that Elle might be excited to see him.

Luckily, Riko had managed not to take the bait.

It took him a good ten minutes to find them, the Suarez royal garden being one of the most immaculate and extensive this side of Europe. She stood next to their lead housekeeper, listening with her head tilted to whatever the older woman was telling her. Even with her back turned to him, there was no mistaking the thick, long braid of fiery red hair. An insane image of undoing that braid and letting the thick waves of hair flow through his fingers ran through his mind before he forcibly pushed it out.

Riko felt his pulse quicken as he approached. How utterly silly of him to feel such excitement to see her again. It had only been three days, for heaven's sake. What in the world was wrong with him? He almost turned around before the two women could notice he was there. Which only led to more self-disdain. He was the crown prince of Versuvia. He wasn't supposed to turn tail and run from any woman.

"The children particularly like to picnic in this spot," Maribel was explaining, gesturing to the wooden table and matching child-sized chairs. "They often take their lunches here."

Elle bobbed her head up and down in an enthusiastic nod, then seemed to take a quick note on her phone. It appeared Ms. Stanton was taking her nanny duties seriously already.

Suddenly, Elle's shoulders stiffened and her fingers paused in the act of clicking on her phone screen, as if she'd sensed his presence. She turned to face him slowly when he was just a few feet away. The smile that spread over her face when her eyes met his had his steps faltering.

"I can take it from here, Maribel," Riko said once he'd reached them.

The woman's eyes grew wide at the suggestion. "Are you certain, sir?"

Riko made a show of glancing at his watch. "Most certainly. I could use the fresh air, and I find myself between appointments." He added the latter lie with an almost bored tone to try to sound a bit more convincing.

Maribel glanced between the two of them, still clearly confused. A beat passed before she spoke. "Very well, then. Thank you. I'll go check on dinner." She gave him a single nod and bid Elle goodbye.

An awkward moment passed between them once they were alone. Then they both spoke at once, only serving to add to the awkwardness.

"How was your trip here?" Riko asked just as Elle began thanking him again.

Her laughter at the clumsy exchange served to break the ice, dissolving the discomfort. Suddenly, they were the same people who'd shared coffee and pastries at a small café in Majorca a few days ago.

"I met your brother earlier," Elle said as they began walking along the perimeter of the grassy knoll the two ladies had been standing on. "The resemblance is uncanny," she added.

He let out a huff of a chuckle. "Yes, we get that a lot."

"I'm looking forward to meeting the children when they get back. And Princess Isabel when she's up for it."

"I'm sure they will all be delighted to meet you as well. As will my mother and father."

Elle paused for a moment.

"What is it?" Riko asked. She'd gone several shades paler, her eyes wide.

Then it occurred to him. Of course, she was nervous about meeting his mother and father. More accurately, she was nervous about meeting the king and queen.

He leaned in closer to her. "Relax. They don't bite."

Elle's delight at finally seeing Riko was quickly replaced by trepidation at his words. Maybe it had been foolish of her, but she hadn't actually considered that the king and queen would bother meeting an inconsequential nanny in their son's employ. Though she supposed it made sense. What little she'd seen of this family so far told her they were a tight-knit and close one, royal titles notwithstanding. Of course such people would want to meet the person who'd be looking after their precious grandchildren. She should have thought to better prepare herself mentally for this whole experience.

But then Riko leaned over to whisper something flippant about his parents not biting her, and she could hardly think at all. For a time back in Majorca after he'd left, she'd fancied that she'd imagined how handsome he was, how charming. That maybe her mind had embellished his attributes. Seeing him in the flesh again eradicated any such notion. If anything, he was even more strikingly good-looking. His dark hair glistened in the bright sun, the masculine scent of him reached her nose over the gentle breeze to mix with the salt air of the sea. He'd started growing a beard, which lent a hint of ruggedness to his features. A tingle ran through her hands at the thought of running her fingers over his chin to feel the stubble there. She took a step back before she succumbed to the urge and did something ridiculously silly.

"I probably should have warned you about my brother,"

Riko said as they resumed walking. "He can be a bit of a personality."

She let out a small laugh. "On the contrary. I thought he was quite charming."

Riko gave her a small eye roll. "That's Manny all right. Most people, particularly the ladies, and quite a few men, come to think of it, find him charming. Always been that way." His lips tightened as he said the words, but Elle sensed no malice or negativity behind them.

"You're something of a charmer yourself," she said, surprising herself with her candor. Then figured she may as well go all in and continue. "In fact, one might even call you Prince Charming."

He flashed her a playful smile. "Hardly. Besides, if we're going to discuss fairy tales, I'd say our initial watery meeting is more in line with the story of a different prince, is it not?"

A bubble of laughter rose from deep within her chest. How right he was.

They'd come upon a wall of shrubbery several feet tall, trimmed with precise edges. Riko took her gently by the shoulders. "Come here. I want to show you something."

He led her several feet down the wall until they reached an opening several feet wide.

"It's a maze," he explained, gesturing her inside. "There's a stone water fountain in the center. Think you can find it?"

Elle was delighted at the prospect. But she'd never been very good at puzzles. "I don't have much of a sense of direction," she admitted.

"I'll be right behind you if appear to be getting too lost."

"Then I guess I have nothing to lose by trying."

"That's the spirit."

Bolstered by his encouragement, she dove in and tried several different paths with Riko fast on her heels. It didn't take long before Elle was ready to call it quits. Just when she thought she heard the trickling of the water fountain loud and clear, she took what she thought was the right turn only to have the noise grow fainter.

Throwing her hands up, she turned on her heel to concede defeat. Only she'd completely misjudged how close Riko was behind her.

"Umph!" She'd barreled right into his chest.

A pair of strong, steady arms immediately reached around her to hold her steady. Time seemed to stop as neither one of them moved so much as an inch.

They were completely alone, surrounded by greenery. The shrubs around them tall and isolating. As if they were the only two people in the world. The warmth of his breath against her cheek sent a flame through her middle.

Elle couldn't help but shift her gaze to his mouth, hovering so close to hers.

Heaven help her, he was lowering his head, his arms around her waist tightening ever so slightly but just enough to make her head feel light and woozy.

Something flickered behind his eyes and then a curtain suddenly seemed to fall behind their depths. He pulled his head back, away from hers. Whatever had just happened, the moment was over. Elle couldn't decide whether to feel relieved or rife with disappointment.

Finally, some semblance of sanity crawled back into her brain and made her pull away and step out of his arms. With shaky hands, she smoothed her hair out of her face.

Riko's expression was impossible to decipher. Shadows fell over his features, his eyes remained dark and unreadable.

"I should probably head back to the castle," she said, finally managing to get her mouth to work. "I imagine the children are back by now. Wouldn't want to appear to be slacking on my first day."

Riko's lips tightened just before he took a step back also. Despite the small space between them, she suddenly felt as if it might as well have been a chasm miles wide.

What had just happened?

"I suppose you're right," he said. "We'll save the fountain search for some other time."

Not any time soon, Elle thought as she followed him down the path and out of the maze.

Given the way her heart still pounded in her chest as they stepped into the grassy clearing, one thing was certain—being alone with Riko in such a secluded, private way again would be nothing short of foolish.

She was here to do a job until she could figure out what the future had in store for her. The last thing she needed was to lose her heart along the way.

Riko slammed the door of his study shut and began pacing around his desk. What in the world had he been doing?

Silly question. The answer was clear, wasn't it?

He'd behaved like a hormonal teenager with a woman in his family's employ. For heaven's sake, he'd almost kissed her back there. How inappropriate. He was the heir to the throne. He needed to maintain decorum at all times, behave in a manner fitting his station. Coming on to the family's new nanny definitely fell outside such parameters.

Nothing like that could ever happen again. He had to make sure of it. He had nothing to offer Arielle Stanton.

His future was laid out for him by centuries of prece-
dent. There were expectations he would need to fulfill
as the future king.

His phone vibrated on his desk with a message, pulling him out of his mental rant. When he glanced at it, he
could only shake his head. The irony was almost com-
ical. Like a reminder from the universe, the message
from his father served to emphasize exactly what he'd
just been thinking.

Please see me in my quarters within the hour. Infanta
Gina's visit will move forward.

Riko made his way to his chair and dropped into it
with a huff of exasperation. The king had been working
on getting Infanta Gina to Versuvia for weeks now. She
was the latest candidate his father had in mind to be the
next Princess Suarez.

A potential bride for Riko.

The urge to stride to his father's wing and demand he
rescind the invitation was so powerful, Riko found himself at his door to do just that before he bit out a curse
and returned to his chair.

What exactly would his argument be? That he had
complicated feelings for the children's new nanny?

No, there was no way around it. Infanta Gina would
be arriving to attend the Versuvia National Spirit Festival scheduled in a few weeks' time. And Riko would do
his princely duties and entertain her as expected.

Hands shaking with frustration, he typed out a response to his father. The only response he could send.

Be there in twenty.

It wasn't as if he had a choice. The vision of Elle staring up at him in the maze just moments ago invaded his mind. Her eyes hooded, desire flooding her features. Desire for him.

He hadn't known her for long, but her face was imbedded in his mind. The hazel-green hue of her eyes, the slight upward tilt of her nose, how her hair changed color depending on how and where the light hit it.

By contrast, despite having run into her several times over the years, he'd be hard pressed to recall what the infanta so much as looked like.

Riko made his way to his father's quarters.

The family resemblance was unmistakable. Elle took in the two small faces looking up at her, full of curiosity and wonder. The Suarez genes were strong with these two. Poor Isabel. It appeared her children had inherited very little of their mom's features and quite the cornucopia from their father and uncle.

There she went again. Her thoughts seemed to drift to Riko all too often and much too easily. Being alone with him in the maze, feeling his closeness as they were completely isolated together. Anything could have happened. Heaven help her, she might have let it if she hadn't come to her senses in the nick of time.

Enough. Her sole focus had to be on the present moment. And meeting the children she'd be caring for, for the first time.

The little boy, Ramon, stepped forward with his hand extended toward her. "Pleased to meet you, ma'am. I'm Ramon. I'm six." After letting go of Elle's hand, he pointed to his sister. "This is Tatyana. She's four."

Elle resisted the urge to chuckle at the exaggerated

politeness that bordered on formality coming from such a small human.

"Lovely to meet you both," she said, smiling wide.

The little girl stepped forward, her large brown eyes focused firmly on Elle's face. "I'm four," she declared loudly, holding up three fingers. "How many are you?"

Elle tapped her nose playfully. "Let's just say that to answer I would need all of my fingers and toes and a few more."

That earned her a childish giggle. Elle crouched to get closer to the children's level. "Now that I know how old you both are and your names, why don't you tell me something else about yourselves."

Ramon stepped closer, an excited smile lighting up his face. "I like to play baseball. Like they do in 'Merica."

"That's lovely. Maybe we can play sometimes. I used to play with my sisters in the summer. Back in 'Merica."

Ramon clasped his hands together, excitement flooding his features. Any sense of formality had been completely replaced by pure childish thrill. "Oh, please. Oh, please. Oh, please."

This time Elle didn't bother hiding her chuckle. "You got it. First chance we get outside."

Ramon mimicked swinging a bat then celebrating a successful hit. Elle applauded the pretend home run before turning her attention to Tatyana. "What about you? Is there anything you like to do?"

The little girl nodded enthusiastically, her small chin hitting her chest. "I like stories. Mama reads to me. So does Papa."

"How fun. We can certainly do that too. Maybe we can even make up some stories of our own. Would that be fun?"

"Si!" Both children answered at once.

Elle sat all the way down on her bottom. "Would you like to do that now? Come up with our own story? We could even act it out. Like a play."

She appeared to have their full attention now. Tatyana was practically squealing with excitement, and Ramon stood grinning from ear to ear.

Well, that would take care of the afternoon's activities. "Ramon, would you get me that large pad off the easel in the corner? And a big marker?"

The little boy ran to do as he was told while Tatyana surprised her by climbing onto her lap. Within minutes, the three of them had entered a made-up world full of fairies and rainbows and one very mischievous unicorn.

Not a bad way to start her first day with the children. And not a bad way to keep thoughts of Riko below the surface. For now.

An hour after leaving his parents' wing, Riko wondered if it was too early to pour a stiff drink of *herbero*. The conversation with his father had gone about as well as he'd expected.

Despite Riko's attempts to push back, the king was determined that the formal visit of Infanta Gina move forward as planned. No amount of argument would change his mind.

Riko was usually careful about picking his battles with the king. But this morning he'd fought particularly hard. To no avail.

He needed a distraction. A punishing run along the beach was always an option to vent some frustration. Maybe he'd invite his brother along for a little friendly competition. Manny had beat him the last time; it was time Riko rectified the loss with a challenge to a rematch.

He went in search of his brother only to be the distracted by a squeal of delight coming from the playroom once he reached the Granada wing. That was definitely his niece. And apparently she was having the time of her life, whatever she was doing.

He would have never guessed. The scene that greeted him when he reached the playroom's doorway had Riko doing a double take.

Elle stood in the center of the room dressed as some kind of pirate with his niece and nephew in similar costumes. They were acting out some sort of skit to an audience of Riko's family members. He had to blink to make sure he wasn't seeing things. Was that really his mother and father clapping and laughing to the antics of the three performers before them? His father complained bitterly about having to attend any kind of theater. Yet here he was, paying rapt attention, a wide smile on his face.

Even Isabel was there, upright in a rocking chair, a crocheted blanket covering her lap. Manny stood behind her, his hands on her shoulders while he watched his children and their new nanny act out what was clearly a scene written by the children.

No one even noticed Riko standing off to the side, so engrossed in the little "play" as they were. Finally, Manny looked in his direction but before he could wave him over, Riko gave a small shake of his head to not give him away. He didn't want to disrupt the delightful moment.

His brother turned his attention back to the entertainment, giving his wife's shoulders a little squeeze.

After delivering a few more lines, Elle took the children's hands in her own and they sang a short song Riko guessed was the finale. Afterward, the three of them took a bow. The other adults responded with raucous applause and a standing ovation. Riko joined in, first clapping then with a crescendo of a whistle.

Elle's smile froze on her face and her head whipped in his direction. As he'd intended, she'd had no idea he'd been there.

The shocked expression on her face left no doubt about it.

CHAPTER FOUR

ELLE STOOD FROZEN in her spot, her smile unmoving. How long had Riko been standing there? How had she not noticed his presence? Up until now she'd always been so aware of him. She'd been preoccupied with their little play, anxious beyond words that the king and queen had appeared out of nowhere to watch the little skit Elle had the children create as a way of getting to know them.

Just when she'd gotten her heart rate down enough to actually get through and complete the silly little performance, it had skyrocketed again. Thanks to Riko.

"Bravo!" Prince Manuel shouted, approaching her and clapping. Then he ducked and embraced both of his children in turn. "Who knew you two were such talented thespians."

The queen smiled at her grandchildren. "Indeed, that was quite entertaining, my darlings." She tucked her hand in her husband's elbow. "Thank you all for such a fun display." With that, the two of them walked out of the room.

Little Tatyana ran over to where her mother sat. "Did you like it, Mama?"

Isabel tousled her daughter's hair affectionately. "I absolutely adored it."

Manny returned to his wife's chair and reached for her hand. "I'm glad to hear it, *mi amore*. But I think it's time we get you back to bed. That's enough excitement for one day."

Isabel waved his words away. "I'm fine, Manny. You don't need to be quite so babying," she admonished but with zero venom in her voice.

Manny didn't argue any longer, simply leaned over and lifted his wife gingerly in his arms then began to carry her out of the room.

"Come, you two," he addressed his children over his shoulder. "Help me tuck your mother back into bed." The children followed them, giggling and poking each other playfully.

Which left only her and Riko. Elle swallowed. She hadn't forgotten what had happened the last time they were alone together. In fact, she couldn't get it out of her mind.

"Well done, Señorita Stanton. Color me impressed."

"Thanks. The children came up with the story. They're really quite delightful."

He smiled at her. "I was more so referring to how you seem to have won over my mother and father within hours of arriving. No small accomplishment."

If he only knew. Elle's nerves had gone tighter than a stretched rubber band when the senior royal couple had arrived. "I was petrified. I've never performed in front of an actual king and queen before. Not that it was any kind of real acting I was doing."

"Well, you've clearly won them over."

Elle tried to take the compliment to heart. But she was still nervous about what Riko's family might think of her. So far, so good, it appeared. But she couldn't get too comfortable. She needed this job. And the complication that was her growing attraction to the man standing before her was just that. A complication. One that she couldn't let distract her.

A good start would be to extricate herself from this room and away from his presence.

"If you'll excuse me," she began. "I'll go see about the children."

Riko stopped her with a hand gently on her forearm before she could take a step. "You have some time. The children tend to crawl into bed with their mother around this time of day and they all nap."

"Oh, I didn't realize." There went her excuse to step away from Riko and the temptation that hummed through her entire body whenever he was in close proximity. "I guess I'll just head to my room then until they're ready for me."

He crossed his arms over his chest. "You could do that. But it occurred to me that when I pulled you away from Maribel earlier today, it probably disrupted the schedule set up for you. For instance, have you eaten?"

She had not. In all the excitement since she'd arrived at the castle, it hadn't occurred to her to see about doing so. But now that Riko mentioned it, Elle realized she was downright famished. As if in response, her stomach let out a low growl, clearly audible in the silence of the room. Elle wanted to sink to the floor in embarrassment. This man was probably used to being around the most graceful, most polished women in the world. And here she was, with her stomach loudly grumbling in his presence.

"I guess I'm hungrier than I might have guessed."

Riko threw his head back and released an amused chuckle. "Here." He extended his hand to her. "Follow me. I'll show you to the kitchens and introduce you to the culinary staff."

Elle scrambled for an excuse to turn down his offer. Hadn't she sworn down in the garden that she would do her best to stay away from him? Though she really was rather famished. It wouldn't do for her to faint from hunger on her first day on duty, would it?

Besides, Riko was just being polite. He probably felt responsible for her until she became more comfortable in her new role and with her new surroundings.

They took the same elevator down to the main floor then Riko led her down yet another hallway. She was going to need a detailed map of this place if she had any hope of not getting lost. Honestly, the Suarez castle had to be bigger than the world-class resort on Majorca she'd been just been fired from.

Was that really less than a week ago? It seemed like another lifetime, another reality. Majorca was only a short boat ride away, but once again Elle felt as if she was in a completely different world.

He couldn't very well have had her go hungry. Especially considering he was the reason she'd missed lunch.

As he led Elle through the main dining hall and past the wide stainless-steel doors of the primary kitchen, Riko knew he was only trying to justify commandeering Elle when he'd so recently sworn to himself that he would try to keep his distance.

His phone vibrated in his pocket for an incoming call.

It was Maribel. "Sorry to disturb you, sir. I wondered if you knew where the new nanny might be. I wanted to see if she might be ready for lunch and then a tour of the rest of the palace."

The right thing to do would be to just tell Maribel to come to the kitchen and take over Elle's lunch and touring. But he couldn't seem to bring himself to say the words. Besides, he was already here. What would be the sense in making the other woman go out of her way when he was perfectly capable of the task at hand? Nothing said he and Elle couldn't be on friendly terms. Riko was simply showing his friend where to find something to eat.

"I'm handling it, Maribel. You may tend to your other duties."

A long pause on the other end of the line told him he'd surprised the woman once more. It took a while longer before she answered him. "Oh, I see. In that case, Your Highness, there is a tray prepared for her in the secondary pantry. I'm sure one of the sous-chefs will be able to retrieve it for her."

"I'm sure we'll be able to locate it. Thank you."

"If it's all right," Elle was saying, "I thought I might head outdoors to get some fresh air while I eat."

"That sounds like a lovely idea," he answered. "I can point you to the perfect spot. The patio by the south garden would be perfect on a sunny day such as this one. It even offers a majestic view of the ocean in the distance."

Her eyes lit up. "Would you? Or perhaps you could…"

"What is it?" he asked when she hesitated.

Elle gave a brisk shake of her head. "Nothing. Never mind. It would be too presumptuous of me to ask," she added almost under her breath.

Riko had no doubt what she wasn't risking to ask. She didn't want to eat alone.

What was the harm in joining her? Would it be so bad for him to actually get outdoors during the day, take his midday meal outside until his next international call later this afternoon? Something so simple; eating his lunch outside. Riko couldn't remember the last time he'd done so. Not since he was a child.

And it wasn't as if Elle had any friends in Versuvia just yet. So the two of them enjoying a friendly lunch together was nothing to get worked up about. Besides, what kind of gentleman would he be if he turned down her invitation for a simple picnic lunch her first day here?

"Listen, as it so happens—" he patted his middle for added effect "—I haven't had lunch yet either."

She tilted her head, studying him with a small knowing smile. "Is that so?"

"Would you mind some company while you eat?"

The smile widened. "I would like that very much, Riko."

The way she said his name sent an unfamiliar sensation down his spine.

"No. Thank *you*. I wasn't really looking forward to sitting alone at my desk with a sandwich. This will be an unexpected treat."

Her expression told him she wasn't buying it for a minute. But she didn't say anything, simply followed him to the pantry. Just as Maribel had told him, there was a tray set up with a variety of breads and small tapas dishes, each individually wrapped. A placard with Elle's name etched on it sat on the rack in front.

"Looks like the staff prepared this for you," he told her.

"Wow. That's quite the feast."

"Does that mean you won't mind sharing?"

She laughed. "It would only go to waste if I didn't. We'll probably still have some left over even with the two of us eating."

"Speak for yourself. I happen to be famished. You have no idea the extent of my appetites."

He could have sworn he heard her suck in a breath. Now why had he said it like that? His wording could definitely be interpreted as some kind of double entendre. Granted, it was the direction his thoughts had been heading all day. But he certainly hadn't meant to voice them out loud. Apparently, his subconscious had other ideas.

Riko pushed past the sudden awkwardness in the air by taking hold of the serving tray and pulling it out of the pantry.

He glanced around for a moment, not finding what he was looking for. "What?" Elle asked.

"Maribel usually serves some type of sparkling water with lunch. I'm wondering where that might be."

She tilted her head. "Sparkling water is usually served cold. So my guess would be that it's in the fridge."

Perfectly reasonable assumption. He just needed to ascertain where the fridge might be.

"You do know where the refrigerator is, don't you?"

He wiggled his eyebrows at her in answer. He had no clue. "Aren't those large rectangular appliances that store food?" he asked in an exaggerated tone.

She laughed at that. He could really get used to that laugh of hers. Something dipped in the pit of his stomach whenever he heard it.

"Have you ever even been in here before?" she asked with a playful smile.

"Of course I have. Several times. And each time I was promptly told to leave and that I was in everyone's way as they were trying to prepare the meal. Though in a much more disguised and polite way."

She stepped out of the pantry and crossed the room to another set of doors. "May I?" she asked, reaching for the handle.

"Be my guest."

She pulled one of the doors open and a slight mist of frost drifted above her head.

Huh. Had the palace always had a walk-in refrigerator?

Elle disappeared inside then came back out with two glass bottles. "Bingo," she said, holding up her bounty.

Within moments they were seated at the wicker table on the patio, the bright rays of the sun blocked by a sizable canvas umbrella. Elle unwrapped both sandwiches as he twisted off the caps on the bottles.

"It's absolutely lovely out here," she remarked in between bites.

"Wait until you see it all decked out and decorated for the National Spirit Festival."

"The spirit festival?"

He nodded, swallowed the morsel in his mouth. "It's a yearly tradition the beginning of every summer. Versuvians as well as guests from all over the world will be in attendance."

One of those distinguished guests happened to be a candidate for his hand in marriage. But Elle didn't need to know about that right this moment.

He would tell her. Of course, he would. Only not right now. They were just friends, after all. And he was enjoying her company too much to broach the subject.

First thing tomorrow morning, before Elle started her day, he would stop by and mention that a prominent Spanish noble would be attending the festivities on the personal invitation of the royal family in the hopes that Riko and she would hit it off and the wheels of matrimony would be set in motion. He would also make sure to explain to her that, if given any kind of choice on his part, no such visit would be taking place. That it was singularly the will of the king and queen.

Elle deserved to hear all that from his lips and no one else's. As his friend. He would tell her, he vowed, first thing in the morning.

Elle lay on the most comfortable bed she'd ever had the luxury to sleep on. Although she hadn't done much sleeping despite the fluffy soft mattress beneath her. She tossed from side to side for what had to be at least the dozenth time and groaned in frustration. She wasn't typically prone to insomnia but tonight she couldn't seem to drift off, despite the incredibly long and eventful day she'd just lived through.

The problem was one handsome prince she couldn't seem to get out of her mind. Whenever she closed her eyes, his dark features floated in her mind. The moments she'd spent with him since arriving, every second of their time together lingered in her consciousness. The feel of his palm against the small of her back as he led her around the castle, the slight curve of his lips when he smiled at her, the scent of him.

She couldn't have imagined the desire in his eyes while in the maze, when he'd leaned closer, his breath hot against her cheek. For one ridiculous moment, she thought about letting him kiss her. Maybe she should have. As foolish as it would be to open her heart to someone so inaccessible, it might have been worth the risk of consequences just to be able to taste the man. If only just the once.

Tossing onto her back, she blew out a long, exasperated sigh. She was being fanciful and silly. What was the point of such childish imaginings? She was here to do a job that Riko had been kind enough to arrange for her. Of course she was attracted to him. But she couldn't jeopardize her position as the family's nanny by entertaining lusty thoughts about the future king. Especially while knowing full well that any kind of future with said heir to the throne was an impossibility.

Right now, she desperately needed to get some sleep or she would be useless the following day. Not a good way to start in her new role. The children were absolute darlings from what she'd seen of them so far. But they were spirited and full of energy. Elle would need to be primed and ready if she wanted any hope of keeping up with them.

Plus she was to meet with Isabel first thing in the morning to go over all her responsibilities. Appearing before the princess droopy eyed and tired wouldn't do at all. Was it against protocol to yawn in front of royalty?

A glance at the bedside clock told her it was almost two in the morning. Elle groaned out loud and rubbed her eyes, willing for sleep to come. But it was no use. She'd barely dozed off when her phone alarm rang six hours later.

Elle groaned and turned to her side. How was it morning and time to face the day already?

First things first; she would need coffee. A lot of it. After a quick shower in the private bathroom of her suite, she made her way downstairs and toward the kitchen. The last time she'd walked through these steel doors, Riko had been behind her, touching her, laughing with her.

Elle gave her head a brisk shake and pushed through the doors. She had to get that man out of her head or she was going to be utterly useless. Enough was enough.

"May I help you, miss?" An accented voice stopped her before she'd taken so much as a step into the room.

Elle turned to face a tall, mustached young man in a crisp white jacket and pressed black slacks.

"I was just looking for some coffee." She extended her hand. "I'm Elle, the children's new nanny. I'm afraid I'm still learning my way around."

He actually tapped his heels together! Just like in the movies. "Pleasure to meet you. I'm Sebastian, one of the kitchen staff. Call me Seb. If you'll head back to your room, we'll have a tray delivered to you ASAP."

Oh, dear. Maybe she wasn't meant to be down here. Had she just broken some unspoken rule about being in the kitchens when she didn't work there? She was debating whether to apologize when Sebastian continued. "I will bring it up to you personally," he added with a charming smile. If Elle didn't know better, she may have thought he sounded somewhat flirtatious.

Just went to show, there were plenty of men in the proverbial sea. She really didn't need to spend her days and nights pining over one so far out of her reach.

"Thank you," she answered. "I look forward to it."

"As do I." He gave her a small bow.

When a knock sounded at her door about fifteen minutes later, Elle anxiously swung it open. Only, it wasn't the handsome, friendly staffer she'd met earlier. Riko stood smiling in the hallway. Despite herself, Elle's breath caught in her throat. He was dressed much more casually today. In a Henley type shirt with three buttons at the collar, a shade of green that brought out the dark tone of his hair and eyes. Even first thing in the morning, he looked so devilishly handsome she was having trouble concentrating.

"Good morning."

Between her surprise at seeing him at her door and the way he took her breath away, Elle was having trouble finding her voice.

His smile faded at her continued silence. "Everything all right?" he asked.

Elle managed to pull herself together. "Yes. Everything's fine. I was just expecting someone else."

He lifted an eyebrow. "Oh?"

As if on cue, Seb rounded the corner down the hall, pushing a tray cart full of dishes and one steaming silver carafe. He did a double take as he approached.

The man was just as surprised as she'd been to find the crown prince at her door.

CHAPTER FIVE

THIS WAS WHAT he got for being honorable. The urge to see Elle as soon as he had awoken had been impossible to ignore, despite the unpleasant task he had to see her for. Judging by the way this staff member with the rolling tray was staring at him with his mouth agape, he had to wonder if this was a good idea, after all. He should have found a less private spot to have the conversation about Gina's impending visit. He should have just asked her to meet him for coffee on the veranda.

Now, it appeared someone had already arranged for her to be served with a breakfast tray. Which left Riko standing in this hallway awkwardly while a kitchen staffer no doubt wondered why his prince was outside the door of another employee.

He swore silently under his breath. What if this man was reaching the disastrous conclusion that Riko might be leaving rather than just arriving at Elle's door? Great. He could just imagine the gossip fiasco that idea might generate within the palace walls.

The other man immediately stepped out from behind his trolley and gave Riko a bow. "Your Highness. I'm so terribly sorry. I didn't realize I'd be delivering a serving for two. I'll go remedy that right away."

Riko stopped him before he could turn back around

and leave. "That won't be necessary. I don't intend to stay." He turned back to face Elle. "I was just stopping by on my way to my office to see how the palace's latest hire had fared on her first day and night. I won't be here long."

Elle's lips tightened into a thin line before she spoke. "How very kind of you, Your Highness," she said, her voice stiff. "I had a very enjoyable first day and slept soundly." She'd never addressed him quite so formally before. But he didn't have the luxury of exploring why right now.

"Glad to hear it, Ms. Stanton," he answered. Probably best to refer to her by her surname, given that they had an audience. He shot her what he hoped was an apologetic look before turning to leave. The staffer gave him one more bow as Riko walked past.

Well, that hadn't turned out at all the way he'd imagined. He hadn't even managed to tell her about Infanta Gina. Riko heard the staffer's voice shortly after he rounded the corner.

"Wow. That was unexpected," the man said. "It isn't often the prince himself checks on a new hire personally."

If he wasn't mistaken, there was a level of familiarity in his tone. When exactly had Elle met this man?

Riko couldn't help but linger. Though the impropriety of the situation wasn't lost on him. He was actually eavesdropping. How unbecoming of someone in his position.

Elle's voice sounded tight when she answered. "Probably because he happened to hire me himself. I'm sure that's the only reason."

Did she really believe that? She sounded so convincing. So convinced.

"You didn't need to bring all this up for me person-ally," he heard her tell the other man.

"But I promised to do just that. What kind of man would I be if I went back on my word?"

Elle's soft laughter echoed down the hall, and Riko felt his jaw tighten. This man was clearly flirting with her. And she sounded as if she was enjoying it.

"I also had an ulterior motive."

Riko's pulse picked up. He knew he should move on and stop listening, but there was no way he was going to miss the rest. Ulterior motive, indeed.

"You did?" Elle asked.

"That's right. The kitchen staff and a few others typi-cally get together late in the evening for a bite and a quick drink at the beach after our shifts. I wanted to see if you'd like to join us tonight."

Riko silently willed her to turn him down, to say no. Despite how selfish it was of him to wish such a thing. But Elle's response was almost immediate.

"I'd like that very much. Thank you."

"My pleasure."

It certainly was. This server sounded beyond pleased. Riko could just imagine the satisfaction on the man's face as he stared at Elle. He was no doubt admiring the thick curls of her fiery red hair that she wore in a loose bun atop her head this morning. The way the color of her tank top brought out the highlights in those curls and showed off her slight tan. Riko had half a mind to turn right back around and interrupt them, stop their conversation before it could go any further.

Stop.

It was no concern of his. Elle was the type to make friends and attract suitors. As pretty and outgoing as she was, what human male with breath in his lungs wouldn't take the opportunity to invite her to events and try to get to know her better. Wasn't that exactly what he'd been doing?

And he had absolutely no standing to do so. Certainly less so than the man she was currently speaking with. He was due to entertain the infanta in just a couple of weeks. A woman who might very well become the wife his parents wanted by his side.

He had no right to resent what he was hearing between Elle and this staffer. And he certainly had no right to stand here and continue listening.

With great reluctance, he forced his feet to move down the hall to his study to finally begin some work.

It was going to be a long day. His focus was sure to be shot for the rest of the morning. If not the entire day and into the night, when Elle would be joining her new friends on the beach.

He'd behaved like a completely different person. Elle wanted to believe she might have imagined it, but there was no use denying it. Riko had been very careful to keep his distance this morning when he'd come to see her. Both literally and figuratively. The way he'd answered Seb when the other man had asked about bringing up another breakfast for him left no room for error regarding exactly who she was to him. And here she'd thought maybe they were becoming friends.

Ha! Served her right for even going there. He was heir to a throne. While she was simply a palace employee.

Elle scurried out of the elevator and down the hallway to the room she'd been told was Isabel's. She wasn't running late, but she didn't want to risk running into some kind of delay along the way. This was her first one-on-one meeting with the children's mother, and she wanted things to go smoothly. It was going to be hard enough to stay focused, between her sleepless night and the way the events of the morning kept replaying in her head.

Didn't her father always say her lack of focus was her biggest flaw? Or was it her lack of drive he kept harping on? Probably both.

When she reached and knocked on Isabel's door, she got an immediate response to enter. The princess was propped up on a large four-poster bed when Elle stepped into the room and shut the door behind her.

Isabel's ebony hair fell in waves over her shoulders; a thin crochet blanket covered her up to her waist. Even on bed rest, the woman was stunning. Despite the dark circles under her eyes, and the tight lines around her mouth, Isabel struck a commanding picture. Now this was the type of woman a royal prince fell for and wed.

Isabel offered her a friendly smile and waved her closer. "Come, Elle. Sit and let's chat for a bit," she said in a soft friendly voice.

Elle pulled over the only chair in the room that looked movable.

"I must apologize for being so ill prepared for your arrival," Isabel said, adjusting the pillow behind her to sit straighter.

Elle was taken aback by her words. She hadn't been expecting an apology from a member of the royal family.

Isabel continued. "My pregnancy has not been a smooth one, and I'm a bit less organized than usual."

"Your Highness, there is no need to apologize."

"You must call me Isabel, please."

"If you insist."

The princess nodded once. "I do. And if you won't hear of an apology then at least allow me to thank you for coming to our aid on such short notice. We are so fortunate Riko found you when he did."

"I'm the one who's fortunate, Your Hi—" Elle caught herself. "Isabel," she corrected. "Riko was beyond generous to arrange for my employment."

"Well, you did save him from drowning. I'd say you're still in the lead." She chuckled softly. "To think, given the way he described the incident, we thought he'd imaged you. His recollection sounded preposterous with visions of a mermaid pulling him out of the water."

"I imagine some confusion is fairly common after a traumatic incident," Elle said, though it did strike her ego ever so slightly that Riko had such a hazy recollection of her from that moment.

"Well, however much he remembers, he's spoken so highly of you. I've never heard him sing anyone's praises quite so effusively."

Elle couldn't help but feel touched at those words. Still, be that as it may, Isabel was referring to the same man who'd earlier acted as if he barely knew her.

"He's very kind to do so."

Isabel tilted her head, her eyes roaming over her. "Right. He is indeed a very kind man. Though I dare say, the regard he has for you seems to be particularly high. It's rather uncharacteristic of him to grow so fond of someone quite so quickly."

Elle shifted in her chair, unsure how to respond. As much as she wanted to take Isabel's words to heart, it would be dangerous to assume anything as far as Riko was concerned.

Luckily, Isabel changed the subject and shifted to the

reason Elle was here. "Let's start with the children's schedule, shall we?"

Elle pulled her phone out of her pocket and clicked on the appropriate app then began taking notes. For the next several minutes, Isabel gave her detailed information about the children she'd be caring for over the next several weeks. It was clear that the woman was a very hands-on parent who loved her children dearly. It was hard not to compare that type of upbringing with the one she'd lived herself as a child. She and her sisters had had a revolving door of sitters and nannies with both parents much too busy to make time for family. Even vacations had been taken with paid strangers.

"To conclude," Isabel said, "I will warn you that my son and daughter are perilously close to being spoiled rotten, the way they're doted on by their father, grandparents and uncle. The latter being the worst offender."

That didn't surprise her in the least. Riko's eyes lit up with true affection whenever he spoke of his niece and nephew.

"So, you and I must be united in our efforts to curb all that spoiling, deal?"

Elle smiled and nodded. "Deal."

"And of course, you'll be accompanying them and helping to prep them for their roles in the National Spirit festivities. Has anyone mentioned that event to you at all?"

"Very briefly. And only in passing."

Isabel inhaled deeply then released a long breath. It was obvious she was beginning to tucker out. Elle didn't want the princess to overexert herself on Elle's account.

"But I know there's a detailed file about it in the laptop I was given. I'll be sure to study it while the children are taking their lessons this afternoon."

"Lovely. And perhaps Riko can fill you in on any missing pieces. The biggest concern with the children will be introducing them to all the special guests who will be in attendance. Not least the infanta."

A chill of trepidation ran down Elle's spine. She was about to hear something that would crush her, she just knew it. "Why her in particular?"

"In the event the king and queen get their wish and she's fast-tracked to become the children's auntie."

Auntie? But that would mean...

"She is a top candidate in their eyes as a potential future daughter-in-law," Isabel added, confirming Elle had been right to feel the apprehension spiking through her.

A brick dropped to the pit of her stomach and her vision blurred at Isabel's words. So part of this festival would involve matchmaking for the royal heir.

And Riko hadn't seen fit to mention it to her.

Elle tried in vain to stay involved in the conversation and listen intently to what Sebastian was telling her. But it was no use. Her mind was a mishmash of thoughts. Thoughts that centered around one main theme—Prince Eriko Rafael Suarez.

It had been a mistake to come to the staff beach party tonight. She didn't have the energy or the mental capacity to be sociable right now. Which was a shame. Everyone she'd met so far had been personable and friendly. Bouncy Spanish pop played from a speaker on the sand, with a small bonfire providing just the right amount of heat and light for the group of ten people gathered around it.

All the makings of a fun evening and she couldn't seem to enjoy it.

It didn't help that a lot of the conversation among the partygoers centered around the buzz about the potential new princess-slash-bride who'd be visiting within the week. Apparently, she was a highly accomplished musician with a litany of achievements and awards. With the beauty to match. She sounded perfect.

"So what do you think, Elle?" Sebastian ask.

Think about what? She hadn't even heard the last several things he'd said. "I think you're absolutely correct," she replied, hedging a chance that a universal answer might suffice to whatever his question had been about.

His expression told her she'd guessed wrong. He blinked at her in clear confusion. Then he tipped his head back and laughed out loud. "You seem a bit distracted. Does it have anything to do with your morning visitor?"

How obvious was she? While she scrambled for a response to that impossible question, Sebastian spared her the effort with his next words. "Let me just tell you, it's unheard-of for the prince to be checking in on a member of the staff. I've been working here for over five years and I've never heard of such a thing. He looked like the cat that had been caught with the canary when I turned that corner this morning."

Elle didn't have the wherewithal for the direction this conversation was headed in. Little did Seb know. "He's just being kind, Seb. He hired me personally and wants to make sure it works out." And no doubt, he felt responsible for her, given the way they'd met.

"Si usted lo dice..." he answered. She could guess what that meant. Right now, she just wanted to leave.

"It was so nice of you to invite me out, Seb. But my

battery seems to be draining of all energy. If you'd please excuse me, I think I'm ready to call it a day and head back for some rest," she told him, then turned to wave at the others. Several voices responded with protests but she simply smiled and made a gesture of sleeping, closing her eyes with her hands cupped under her tilted head.

"Sure. I'll walk you back to the palace."

Elle lifted a hand to stop him. She didn't want to cut his night short on account of her sour mood. "No. That's not necessary. I know my way, and I'd hate to take you away from the gathering."

Seb gave a shrug of acceptance and leaned over to give her a friendly peck on the cheek. *"Buenas noches."*

Elle started making her way back, the castle lit up like Lake Shore Drive during Christmastime before her. What part of the building was Riko in right this moment? What might he be doing? Had he given her another thought all day?

What did any of those questions matter to her. They shouldn't. She shouldn't be wondering about him at all.

He hadn't mentioned that the woman his parents wanted him to consider marrying would be arriving in a few short days. Which Elle had no right to even be upset about. Riko didn't owe her that kind of personal information. She was essentially a palace employee, no different from the crowd she'd just been introduced to. The only reason Riko even knew her name was because he'd hired her himself after a chance encounter. An encounter he barely even remembered.

So that was quite enough of her constant girlish romanticizing of Riko.

Elle quickened her pace and summoned up all her resolve as she made her way up the long, paved roadway leading to the main doors. From now on, she was going to know her place. She'd make sure to go to the next staff beach party and she'd be much more outgoing than she'd been tonight. She worked for the royal family, and her rightful place was with the staff.

And she was absolutely going to stop obsessively thinking about Prince Eriko Suarez and imagining there was anything more between them than a simple contractual, professional relationship.

By the time she reached the doors and pulled them open, she was determined to keep to her new resolution no matter what it might take.

Her resolve was tested immediately. When she made it to the castle doors, she literally ran into the man.

CHAPTER SIX

RIKO GLANCED AT his watch yet again. Then he looked up at the tall mahogany grandfather clock that loomed by the doorway as if it might tell him something different.

Isabel had mentioned in passing that Elle had left the castle. His niece and nephew were already in bed at this hour. Which meant she'd taken the man's offer from this morning to join him at some kind of beach party the staff was attending. The same party where she'd be meeting up with the handsome staff member who'd personally delivered her breakfast this morning.

Well, good for her. Riko was glad she was getting acclimated and getting to know the others who worked at the palace. This was her personal time to do with as she wished. To spend with whoever she wished. And anyway, it was none of his concern, really. So why was he down here pacing the foyer instead of studying the spreadsheets that urgently required his attention before tomorrow morning?

Because he hadn't been able to concentrate on any of the numbers for more than a few seconds at a time. He'd nearly launched his tablet across the room and against the wall in frustration after his umpteenth attempt. For someone who normally prided himself on focus, it was beyond galling. All because he couldn't stop thinking about what Elle might be doing at that party and who she might be doing it with.

Maybe he'd take a walk along the beach. Though it was completely against protocol for him to try and crash a staff event, that wasn't necessarily what he'd be doing. It was a beautiful night, after all. Even the prince couldn't be faulted for wanting to get some air.

Who was he kidding?

The staffers would be suspicious; he'd never randomly appeared at one of their events before. And Elle would see right through him.

Riko bit out a curse and paced some more.

Then he made a decision. While he'd sensibly established that he couldn't very well crash this get-together, getting some air would actually do him some good. That's all he would do; he wouldn't even go near the beach where Elle might be with her new friends. Besides, he couldn't very well just stand here pacing a track on the Italian marble tiled floor. He didn't even want to think about the possibility of Manny appearing and asking him what he was up to. The teasing would never cease if his brother even suspected the source of Riko's agitation right now.

His mind made up, he strode to the door and yanked it open, startled to find Elle on the other side. Though "finding" wasn't quite the correct term. Rather, he caught her just as she was about to topple through the doorway.

"Oh!"

Riko took a moment to process what was happening. He'd just been agitated and pacing about, wondering what Elle was up to. Now, she was literally falling into his arms. It was almost an exact replay of what had happened yesterday in the maze.

She straightened, her eyes wide with shock. His arms were still wrapped around her waist and shoulders; he knew she'd regained her balance but hesitated letting her go just yet. She felt so right where she was. With him holding her, her skin warm everywhere it touched his.

"Uh, hi there," he finally managed to say. "Nice of you to drop in."

Pretty terrible attempt at humor, but he wasn't exactly operating with all his wits about him at the moment.

"Riko. I…uh…was about to open the door when it disappeared from my grasp. I guess I lost my balance as a result."

He almost thanked her for doing so then stopped himself. How inappropriate. As was the way he still held her, tight against him in front of an open doorway right in the foyer where anyone could walk by. With great reluctance, he finally released her.

"I apologize," he began after the two beats it took regain his senses. "I didn't mean to startle or unbalance you. I was just headed out to get some air. Is that what you were doing?" he couldn't help but ask, though he knew he had no right to.

"No. Well, sort of. I was out with some other staffers. They were having a little get-together on the beach."

He made a show of lifting his wrist to look at his watch. Totally unnecessarily. He knew exactly what time it was; he'd been staring at his blasted watch for the past half hour. "Kind of early still."

She shrugged. "I just didn't have the energy or stamina. I had a bout of insomnia last night. I'm afraid it's finally caught up to me."

So, she'd been fibbing this morning when she'd told him how well she'd slept. How curious. "Sorry to hear that. Was the bed or room not to your liking? We can see about other accommodations if that is the case."

She shook her head. "No. It was all lovely. One of the most comfortable beds I've ever slept on, in fact. That wasn't the issue," she said, not looking him in the eye for some reason.

"Glad to hear it. You know, we happen to have a cure-all for insomnia in this part of the world."

"You do?"

He nodded. "It's called horchata. A very soothing, warm drink that brings immediate calm."

"What is it?"

"Around here we like to make it with almond milk. Along with some real vanilla and a touch of cinnamon."

She licked her bottom lip at the description and he had to turn away. "That sounds delicious."

"We could try some now. There's always a pot of it brewed and kept warm in the sitting hall. If you're not too tired that is."

"Not too tired to turn down such a tempting sounding treat. But I don't want to impose on you. Didn't you say you were heading out to get some fresh air?"

If she only knew. The only reason Riko had even felt a need to get out had been because he hadn't been able to stop thinking about her. Now, here she was. He couldn't very well tell her that, of course.

"Hmm. I did. But now I find myself craving the horchata I just told you about. But I might have a way to do both."

About ten minutes after she'd stumbled through the front doors and into Riko's arms, Elle found herself sitting outside under the sparkling stars. The veranda Riko had taken her to was expansive, decorated with several potted plants taller than even her companion. She could hear the ocean in the distance, the sea breeze carrying the scent of the sea and sand with it.

She took another sip of the horchata from her porcelain mug. Riko was right. It was delicious and went down smooth, in a calming and relaxing way. The taste of almonds and subtle vanilla lingered on her tongue after swallowing. The dusting of cinnamon added just the right amount of spice. Between the delicious soothing drink he'd served her and the romantic setting, she was finding it harder and harder to remind herself she was annoyed with him.

She had to wonder if he had any idea that the palace staff was already speculating about the infanta who might be his intended.

"You appear deep in thought," he said, pulling her out of the questions running through her head. Questions that were beginning to dampen the tranquility she'd been enjoying up until they surfaced. "What are you thinking about?" he added after a beat.

If only she could tell him the truth. Somehow let him know that she was drawn to him in a way that both surprised and horrified her. That she was more aware of him than any man she'd ever encountered. The way the corners of his mouth crinkled when he flashed her that devilish smile. How he made her stomach flutter whenever he walked into the room.

How much it bothered her that he'd be entertaining a woman next week whom he'd most likely propose to.

No. She had to keep all that to herself. It was her burden to bear, the way she felt about him, how swiftly and strongly her feelings had developed in such a short time.

She offered a small fib instead as her answer. "I was just thinking how I haven't called my sisters in a while. They're probably getting antsy about my lack of contact."

"Hmm. You should remedy that first thing, then. I myself am quite aware how pesky siblings can be."

She chuckled at that, relieved the conversation had steered toward a subject that allowed her to keep her head straight. "You and your brother seem close."

"Are you close with your sisters?"

She shrugged; the answer to that question was complicated. "Mostly. I'm the youngest of four. And they're all rather protective to the point where they can be a bit smothering."

He took another sip of his drink, his eyes trained on her over the rim of his cup. "Tell me about them."

Elle shifted in her chair. When he found out how accomplished her sisters were, she was going to appear so much less successful in comparison. She was proud of all her sisters, she really was. Loved them all dearly. It was just that her accomplishments were so trivial compared to all that her three older siblings had done. A fact not lost on their parents.

"Well, Maysie and Trina are doctors, like my mom. And Lizzie's an attorney like my father."

Riko merely lifted an eyebrow, so she continued. "I was supposed to follow in Lizzie's and my dad's footsteps and complete the circle."

"But that wasn't the life you wanted," Riko suggested.

Elle put her cup down, leaned her elbows on the table. "I tried. I really did. I studied international politics in college then applied to law schools throughout the Midwest. And then when the time came, I just couldn't do it."

"Let me guess. Your father was disappointed."

She nodded, her mind calling up the memories of that awful afternoon when she'd announced her intention to cease her studies. The looks of disappointment on her parents' faces. The disdain in their voice. Prominent attorney that he was, her father was impossible to argue with. She'd stammered and stuttered, sounding exactly like the scatterbrained young nitwit her parents were convinced she was.

"They both were, Mom and Dad. My sisters weren't exactly thrilled either. Turns out one's family isn't terribly enthusiastic when you announce that you're quitting school to join a traveling band to sing for a living. They were certain I was throwing my future away."

"But you did it anyway. You followed your dreams."

She had. Though she hadn't managed to achieve any level of success. "Maybe. But I didn't get very far. The band broke up. And I was on another continent from home with no other prospects. A complete failure."

His forehead creased. "You can't really think that."

"What other way is there to think? I fell flat on my face. Just like everyone warned me I would."

"Or you've hit a small obstacle until another opportunity comes along. In the meantime, you're gainfully employed helping to care for two children whose mother is temporarily not able to."

"It's kind of you to say that, Riko. Thank you."

He shrugged. "I only say it because it happens to be true."

"Unfortunately, my parents and sisters will not see things in quite so favorable a light. My last conversation with my father back in Majorca involved a lot of 'I told you so's."

"I'm sorry to hear that, Elle. He might come around."

She shook her head, sadness washing over her. In her father's eyes, she was a failure and probably always would be. "I don't think so. But thank you for trying to make me feel better. I've just come to accept that I'll never be the daughter my mother or father hoped that their youngest child could be. Certainly not comparable to their other children."

He released a long sigh. "Family expectations can be quite the burden, can't they?"

She studied him as a heaviness fell behind his eyes. "You sound like you might be speaking from experience."

She would be guessing correctly.

"I can't imagine having your parents also be your king and queen. What is it like?"

Riko wasn't sure how the subject matter had turned to him. Surprisingly, his first impulse wasn't to shut the conversation down as he normally would whenever he was asked a personal question. Instead, he found himself wanting to open up to Elle. To tell her exactly how heavy it weighed on him that he would be the inheriting the throne. To tell her how he'd been experiencing anxiety attacks ever since it had truly sunk into his brain that he would be the one leading this island kingdom someday soon. Attacks strong enough to wake him up at night.

Maybe it was the novelty of simply sitting with a friendly face, someone willing to listen who had no real connection to the royal family he was part of. He'd never had the pleasure of a casual conversation with a friend sitting outside on a pleasantly warm evening with the clear night sky overhead. Or maybe it was just so Elle could see she wasn't alone in the pressure that her family unduly forced on her. That sitting right across from her was a kindred spirit who could relate to such pressure.

But he couldn't deny that was only a portion of it. The rest was more selfish on his part. This was the most relaxed he'd felt since childhood. And it had everything to do with being in Elle's company.

He toyed with his cup, now empty, before answering her question. "It can feel overwhelming, to be honest," he confided, surprising himself some more. "It's much harder to defy your father when he also happens to be ruler of your nation. And your mother because she's also the queen."

Her eyes softened with understanding and sympathy. Which encouraged him to add, "So I just made sure to not defy them."

Then he went on. "I studied what they and the kingdom expected me to study. After university, I served in the Versuvian military, and I learned everything there was to know about Versuvia and its history."

"What did you want to study?" she asked.

"When I was very young and didn't know any better, I liked to sketch and draw. If given the choice, I might have pursued architecture."

"But you weren't given the choice."

He shook his head. "I studied economics and European history instead. Just as my father did. Much more acceptable fields for future kings."

"Do you still sketch? Even just for fun?"

Riko blew out a puff of air. He couldn't remember the last time he'd held a pencil and clear sheet of sketch paper. "No. I put it behind me. What would be the use? Even if I wanted to, I would hardly have the free time."

"I'm sorry to hear that, Riko. That you had to give up something that you enjoyed and were talented at."

He chuckled at that. "I have no indication that I had any kind of talent. Didn't pursue it long enough to find out."

The small smile she gave him made him want to reach over the table and take her hand in his. He leaned back in his chair instead, increasing the distance between them before he gave in to such an impulsive and foolish urge.

"I have no doubt you're talented. You seem to be good at a lot of things." She looked down after speaking, as if surprised she'd said the words.

Riko cleared his throat, disarmingly touched by the statement.

The conversation was a getting a bit too heavy, and he was getting dangerously close to sounding like a poor, self-pitying prince when he had a life more privileged than most, so Riko decided a change of subject was in order.

"If only Manny had had the courtesy to arrive first by mere minutes, he would have been the one to deal with all the protocol and expectations, leaving me to a life of carefree luxury."

She laughed. "I agree. That was very rude of him."

"Well, he's always been rather inconsiderate. Isabel is a saint for putting up with him. The children definitely take after her. Luckily." He offered a silent apology to his brother for using him as a distraction in such a ridiculing way. Manny would understand if he were here.

"Well, your brother has been lovely to me so far. As has Princess Isabel. And the children are absolute delights. They're quite looking forward to the national day festivities." The smile faded from her face and her voice caught as she mentioned the event. She ducked her head before continuing. "I understand there will be visitors arriving from all over Europe to join the celebrations."

When she looked back up again, the reason for her question hit Riko square in the chest. She'd heard about Infanta Gina and why she would be arriving in Versuvia in a few days. He should have found a way to tell her himself after being thwarted that morning at her door by the staffer. Foolish of him to not think that it would come up in her conversations with others. For all he knew, the staffer was the one who let the cat out of the bag, trying to get into Elle's good graces by showing off how well informed he was.

First things first. He had to make amends with Elle.

A torrent of conflicting emotions collided in his chest. That Elle might be affected at the thought of him spending time with someone else warred with the truth that he had no right to feel any kind of pleasure at that knowledge. Added was the guilt that she'd had to find out from someone else. He felt like a heel in more ways than one.

"Elle, every once in a while my father insists on having me entertain someone he refers to as 'fitting.' As modern and progressive as he is, there are certain things he's still rather traditional about." Stubbornly so, he added silently.

She held a hand up before he could continue. "You don't have to explain anything to me, Riko."

Maybe she was right. The only problem was, he wanted so badly to do exactly that.

CHAPTER SEVEN

THE FIRST DAY of the National Spirit Festival always seemed to bring on a buzz of excitement throughout the kingdom. Riko felt it in the air as soon as he began his morning.

The text from his father that had been waiting for him when he'd awoken served to further heighten his spirits. Apparently, Infanta Gina would have to delay her arrival due to a labor dispute within her country's borders. She wasn't sure how long she might be put off as she mediated the negotiations.

Riko had nothing against the woman. In fact, the few brief interactions he'd had with her in the past had been perfectly pleasant. And he certainly hoped any strife within her nation was resolved quickly so that she may travel again. He just hadn't been terribly enthusiastic about her arrival. He'd wanted to be able to enjoy the day of festivities without having to play charming suitor under his dad's scrutiny. Was that wrong of him?

Not if he kept those thoughts to himself, he figured.

A nagging voice in the back of his mind teased that he had a deeper reason for wanting to be free of the infanta a little longer. One that brought to mind hazel-green eyes and wavy red hair.

He pushed that thought aside.

The celebrations would start late morning with games and activities set up on the palace grounds for young children. He and Manny along with his parents always gave out prizes to the winners of various games and challenges. A few of which he even participated in.

Of course, Elle would have to be there to accompany his niece and nephew. He hadn't seen her since their time on the veranda. He had to wonder if that was by her design. Did she regret the way they'd confided in each other?

Just as well. As much as he enjoyed her company, he had no right to seek it. Now that Elle was acclimated in her new role and her place at the palace, there was no reason to keep checking on her.

A sinking feeling manifested in the vicinity of his heart. He hadn't intended it, but he'd grown quite fond of Elle's company. Being with her felt freeing and easy. As if he could be his true self without fear of dropping the prince face mask. In a different reality, he would have pursued what it meant that Elle invoked such carefree feelings in him.

Still, he didn't regret a single minute of that time on the veranda with Elle, simply chatting. Today, he'd take the opportunity to speak to her again about what the deal was with Infanta Gina. That he had nothing to do with her impending visit. The king had made the arrangements with zero input from Riko. Maybe he was being presumptuous in assuming that Elle should know that. But be that as it may, it was important to Riko for her to know it.

When he made it out to the grounds, there was already a flurry of activity. Several stands had been set up. The obstacle course and path for the three-legged race were arranged in their usual spots in the middle of everything.

A deejay was setting up across the square near a temporary wooden stage and in front of an impromptu dance
floor. There'd be music and dancing all day.

Riko was looking forward to it all even more so than
usual. A large part of that could be attributed to seeing
Elle's reaction to it. What was she like when she was simply having fun? He wanted badly to find out.

As if he'd summoned her with his thoughts, Riko
sensed the moment Elle stepped outside. He turned to
greet her, beyond pleased with the look on her face.

"Oh, my," she said breathlessly when she reached his
side. "I came out to see what all the commotion and noise
was that I'd been hearing since the wee hours."

"Good morning."

"Morning. This is quite the production."

"Just wait until it's in full swing."

She smiled, scanning the grounds. "Well, there are
two little ones inside having breakfast that are having
a great deal of trouble waiting for it." Her smile faded.
"It's too bad Isabel can't participate. She's been talking
about it endlessly."

"I'm sure Manny will figure out a way for her to at
least watch some of the events," he reassured her.

"I hope so. The children are beyond excited about the
day, but Tatyana in particular seems sad that Isabel won't
be able to take part."

"It's a good thing they have you to step in."

"Care to tell me exactly what I'm in for?"

Riko gestured toward the obstacle course. "Well, I
have no doubt you'll be dragged into both those races.
Will absolutely have to get your face painted." He pointed
toward the stage. "Plus there's a lot of dancing in your

future. And food. Lots and lots of food. There'll be everything from empanadas to flan."

Elle laughed. "I think I can handle all that. Though the children are going to be exhausted."

"As will you."

She chuckled once more, and the tightness that had grown in his chest at the thought that Elle had been avoiding him loosened.

She looked away, her gaze focused on the field before she spoke. "But won't you be too busy entertaining the infanta once she arrives?"

"Turns out Infanta Gina will not make it today, after all. She sent her deep regrets and is not quite certain when she might arrive."

If Elle had any kind of reaction to that bit of news, she managed to conceal it completely.

"I hope everything is all right," she said after several beats of silence. Riko had been about to ask if she'd even heard him.

"Nothing concerning. She's just busy with some official business that's keeping her from leaving the country just yet. I'll be free to roam around and enjoy the festivities with everyone else all day."

"I see."

Again, he waited for some kind of real reaction. Once again, he waited in vain.

She had to get her inconvenient jealousy in check. Elle strode through the main hallway and toward the children's dining area trying to get her breathing under control. The amount of relief and giddiness she'd just experienced upon learning that Infanta Gina wouldn't be arriving today had shocked her through to her core.

She'd had no idea how badly she'd been dreading the infanta's visit. The sight of Riko accompanying her around the palace, how he'd grant her all his attention...

Despite herself, she'd spent a considerable portion of her evening the previous night scrolling through social media posts about the woman. She looked more and more beautiful with each photo Elle had found of her.

She'd made sure to avoid Riko these past few days to get used to the idea that she'd be staying away from him once his guest arrived. Now, given the reprieve, Elle wasn't sure how to react. After all, the reprieve was only temporary. Infanta Gina would be here soon enough.

Then she'd have to go through the same dread that she'd been dealing with all over again. No, best to stick to her original plan to stay away from Riko. She could do it if she really set her mind to it.

Two hours later, Elle realized just how wrong she'd been to think that. Her plan was utterly doomed to fail. She didn't stand a chance.

The children made a beeline for their uncle the moment they saw him upon arriving at the festival, which was now in full swing. It appeared the entire kingdom was on the palace grounds. Hordes of children ran around, loud bouncy music echoed through the air and some kind of folk dance performance was happening on the stage with a line of dancers in full costume. She had no choice but to follow Ramon and Tatyana to where Riko stood in the center of it all. He was dressed much more casually than usual in a pair of tan slacks and a V-neck sky blue short-sleeved top that fit him like a glove and showed off his toned chest and muscular arms.

Stop it.

"Uncle Riko!" Riko's face broke into a wide smile as

soon as he saw them. Bending down, he somehow managed to grab hold of both children and lift them in the air to loud shrieks of delight before lowering them to the ground.

Elle stifled a gasp at the image. The man would make a wonderful father someday. Oh, dear. That was exactly the type of thought she had to make sure to avoid. True or not.

"This is quite the gathering," she said when she reached them.

"Trust me, it's just getting started," Riko answered, while simultaneously tousling his nephew's hair.

"Uncle Riko, I bet I can beat you at the crown toss again this year," Ramon declared, tugging on his uncle's pant leg.

"I wouldn't be so sure about that, little man," Riko answered, with mock seriousness.

"Let's go see!" Ramon demanded, not waiting for an answer as he turned and ran to a gold canvas tent that had all sorts of games set up inside.

"I wanna try too," Tatyana shouted, following her brother.

Riko and Elle trailed behind. "Beat you again? You let him win, don't you?" Elle asked needlessly. She was pretty sure she knew the answer.

"Maybe," he answered in a hushed tone. "Or maybe I just have really bad aim."

"Sure you do." She highly doubted it. From what she'd seen so far, Eriko Suarez wasn't bad at anything.

Sure enough, when they reached the table with a slew of plastic crowns and a short pole in the center, Riko was comically off target. Ramon managed to toss the crown onto the pole after his tenth try.

"I won! I won!" the little boy shouted, pumping his fist and earning a laugh from his uncle. Tatyana had seemingly forgotten the object of the game and was simply putting the crowns on her head.

"Let's do the leg race now!" Ramon shouted, running out of the tent and across the field to where several people were already gathered.

Ramon picked up one of the burlap sacks lying on the ground and stuck one leg in. His sister ran over to join him and did the same, sticking her leg in the same sack her brother had stepped into.

Elle's stomach froze as she realized what was bound to happen next. If Ramon and Tatyana were sharing a sack, and Riko intended to race too, then that would mean…

"Come on, Elle," Riko said, bending to retrieve one of the empty bags and stepping his right foot into it. "We'll have to let them win this too." He motioned to her left leg.

Elle thought about saying no, desperately wanted to do just that. But then she looked at the expectant faces of the two children. Their smiles as they waited patiently for her to do as Riko asked.

It was just a silly race. She could do this. They wouldn't even really be running; he was going to allow the children to win. If she was lucky, they wouldn't take more than a step or two. That had to be what Riko was thinking. It made sense. With a deep breath, she stepped into the bag and tried in vain to ignore the warmth of Riko's body so close to hers. The scent of him filling her nostrils.

A horn sounded behind them and the children took off. To her shock, Riko did the same. He apparently had no intention of going slowly. Elle wasn't prepared. She tried her best to keep up, but it was no use. They'd only gone three or four steps when she completely lost her balance. She was going down, and she'd be taking Riko with her. There was no way to stop it.

The next instant, she felt a pair of strong arms wrap around her waist. Instead of the impact with the ground she'd been expecting, she was cradled. Somehow Riko managed to catch her before she fell and twisted around so he would hit the ground first.

She landed square on top of him.

It took Riko several moments before he could catch his breath. Not necessarily because he'd just had the wind knocked out of him. No, it was more because of the woman sprawled over him. The same woman he hadn't been able to stop thinking about since he'd met her, the one who'd crept into his dreams at night and into his thoughts during his waking hours. Plenty of those thoughts had come up with exactly the scenario he was in right now—him flat on his back with Elle draped atop him.

Well, maybe not the exact scenario. Actually, the pictures in his mind had been quite different. Also, they hadn't been surrounded by laughing children with a crowd of other onlookers watching in amusement.

Elle appeared stunned, her wide eyes boring into his. Heaven help him, then those hazel-green eyes fell to his lips, desire and invitation clouding her irises. He gasped for the air that hadn't quite made it into his lungs yet. If it wasn't for their audience, he wouldn't hesitate to take her up on that invitation. And make a few of his own.

He couldn't be sure how much time went by. One thing he was certain of—he had no desire to let her out of his arms just yet, despite their surroundings.

Her tongue darted out to her lips and heat surged

through his body. The way he reacted to this woman was nothing short of jolting. They were in the middle of a literal festival of people, and all his focus was squarely on her. Only her.

"Guess we lost the race, *cariña*," he said when he finally got his voice to work. The last word came out of its own volition. Darling, sweetheart. He'd never called her that before. He'd never called anyone that before.

Her eyes remained fixed on his, her lips parted. What if he just went for it? the devil on his shoulder asked. What if he just gave in to what he so badly wanted and just took her lips with his own? Despite the crowd, despite the flak that would be sure to follow. He could find a way to deal with the repercussions later. He had no doubt the taste of her would be worth it, even if just for a moment.

Elle's eyebrows lifted close to her hairline, as if she might have read his thoughts. Maybe she didn't need to. Perhaps they were written clearly on his face for anyone to see.

Her breath brushed against his chin in puffs. She felt soft and warm everywhere her body touched his. She scrambled in a futile effort to get off him. Of course, it was no use. They were literally tied together at a limb. The squirming only served to heighten his awareness of how intimate their position was.

The sudden sound of an airplane flying above was immediately followed by a chorus of cheers erupting around them. The skywriter. The king employed one every year on the first day to write patriotic message high among the clouds. The feat was one of the most anticipated events of the festival. Everyone anxiously waited to learn what this year's inspiring words might be. As far as Riko was concerned, he was just grateful for the distraction it provided at the moment.

Elle made yet another futile effort to flee. He stilled her with a finger under her chin, lifting her face to his. "Elle."

A glance around told him everyone's attention was still focused on the show overhead. All except for the two of them. They were so close now, a hair's width separated their faces. He couldn't take any more. He leaned even closer and brushed his lips to hers, ever so softly. Just enough to finally get the taste of her he'd been craving for so long. Without lingering he pulled back. Anyone watching would not have even noticed the subtle and rapid touch of his lips to hers.

Elle's eyes squeezed shut. She was trembling in his arms now just as he was shaking inside. Heaven help him, now that he'd tasted her, he couldn't wait to do it again.

"Do you two need a hand?"

Riko looked to the side to see a pair of athletic shoes about a foot away from his nose. Then he looked up to find Manny standing over them. Despite his question, it didn't appear he was at all ready to give them any kind of hand. His arms were crossed at his chest. A smirk on his face.

No doubt his brother found this very funny.

Riko ignored him and addressed Elle. "We have got to stop meeting like this," he said in an attempt to lighten the intensity of what had just happened.

Elle didn't bother to acknowledge his poor attempt at a joke. "Maybe if you tried to sit up," she offered.

He tried to do as she said, which only made things worse. To anyone watching, it would appear as if Elle was sitting on his lap. Thank heavens for the distraction of the skywriting show. Of course, Manny had somehow still managed to witness the debacle. Just like the typical thorn in Riko's side that he was.

His brother wasn't even trying to hide his amusement now. His smirk had grown into a wide grin. Riko figured it could be worse. It could be his mother or father standing above them watching this spectacle. Somehow, he didn't think the king or queen would be as amused by the scene as his brother seemed to be.

Elle's face was growing redder by the second. He did his best to kick off the sack. It had gotten good and tangled during their fall and subsequent struggle. Manny still made no effort to help. Darned if Riko was going to ask him to. Finally, the damn thing slipped off. Elle immediately jumped to her feet.

Shame. She had felt really good cradled in his arms, despite the circumstances that had brought her there. Her face was now the exact crimson of the carnation flowers that grew all over the island kingdom. "Elle," he began, not even certain what he would possibly say.

She didn't give him a chance to figure it out. "I'll go find the children," she announced, and practically bounded away.

Riko stood and brushed the dirt off his pants. His brother hadn't so much as moved. But he was now actively chuckling.

Riko glared at him. "You appeared to be enjoying that way too much."

"As did you, big brother," Manny said through his growing laughter.

CHAPTER EIGHT

SHE HAD TO have imagined it. It couldn't have really happened. Riko hadn't just kissed her, slight as it had been, while she'd been sprawled on top of him. Heat still burned in her cheeks. Her body still held the warmth of his in every place they'd touched. Her lips still tingled with the taste of him.

Stop it.

She had to stop thinking about it. She had to stop thinking about him. The kiss didn't mean anything. It was barely even a kiss. A mere touching of his lips to hers. Soft and subtle.

So why was her stomach quaking like an active fault line? It had been foolish to go back on her original plan of trying to avoid Riko. She should have done exactly that. Even if the children dragged her to where he was, now she would keep her distance.

That meant no more races where they were tied together, for heaven's sake. Curse the complication that had delayed Infanta Gina's visit. Unlike Elle, the infanta would never get caught in such an undignified position. She probably had too much class. Too much grace.

Just like with her sisters, Elle couldn't compare.

And now she'd be thinking about that kiss to distraction. The last thing she needed. But it was impossible to get Riko out of her head while she could still taste him on her lips.

The rest of the afternoon into early evening passed by with her mind a blur. On automatic pilot, she followed the children from one activity to another, face painting followed by a balloon toss followed by more games. She somehow managed to get them to eat their lunch along the way.

Luckily for her, Riko seemed to be busy with his parents as soon as they arrived. He really was quite different when he was around the king and queen. He appeared stiffer, stood that much straighter.

Not that it was surprising. Parents or not, one had to demonstrate a certain level of decorum around a king and queen.

Glancing at him now across the square, her pulse skipped a beat. His head tilted in the king's direction, he was listening intently to whatever the other man was saying. Riko nodded in agreement to whatever it was he was hearing. Maybe they were discussing how disappointing it was that the Infanta Gina wasn't here. Was Riko disappointed that she hadn't made it? Had he been looking forward to spending time with her at such a fun event? She didn't want to think too long and hard about the potential answers.

Ramon ran over to her, distracting her from the disconcerting thoughts she had no business wondering about.

"This is my favorite song, Ms. Elle," he said, tugging at her pant leg. "Tatyana is dancing with Dad. Will you dance with me?"

She bowed to his height. "I would love to, young man."

The little boy thrust his hand in hers and led her to the makeshift dance floor. The bright afternoon was slowly giving way to a pleasant early evening with the stars faintly beginning to twinkle in the sky.

Elle walked with Ramon to the center of the throng of dancing bodies. The song was a fast and bouncy one. Some hip version of a Spanish pop song.

Ramon didn't so much as dance as hop from one foot to the other with a total disregard for the rhythm. His enthusiasm and energy were charmingly sweet, making Elle laugh at the sight of him.

Elle's gaze drifted over to the right of the stage where she'd last seen Riko with his parents. But the king and queen were the only ones there now. Her eyes scanned the periphery for him though she chastised herself for even wondering. She really had to find a way to stop thinking about the man.

At the next song, Tatyana came over to dance with them and the two children circled around her while trying to outdo each other with goofy moves.

Their antics had Elle laughing to the point of developing a cramp in her middle. She'd grown increasingly fond of them both in such a short span of time. It was going to be hard to walk away from the two of them when the time came.

The amusement suddenly faded and a sadness washed over her that she did her best to mask. It wasn't easy. She couldn't forget how temporary all this was. A year from now, her time spent on Versuvia would be a distant memory. This all may be a once in a lifetime experience for her, but she was nothing more than a blip in the life of the Suarez royal family. And that included Riko. Would he even remember her years from now? When he was crowned king and had a suitable wife as queen, how many thoughts would he give to the woman who'd pulled him onto the beach that fateful day then hired her to work at his family palace?

The odds were he wouldn't give her a passing thought. She was fooling herself if she thought otherwise.

Ramon suddenly stopped midswing, his attention focused on the distance toward the palace. Elle followed the direction of his gaze and saw what had drawn the little boy's attention.

"Mama!" he yelled, then made a beeline to where Manny was wheeling Isabel toward him. Tatyana was fast on his heels a moment later.

Just as well. Elle was suddenly feeling too melancholy to continue anyway.

But a hand on her arm stopped her before she could leave the dance floor. She looked up to find Riko had approached her when she hadn't been paying attention. He gave her a small bow then extended his other hand.

"May I?"

Riko knew he wasn't thinking straight. And that he was about to do something foolish and ill-advised. But he strode toward Elle on the dance floor, approaching her anyway. Today was about celebrating the kingdom. The only woman he wanted to celebrate with happened to be the one standing across him now. Watching her dance with the children had been an entertaining delight. All eyes had been on her. He would guess she probably had no idea.

She also probably didn't notice that no less than three men were getting ready to approach her to ask her to dance, including the staffer who had delivered her breakfast the other day. So Riko had made sure to beat them all to it. More than a few surprised gasps had reached his ears when he'd extended his hand to her.

He didn't much care. Right now, Riko's focus was solely on Elle. The garden lights had been turned on and they cast a golden hue that brought out the auburn highlights in her hair. Her eyes sparkled in the dimming light as the sun slowly began to set. He'd gone from amusement while watching her dance with Ramon to a sensation he didn't want to examine.

She still hadn't given him an answer. Wouldn't that be a gallon of fuel for the gossip mill if his kinsmen witnessed their crown prince being rejected for a casual dance.

Elle must have come to the same conclusion because she finally nodded reluctantly. "It would be an honor, Your Highness," she said before moving her feet to the beat of the song with zero enthusiasm. So, she was back to using his title. That didn't settle well in his gut. She couldn't honestly believe they could be so formal with each other. Not now. Too much had happened between them.

"The children are clearly enjoying your company," he said over the loud music. "Ramon doesn't often dance except with his mother or grandmother."

"I was just trying to keep up with him on the dance floor. Not sure how successful I was."

"It looked all good from where I was standing."

That was the absolute truth. The picture she'd made dancing and laughing with his little nephew on the dance floor was impossible to look away from. No wonder she'd garnered the attention of so many. The irritation and ire that attention drew from him shocked him in its intensity. Sebastian had been standing in the periphery of the dance floor, waiting to make his move, Riko was sure. The other man had made a step in Elle's direction as soon as the children left her side. Riko's need to intervene and stop him in his tracks had been both reflexive and powerful. There was no way he was going to let another man ask her to dance while he drew breath only a few feet away.

He knew he'd surprised his parents with the move. Well, he'd surprised himself as well.

A glance at his father across the way near the stage confirmed Riko's suspicions. His father looked beyond annoyed. So be it.

Elle followed his gaze. Astute as she was, she picked up on exactly what was happening. Not that the king's displeased expression as he watched his son was hard to read.

"Your father looks none too happy."

He wasn't. "We had a bit of a disagreement earlier, that's all. We will resolve it in due time."

He wasn't lying to her. The king made it clear that he thought Riko should have tried harder to reschedule Infanta Gina's visit, that he dropped the matter too easily and should have tried harder to have their respective people secure a set date rather than leave it up in the air.

But Riko had felt nothing but relief at the news that the Infanta Gina had matters to attend to in her country. He was able to enjoy the festival this way, not having to play tour guide and doting suitor to a woman he'd only met a handful of times.

Spending time in Elle's company instead.

"Are you sure that's the only reason?" she asked, her worried eyes still trained on the king.

Just like the other night on the veranda, he found himself confiding in her once again. Stepping closer so he didn't need to shout over the noise, he leaned to speak into her ear. "He's disappointed Infanta Gina couldn't make it today."

Elle's eyebrows furrowed. "Surely he can't fault you for that. You told me it was a decision she made herself over a circumstance that couldn't be helped."

He shook his head. "You're right. What he's faulting me for is not trying harder to convince her how disappointed I am about the delay."

"I see," she answered, her lips tight. "And are you? Disappointed about not seeing her today?"

There was no way to answer that question without admitting much more than he was ready to tell her. So he simply shrugged. "She'll be here soon enough. It's only a postponement. My father is simply used to getting his own way and gets out of sorts when that doesn't happen."

"I see," she repeated, her voice so low that he had to strain to hear her.

For one insane moment, Riko had the urge to just take her by the hand and leave the floor with her. Leave the party altogether. He wanted her all to himself without a crowd of people around them.

And then he wanted to continue what they'd started when she'd fallen on him earlier today during that ridiculous race. How soft she'd felt everywhere their bodies touched. The taste of her lips, the pounding of her heart against his chest. He'd been thinking about that kiss ever since. Saints above, it had only served to whet his appetite. He wanted more from where that had come from.

And he desperately needed to know if she wanted the same. If Elle gave him the slightest indication that she may be interested in exploring something more, then

Riko would do everything in his power to persuade his parents that he wasn't ready or willing to marry Gina.

He stopped any pretense of dancing and leaned in toward her. "I think I've had enough of the pounding music and big crowds for a while. Care to join me for a stroll in a much quieter area of the garden?"

She blinked up at him, worked her lips. "I don't think that's a good idea, Riko," she finally said after several beats.

A flood of disappointment rushed through his core. She couldn't mean because of the children; they were still with their parents. Looked like he had his answer, didn't he?

It was confirmed when she excused herself and walked away as soon as the song ended.

Riko watched Elle's back as she walked away toward the children. The party was in full swing, but he didn't feel much like partying anymore.

Was she simply skittish about pursuing a relationship? The other possibility had his blood pressure spiking. That she might be more interested in the staffer who had invited her to the beach party.

Well, he couldn't just stand out here staring after her. No doubt several eyes were on him right now. Besides, he could use a drink. He'd almost made it to the bar in the main sitting room before the deep baritone of his father's voice stopped him in his tracks. "Son, a word please."

He'd been so lost in thought, Riko hadn't even noticed that both his parents had been fast on his heels.

They entered the room somber-faced and tight-lipped. A palace staffer immediately appeared to wait on them before the king waved her away with a flick of his hand.

The woman left, shutting the double doors firmly behind her. Clearly, she knew how to read a room.

His father didn't wait long to begin. "What in the devil's name are you thinking, son?"

Riko merely lifted an eyebrow.

His father was all too happy to clarify. "Why would you dance with your brother's nanny at all, let alone during such a public event?"

"It was one dance, Father. A silly one at that after the children left her standing on the dance floor." He would leave out the part about at least three other men waiting in the wings to pick up where Ramon and Tatyana had left off.

"So, you felt the need to fill the empty space on her dance card yourself? Is that it?"

Riko inhaled deeply. "If you noticed, Elle didn't stick around to do much dancing at all. She took off after the first song ended." A fact that still stung, he had to admit.

"Well, then, she's got more sense than you do. What are we supposed to tell our press office to say when they're asked about this?" his father demanded to know.

Riko shrugged. "Tell them that Elle and I are friends. I enjoy her company."

The king visibly bristled. "We will absolutely not be telling them that last part. The only woman whose company you should be entertaining is the infanta."

Riko almost chuckled at how ridiculous that sounded. Somehow, he managed to keep it suppressed. "It was just a dance, Father. Nothing more."

His father rubbed a hand down his face, his expression so weary, Riko almost felt the need to apologize. Almost.

"If it makes things any better, I don't foresee any more dancing in Elle's and my future."

His father's features softened ever so slightly. "See that there isn't."

"Yes, sir," Riko assured him, not that it had been his decision in the least. With a respectful bow to each parent, he turned and left the room.

He wasn't surprised when the queen caught up with him a few short moments later in the main hallway. His mother had appeared to be holding back what she'd wanted to say during the king's tirade.

"Son, wait."

Riko closed his eyes before turning to face her, doing his best to summon some of his swiftly dwindling patience. "Yes, Mother?"

She turned to look over her shoulder, as if to make sure no one else was in the vicinity. There was no one. They were alone. So why the cautious glance?

"I'd like you to consider something," she told Riko, turning back to face him.

"What's that?"

"Your father isn't getting any younger. Neither of us are. Please keep that in mind as you follow your impulses."

Impulses. Was that really how she was going to refer to his attempts at having some say in the direction his life might take? "What does that mean exactly, Mother?"

She tilted her head, as if disappointed with his question. "It means he's not the young, energetic man who inherited the throne decades ago. He tires more easily. He needs more rest."

He studied his mother's face. The concern there was unmistakable. "He's not a young man any longer," she added.

Riko pinched the bridge of his nose. "Point taken, Mother. I understand."

She lifted her chin as she studied him. "I hope you do."

With that, the queen spun on her heel and walked back toward the king and queen's wing.

Riko watched her for several beats before making his way back to his own wing, his thoughts even murkier than they'd been just moments ago.

There had to be some kind of mistake. Elle just knew it couldn't be morning yet. She'd only just crawled into bed and shut her eyes. Unlike the insomnia-laden hours of her first night at the palace, she'd been out as soon as her head had hit the pillow. A physically tiring and emotionally exhausting day could do that to a girl, she supposed.

On one hand, she should be surprised that her insomnia seemed to have cured itself. On the other, the same thoughts and images had still managed to invade her dreams. Not surprisingly, they all involved one charming and handsome prince she couldn't erase from her mind even during sleep.

Pictures from the previous day ran through her mind like a slideshow. Dancing with Riko. His arms around her as she fell. The touch of his lips softly brushing against hers. Heaven help her, she could still taste him now over the mint from her nightly toothpaste.

What was wrong with her? How had she ended up in such a position? Pining after a man, thinking of him non-stop. It just wasn't like her. She'd had her share of crushes, had dated a couple of men regularly. None of them had lasted long. She couldn't recall ever actually feeling as if she might be falling for someone.

Just her luck that the first time she had those feelings,

they had to be for a man who was so far out of her reach he might as well be in another stratosphere.

A crown prince. One who was supposed to be entertaining an infanta he might become engaged to.

She groaned as she thought of the way she'd asked him point-blank whether he was disappointed that Gina's arrival had been delayed. What had possessed her to do such a thing? Riko hadn't given her any kind of answer. Which was answer enough in itself, wasn't it? He really was ready to marry the infanta. A woman much more fitting for him given his station in life. Elle would be fooling herself to think otherwise for even a moment.

With another groan of frustration, she reached for her phone where it was charging on the bedside table. Her screen was covered in message alerts when she lifted it. All from her sisters. All said different versions of essentially the same thing.

...saw you online...

...dancing in front of a grand palace...

...an actual prince!

There'd been photographers at the festivities yesterday, plenty of them. She hadn't realized that she'd been the subject of any photographs. Elle felt a jolt of panic spark through her as the thought crossed her mind. Had a photo been taken when she and Riko had been on the ground, during the ever so brief moment when he'd kissed her?

She inhaled a deep breath and aimed for some calm. Surely not, or her sisters would have most certainly led with that. Scrolling through the rest, she was further relieved that no mention was made of any such thing.

The relief was short-lived. At the bottom was a message that was much more serious and much more crushing. Her father.

Are you really over in Europe to babysit, Elle? Isn't it time to come home and begin working toward a real future?

A blanket of weariness settled over her at the words on her screen. Her father was actually referring to her highly appreciated, so far genuinely rewarding, new nanny position as if she were a teenager looking for pocket money hired to watch a couple of toddlers during their parents' date night.

Well, he might be a brilliant and successful man, but in this case he was wrong. Elle already adored Tatyana and Ramon. Manny and Isabel had made her feel more like a family friend than an employee since she'd arrived. She was responsible for making sure the children did their studies, ate at their scheduled times, and were entertained and safe in her care. So much more than simply babysitting. Of course, her father would never see it that way, even if she bothered trying to explain. The two of them didn't often see eye to eye on much, if anything.

She didn't have it in her to reply to him. What would she even say? Or to her sisters for that matter.

Reluctantly, she got out of bed though it was so tempting to crawl back under the covers and hit the snooze button. But that was a slippery slope. And she didn't want to be late for the second day of the National Spirit Festival.

Another alert sounded on her phone just as she was

done showering. Worried that it might be her father again to drive his point home, or her mother this time, Elle hesitated. But it was Isabel's contact info that appeared on her screen when she glanced at it. A text requesting to meet with her before she gathered the children from their breakfast.

Curiosity piqued, Elle made her way to Manny and Isabel's wing. The princess lay reclined on her bed again this morning when Elle entered the room.

"Good morning, Elle," she said, greeting her with a warm, friendly smile. "I hope you slept well."

"Like a brick," Elle answered.

Isabel blinked at her in confusion.

"Sorry. It's an American idiom that doesn't translate well."

"Hmm." She patted the mattress next to her. "Come sit, dear. There's something I need to run by you."

"What is it?" Elle asked, sitting on the bed.

"Part of the celebrations tomorrow evening involve a symphony concert followed by a rather formal dinner."

"That sounds lovely. How will the children be participating?"

"That's just it. They won't be. The concert is rather late, past their bedtime."

Sounded like she might be about to get the evening off. Which should have been welcome. But Elle wasn't sure what she'd do with herself.

But Isabel's next words threw her for a loop. "With the absence of Infanta Gina, there'll be an empty chair in the box and an uneven number at the table. It just won't do given how many pictures are taken at these things."

Elle merely nodded, not sure what any of this might have to do with her.

"I was wondering if you might attend both events. Just to sort of fill in."

It was Elle's turn to be surprised. "Me? I don't understand."

Isabel smiled at her. "Well, I simply don't have the time or energy to try to come up with a replacement for the infanta at this stage. And Manny is of absolutely no help. And such mundane matters are beneath the king and queen."

Elle stammered for a way to respond. She was certain to feel and look out of place. But the concept of attending royal events as an actual guest seemed like a once in a lifetime opportunity too good to pass up. On the other hand, what if she made a fool of herself by using the wrong fork or something?

"Would you like to attend then, Elle?" Isabel asked. "I know it's short notice, but the schedule really has gotten rather chaotic given the change." She glanced outside the window. The sky was gray and covered in rolling clouds. "And it looks like we're going to have to postpone today's festivities given the weather. Just adding more overall chaos."

Elle swallowed through the confusion causing a rock-like lump in her throat when Isabel delivered the coup de grâce. "Consider it a favor to me."

How in the world would she say no to that? One didn't simply turn down such a request from a princess.

"It would be an honor," she told her. "Thank you for thinking to ask me."

"Well, if I'm to be honest, I should tell you that it wasn't originally my idea."

"Oh?"

Isabel shook her head. "I must admit that it was Riko's idea."

Elle tried to hide her reaction at that bit of news. Riko had been the one to think of her?

"Huh."

"That's right. He mentioned you've been pursuing a career in music before being waylaid for a while. He thought a concert would be something you might enjoy."

Elle's mouth went dry. "How very kind of him. I will have to thank him first chance I get."

CHAPTER NINE

ELLE STEPPED BACK into her room to try and regroup before going to get the children for the day. She was still processing what had just happened and exactly how she felt about it.

The morning had grown even darker on her way back, casting shadows over the walls and furniture. It had been Riko's idea to invite her. She didn't dare look too far into that. She'd simply been the easiest choice—free for the evening and already residing at the palace. Thoughts of Riko brought other questions to mind. Like how good would the man look in a tuxedo? Would they be sitting anywhere close to each other at the concert? Or at dinner?

Her phone dinged. Her sister Lizzie again.

Are you there? You've gone silent and we are dying of curiosity back home.

She'd added several sad face emojis at the end. This time Elle began to answer back. Wait till her sisters heard about her invitation to attend a concert and a formal dinner with the royal family.

Lizzie picked up on the first ring.

Elle breathlessly answered her myriad questions then told her about the morning's conversation with Isabel.

Lizzie actually squealed. "How exciting, Elle! What do you think you'll wear?"

Elle jolted at the question. How could that have not even occurred to her? Leave it to her logical, pragmatic, state's attorney sister to immediately bring it up. "Lizzie, I'll have to call you back," she said into the phone then began to pace after hanging up.

There was nothing in her closet that would even remotely suffice. In fact, she'd actually felt underdressed at even the casual activities she'd been to so far at the castle. Were there boutiques near the palace? Surely they wouldn't be within walking distance. Who would she ask for a ride?

She was loath to ask Riko, further cementing her out of place status in his eyes. And she didn't want to bother Isabel; the woman had enough to deal with.

A ringing sound interrupted her panicked thoughts. The landline phone that hung on the wall near the door. It had to be some kind of internal palace communication system. Elle hadn't really noticed it until this very moment.

Curious about who would try to contact her in such a way, she went to answer it. A woman with an accent responded when she said hello.

"Hello, miss. I am just calling to schedule your fitting."

"Fitting?"

"Yes, miss. Would this afternoon work for your schedule? Say around one?"

That was right around the time the children sat down

for their lunch with their parents. Which would leave her free. "Yes. Thank you. That would be fine."

Elle stared at the receiver as she replaced it. Had she just gotten a solution to her wardrobe problem?

Four hours later, after a hectic and busy morning with the children, Elle got her answer when a knock sounded on her door.

She opened it to find a short, smiling woman in a smart business suit and sensible heels.

"Hello, I am Seema. Are you ready?"

Elle couldn't be sure. But she stepped aside to let the woman in then gasped in surprise when she realized Seema wasn't alone. Two men walked in behind her wheeling several racks full of clothing. A third man walked in carrying a large boxy briefcase.

They deposited the items in the middle of the room then left, shutting the door behind them.

Elle didn't know what hit her. The next ninety minutes passed by in a flurry of fittings and slipping in and out of shoes. Seema was friendly and personable, making the experience less daunting and nerve-racking than it otherwise might have been.

"Eight hours ago, I had no idea I'd even be attending such an event," she found herself admitting to Seema. "I'm invited only because there's an open chair due to the infanta's unexpected absence."

"Nature hates a vacuum. And so does the royal family," Seema quipped as she pinned yet another spot on the dress she currently wore.

"There," the other woman said, stepping back to look Elle over. "I believe this is the one."

Elle summoned the courage to turn and look at herself in the mirror. Her breath caught at the image. Was that really her? She was draped in a silky dress of emerald green that brought out the fiery red shade of her hair and accented the hazel in her eyes. She looked like she might even be an actual princess herself.

Oh, Seema was so very right. The dress was indeed the one.

Riko ran up the main stairway to the staff residence hallway, a million and one thoughts scrambling through his head. He normally resented having to attend symphony concerts, the music much too slow and stuffy for his liking. And the formal dinners afterward were always such a strained bore of a time. The two events were really the only part of the National Spirit Festival week that Riko didn't enjoy.

But tonight, he found himself looking forward to both activities. There was only one reason for that. And that reason would be the woman who was to be his unofficial date tonight.

When he knocked on her door minutes later, she opened it within a heartbeat. But then his heart almost stopped when took in the sight of her.

The dress she wore was the color of the emerald jewels that glimmered on the royal crown and crest. Her hair was done up in some complicated style and shimmered with thin strands of some kind of glittery thread. The strapless dress showed off her elegant shoulders and the arch of her delicate neck. And heaven help him, it clung to her in all the right places. She looked like a vision out of a skilled painter's masterpiece.

"Elle?" He didn't even know why he'd said her name

like a question. His mind wasn't working straight. He couldn't even think, could barely breathe.

"Good evening, Riko," she said. Even her voice sounded different. Smoother, softer, like a light breeze floating to his ears.

She glanced up and down the hallway.

"Apologies. I didn't get a chance to notify you. I'll be accompanying you in the car on the way to the symphony."

Her lips tightened and a rosy spot of color appeared on her cheeks. "I see. What about the others?"

"Just us in the car. The king and queen have to make a formal entrance, of course. And Isabel needed more time. They'll join us shortly."

Elle looked off to the side. Was she dreading his company then? Why was she apprehensive that the two of them would be alone for the duration of the ride? It vexed him that he couldn't read her.

He offered her his elbow when she stepped into the hallway and led her down the marble staircase unsure what to say. His head was still spinning, in shock at the vision Elle made on his arm. In a true grasp at cliché, he settled on the weather. "I must apologize for all this rain when you're dressed so sharply."

She chuckled before answering. "You can hardly be blamed for the weather, Riko. Even you don't wield that kind of command."

She thought him commanding? The idea pleased him more than was logical.

When they reached the main doors, two guards appeared at either side with umbrellas to ward off the rain that had started this morning and lasted throughout the whole day. The day might have been a bust with all the planned outdoor activities being postponed, but this evening was starting off quite to his liking.

One of the official limousines with the royal Suarez crest on the hood sat waiting at the bottom of the steps.

He led Elle with a hand to the small of her back, the skin on his palm tingling at the contact point. His whole body was strumming. A staffer held the door of the stretch limousine open for them, and he guided her inside before joining her in the seat. His heart skipped as his thigh brushed against her silk-clad one.

"The children were awfully disappointed that today's festivities had to be moved to the rain date in a couple days," she said.

"I can't say I blame them. Today would have been the much anticipated kayak races along the river."

"Yes, they mentioned it more than once."

Riko barely heard what she'd said, his attention drifting to the way her hair glimmered from the soft blue glow of the roof lights. He couldn't help but let his gaze wander from the top of her magnificent head to the tips of her painted toes.

Since when had he been the type of man to appreciate a woman's toes?

He gave his head a shake and looked up to find her eyes on him. Great. He'd been caught ogling her like some sort of lovesick teenager. Her hand drifted up to the back of her neck and then to her chest.

"Is something wrong? Is this dress okay? It isn't my usual style, but I wanted to try something different. I'm terribly sorry if it's not working for the evening that's planned."

Riko blinked at her. Was she really apologizing because she thought she wasn't dressed right? How could she even consider the possibility?

He shook his head ever so slowly. "Believe me, Elle. The dress is more than just okay. You look incredible." He figured he should stop there. If he continued, he seriously ran the risk of overcomplimenting her and stammering his praise like the aforementioned teenager.

She swallowed. "You're sure? I probably should have asked Isabel before making a choice. I just don't want to intrude on her too often as she's resting."

"Trust me. You didn't need to confer with anyone. The choice of dress is perfect for tonight."

In his eyes, Elle herself was perfect. A knowledge that was becoming increasingly harder to deny.

She'd stepped into a fairy tale. Complete with a dreamy prince.

Elle watched the glowing lights of the kingdom below as they drove away from the palace and along the winding road that meandered down the mountain.

How was any of this happening? To her, Arielle Stanton of Chicago, Illinois? To think, it had all started during a storm much like this one. From this day on, she would consider stormy days lucky and never complain about lightning or rain or thunder. Then she felt guilty for even thinking that first storm was good luck in any way because of the danger Riko had been in. Lucky or not, it had brought the two of them to this very moment.

The shock of finding Riko at her door announcing that he'd be accompanying her personally had yet to wear off. It didn't help that the man looked like temptation in physical form the way he wore the tuxedo that had clearly been tailored to fit him to a tee.

When they arrived at the concert hall and Riko walked her through the grand lobby and up to the balcony, pretending to be a princess was becoming all too easy.

"I haven't thanked you yet for agreeing to come tonight," Riko said once they'd taken their seats.

Elle had to stifle a laugh at that comment. She should be the one thanking him.

He glanced at the gold watch on his wrist. "The concert should be over in under two hours or so."

She didn't hide her chuckle this time. "It hasn't even started yet. And I'm looking forward to it."

"That's where we differ. I'm looking forward to it being over."

"Not a fan of classical music, I take it?"

He shook his head. "Probably due to all the hours of violin I was made to practice as a child. All I wanted to do was run around outside or at least study an instrument a bit more exciting."

"Like what?"

He shrugged. "The drums maybe. Or guitar. Electric preferably. Maybe even the tuba."

Elle's laughter grew and she clamped a hand to her mouth. The people already assembled in the seats below didn't seem the type to giggle their way into an auditorium. "Somehow I can't picture you roaming around the palace blowing on a tuba."

"Neither could my mother and father. I was told any prince worth his salt had to master a classical instrument. No one seemed able to tell me why. Especially considering Manny was allowed to try his hand at the ukulele of all things."

It occurred to her just how different the lives of the two princes had been. By a twist of fate that had literally amounted to minutes.

Not all that different from her upbringing with her sisters. Elle wasn't the only daughter in the family with a singing voice. But while her sisters had only sung recreationally or for school plays, Elle was the only one who insisted on training her voice in the hopes of a vocal career someday.

"I wasn't given the opportunity to study what I wanted until I reached the age when I could pursue it on my own."

He laid his hand over hers. "Your singing."

So he had been listening to her that night on the veranda. And he did remember what she'd told him. "That's right. Mom and Dad absolutely refused to pay for any kind of singing lessons."

"So you can sing and you're a great swimmer. Quite the talented young woman."

It was going to be hard not to let his compliments go to her head.

She explained the history behind her abilities in the water. "We lived near Lake Michigan, so the water was my refuge when I needed to get away from all the structure and rules rampant in my house. I would take every opportunity to swim in the summer. During the colder months, I found any indoor pool there was until I could jump into the lake again. It made sense to join the swim team in high school when the time came."

"Lucky for me," Riko said. "Though I wish I could remember more precisely how you saved me that day."

It hardly mattered whether he did or not given all that

had transpired since. "Who knows. Maybe you will some-day," she answered.

"Hopefully. And who knows, maybe someday I can pick up the electric guitar," he said, though didn't sound convinced of his statement at all. Then he grunted a laugh. "Can you imagine?" Riko added after a beat, amusement laced in his voice. "A ukulele."

She could. Her imagination was in full force, actually. For instance, just for tonight, she wanted to pretend that the fairy tale she'd stepped into could somehow be real. That she was here as part of this life. A part of Riko's world in truth. Not because she was filling in for the woman who rightfully should be here.

What would be the harm in that?

The nagging voice inside her head told her exactly how damaging such dreaming might be. For her heart. She had to believe the memories alone would be worth it.

Isabel and Manny arrived not long after. Manny wheeled his wife to the row behind them. He gave Elle an appraising look and blew out a whistle of apprecia-tion. "Wow. Elle, you clean up good."

The comment earned him a chuckle from his wife and a glare from Riko.

A commotion from her left drew her attention and Riko clasped her hand, signaling her to rise as he did. Manny stood as well while Isabel bowed her head. The king and queen had arrived and were settling into their seats in an adjacent balcony. She remained standing with the two brothers until their parents sat down.

The lights began to dim lower and lower but not before Elle stole a glance at the royal couple to catch a clearly displeased expression on the king's face as he looked upon his heir.

Surprisingly, his look of disapproval didn't upset her as much as it perhaps should have. For all their differences, maybe she and Riko actually did have some similarities.

After all, she was familiar with such looks. Her father's icy cold glare could give the Versuvian king a run for his money.

CHAPTER TEN

RIKO SHOULD HAVE checked the seating arrangements before dinner started. To his disappointment, Elle wasn't seated anywhere near him. Of course, he was seated to the right of his father with his mother two chairs away next to his father. Would it have been too much to ask that Elle be seated on his other side. Instead, it was one of the kingdom's economic ministers who was probably going to talk his ear off about the European markets, which was boring enough under normal circumstances. Tonight would be much worse given how distracted Riko was. He didn't think he could even feign indifference the way he normally did with the man.

He watched her now at the other end of the table. She was sitting next to one of the country's top journalists and apparently he was telling her something very interesting based on the way she kept nodding and smiling at the man.

He had a ridiculous urge to walk over there and ask the reporter to switch chairs with him. He almost laughed out loud at that suggestion. He could just imagine how that might go over with the king and queen.

"Do you have time in your schedule first thing tomorrow to do that, son?" he heard his father ask as the first course of garden salad and fresh rolls was brought out by the wait staff.

Do what? Riko hadn't heard his father speak let alone knew what question he was being asked. He scrambled to come up with a generic answer that might cover a wide range of the king's asks, but his father was on to him. He grunted with displeasure. "You're not even listening to me, are you?"

Riko pinched the bridge of his nose. "I apologize, Father. It has been a rather long day. And I'm afraid I have a slew of emails to answer and calls to make upon our return to the castle."

The king tore apart one of the dinner rolls as if it had caused him injury and then dropped it on his place without even taking a bite. "Perhaps one of those calls could be to the infanta?"

Riko tried not to physically react to the suggestion. The truth was, he'd forgotten all about Infanta Gina and her as yet not rescheduled visit.

"What would you have me say to her, Your Highness?" Mistake. Riko should have simply answered in the affirmative and worried about it tomorrow. Now he was going to get an earful.

The king lowered his fork, which had been about to spear a slice of tomato in his salad. "I can write you a script, son. But I think the gist of it should be that you inquire how she's doing and remind her she has an invitation to Palacio Suarez which we hope she will honor within the next day or so."

His mother leaned over to join the conversation. "Better yet, maybe he should be the one to go visit her."

Not going to happen. He had to stop this train in its tracks. The only way Riko could think to do that was to agree to the original ask. "I'll be certain to call her first thing tomorrow." As loath as he was to give so much as an inch, he hoped that would be the end of the conversation. No such luck.

His father went on, "Be sure to tell her that we all await her visit with great anticipation."

Riko merely nodded at that, unwilling to lie to his father outright. His attention drifted back to Elle's end of the table. She hadn't so much as glanced in his direction. Could the journalist really be that interesting? He willed her to look up at him, to offer him that fetching smile of hers he'd gotten so used to brightening up his days and that floated through his mind at night.

His salad was untouched still when the next course arrived, chilled seafood with an array of dipping sauces. Elle smiled at the waiter when her plate was delivered, the server lingering just a little too long after he'd set the plate down.

Riko swore inside and rubbed a hand down his face. He couldn't very well get annoyed with every man who so much as made eye contact with her. Besides, he could take solace in the fact that he'd be the one sitting next to her in the car later, the one walking her up the stairs of the palace and to her room.

It hit him like a thunderbolt. Oh, man. He had it bad. He was falling for her. Hard. What a completely inappropriate and utterly messy fiasco. He was expected to make a match that would bring gains to the kingdom. His parents had made their decision already about who that match should be with. But he felt nothing for the infanta. Whereas simply seeing Elle made his pulse quicken and his heart race. And his attraction wasn't like some kind of faucet he could turn on and off.

It was as if his father sensed the dangerous direction his thoughts had taken. He leaned over to Riko, close enough that their shoulders were touching. "I'd like to make something very clear, son," he said softly. The timbre and tone of his voice left no doubt that Riko was being addressed by King Guillermo, honored monarch of Versuvia. Not his father.

Riko cleared his throat. "What's that, sir?" he asked, though he could guess.

"I'll be forever grateful to the young lady for coming to your aid after the boating accident. But my indulgence only goes so far."

Message received. Loud and clear.

The only question was, was Riko willing to heed it?

Elle knew this fairy-tale night was coming to an end. No amount of wishing would change that.

But she was so not ready to have the magic stop. The long black limo pulled up in front of the palace doors, and a footman appeared immediately to open her door. But Riko was the one who took her by the hand and helped her out of the car.

He led her up the steps and through the foyer, his palm resting gently on the small of her back. Such an innocent touch. But it was setting her on fire inside. She'd been trying so hard not to stare at him all night. It hadn't been easy, but she knew if he caught her looking at him with all the emotions churning in her chest, there would be no hiding the attraction she felt for him.

"I hope you had a good time, *cariña*," he said now when they made it to her hallway and down to her door.

The last word dripped from his mouth like honey. That

was the second time he'd called her that, and it made her muscles turn to goo.

There were no words for her to answer that question fairly.

"I had a lovely time. I must thank your family for including me first chance I get. And I'll have to thank Isabel for sending the seamstress to make sure I had something fitting to wear."

Riko looked off to the side. "I don't think you need to mention it. I'm sure she was happy to do it."

Something in the tone of his voice and the way he wasn't making eye contact had her suspicions rising. Then she put two and two together. "It was you, wasn't it? You're the one who sent Seema up to see me."

He ducked his head. "Guilty as charged."

Elle was beyond touched at his consideration for her to even think of such a thing let alone making it happen. "Thank you, Riko. Really. That was very kind of you."

"It was more than worthwhile. You looked breathtaking. The most alluring woman there."

Her heart was about to pound out of her chest at his words and the way he was looking at her. That settled it. There was no way she was going to let him walk away and leave her alone just yet.

"If you're not tired," she began, "this is usually the time of night I sit out on my balcony just to stare at the night sky."

Riko leaned his shoulder up against the door frame, bringing his body that much closer to hers. "Are you asking me to join you?"

"Yes," she answered, still not quite believing that she was being bold enough to do just that.

"I'd love to."

She walked through the door and switched the light on. Soft yellow light from the small crystal chandelier washed over the room. Making her way to the balcony, she pulled the double doors open and stepped out. Riko followed behind her.

It might have been a scene out of a movie. Her standing there under the starlit sky, wearing a dress made for a princess, a handsome tuxedoed prince standing behind her. But Riko wasn't just a royal heir. He was charismatic beyond measure. So affectionate that his small niece and nephew appeared to adore him. And considerate enough to make sure that an unprepared nanny was fitted with a dress.

How in the world was she not to fall in love with him?

She heard a rustling behind her and turned to find he'd slipped off his jacket and unbuttoned the top three buttons of his shirt. He proceeded to roll up his sleeves, and her breath caught at the masculine, devastatingly handsome figure he posed. She knew it was, oh, so dangerous for her to be out here alone with him given where her emotions were leading her. But there was no turning back now. She was way past the point of no return.

"It's a beautiful night," he said, casually striding over to where she stood behind the railing. Then he leaned his forearms on the steel bar, so close, her thigh brushed against his hip and sent a bolt of electricity through her limb.

He was right. The diamond-bright twinkling stars above, the crisp post-rain night air, the slight scent of the ocean in the distance made for a spectacular potpourri for the senses.

But she could hardly pay attention to any of it.

Her sole focus was Riko and the currents of longing running through every inch of her body.

"I'm sorry we didn't get a chance to sit together at dinner," he told her. "I didn't think to check the seating arrangements beforehand."

She'd been sorry about that too. Had spent most of the meal wishing he was closer. "That's all right. I understand you had to sit next to your parents. And my seatmates were nice enough."

He continued to stare at the horizon. "Nice, huh? The one gentleman appeared to be talking your ear off."

Did she detect a note of jealousy? "I hardly heard a word he was saying."

He straightened then, turned to face her and stepped even closer. She could feel his breath hot against her cheek, his now familiar scent filling her senses. "Why's that?"

She tilted her head, studying him through the dark shadows the full moon was casting on his face. "Why all the questions about my dinner conversation?"

His eyes darkened. "Because all night I wanted to leap across the table and pull the man out of his chair to take his place beside you," he bit out, his voice full of frustration. "It took all the restraint I had not to do just that."

Elle had to fight for her next breath. "Riko." His name escaped her lips on a soft whisper, her hand reaching for him when she didn't even know she'd lifted it.

The next instant his lips were on hers, his arms wrapped tight around her. His hand traveled lower behind her back until he was cupping her bottom and pulling her even tighter against his length. The contours of his chest pressed deliciously against her skin. The world stopped—

she was convinced her heart had stopped. Nothing else mattered but this man and the way he tasted on her lips. She dragged her hands over his shoulders, thrust her fingers through the thick curls of hair above his neck.

She'd been dreaming of this moment, yearning for it. Still, she wasn't prepared for the sensations Riko's kiss evoked.

Nothing could have prepared her.

He was going to need much more coffee than his usual espresso. Riko was useless this morning and finally shut his laptop cover and leaned back in his office chair, swiveling it around to look out the three-panel bay window that overlooked the elaborate maze in the South Garden. Unlike the rain yesterday, the weather this morning matched his mood to a tee. Bright and sunny, the horizon an aqua blue.

Kissing Elle last night had literally knocked the wind out of him, taking a good portion of the night to get his breathing back to normal. He'd actually needed a cold shower.

He'd wanted to spend the night in that small room with her more than he'd wanted his next breath. But as a gentleman, when a clear and direct invitation hadn't been extended, he'd left her on the balcony after another lingering kiss.

All the pity.

Now, he couldn't wait to kiss her again. See where it might lead this time.

First, he would have the conversation with his parents that he'd been dreading. There was no putting it off any longer. Though it was too late to cancel the infanta's visit without causing an international scandal, he had to make clear to the king and queen that no match would be made. His feelings for Elle had simply grown too strong to ignore.

He glanced at this watch. She'd be gathering the children right about now after their breakfast.

An incoming call required his attention and he clicked the answer icon, only glancing at the screen afterward to see it was Gina on the other end of the line.

He had to stifle a groan.

"Riko!" she said breathlessly through the small speaker, as if she might be in motion. Riko got a squirmy feeling in the pit of his stomach when he thought of what that might mean. "Good news," Gina added. "I'm on my way. Finally! I'll be landing in Versuvia in a couple short hours."

Riko swore under his breath. He'd been right. Gina went on talking. He could hardly concentrate on what she was saying through the panic pounding through his veins. "I'm sorry I didn't go through official channels to announce my travel plans, but when the opportunity came, I just jumped to get started on the journey."

"That's...uh...that's great news. I'm glad to hear it." That might have been the biggest lie he'd ever told in his life. But what was the alternative? He couldn't very well tell the woman not to come, over the phone no less. The international chaos storm insulting the infanta would cause would be monumental and instantaneous. Political strain between the two nations was the last thing anyone needed.

"Isn't this a relief?" she asked, chuckling. "Bet you were worried I'd never get there."

How far from the target she was. "Of course," he lied again.

"I'll text your office the details."

He thanked her, knowing just how stiff he sounded, but his mind was racing with all that this development meant for him.

And for Elle.

"I'll be sure to have them arrange for an official greeting when you land on Versuvian soil," he told her.

"Lovely. Goodbye until we see each other, then."

"Goodbye," Riko replied, ending the call. Then he threw his phone across the room against the wall so hard that the corner of the screen cracked and dislodged a portion of the wall's plaster.

His brother chose that moment to enter the room. Without knocking, of course.

"Not now, Manny. I have a colossal mess on my hands. The infanta just called me personally to announce she'll be arriving in Versuvia before lunch."

"And that's a problem? I thought we were expecting her at some point."

Riko gave him a pointed look. They were twins, had spent their entire lives together. He waited for Manny to figure it out.

It took only a second. "Ah, I see. A certain red-haired former mermaid who happens to be under this roof reading to my children at the moment."

Riko thrust his hands through his hair.

Manny shut the door and strode into the room. "I mean I kind of surmised where your head was at when it came to Elle. But I guess I didn't realize the full extent of the... complication."

"Don't use that word."

Manny shrugged. "No other way to put it, big brother."

He was right, as much as it pained Riko to admit it. Things had gotten unfathomably complicated. He would have to get through the next forty-eight hours performing a balancing act where he treated Gina with the utmost respect and consideration while not giving her the wrong idea about his attraction to her. Or lack thereof.

And there was Elle. "I have to figure out what to tell her."

"Well, you should figure it out soon."

"What do you mean?"

Manny's eyes narrowed on him. "You really aren't yourself, are you?"

What the devil was he talking about? Riko made a circular motion with his hand in a gesture of "come out with it."

"If you were thinking straight, you'd realize that as she was calling you, her office was probably calling the king's staff to officially announce her arrival."

Riko bit out another curse. He was right, again.

Manny continued. "Which means..." He didn't need to finish.

Riko finished for him. "Which means the announcement is traveling through all the family members as we speak so that they may prepare to greet her."

Which in turn meant that Isabel would need to have the children ready for the visit as well.

Riko didn't bother to say goodbye to his brother. He wordlessly walked by him and half jogged, half walked to the children's nursery.

He burst in without bothering to knock. The children cheered with delight when they saw him.

But Elle's reaction to his entrance was anything but cheerful.

He was too late.

Elle wanted to kick herself. Because the first reaction she'd had when Riko burst through the door wasn't one of anger, or frustration. No. Rather it was a tugging in the area of her heart at seeing him for the first time since their passionate kisses last night.

At least she'd quickly recovered.

Enough to turn him down when he asked his question after patting the heads of both the children. "I know you're on duty. But can we go to the corner of the room and talk for a minute?"

She shook her head. "I'm afraid I can't. I have to get the children properly dressed and ready. I've just received a notification text that they are to be greeting a VIP this afternoon." Imagine her surprise when she'd gotten that text. Riko hadn't made any mention of Infanta Gina yesterday. He could have given her the courtesy of a warning at the least. Had he merely been toying with her last night? It was the only explanation that made sense.

"Elle—"

She cut him off. She really didn't have the emotional fortitude for this conversation right now. "This isn't the time or place."

His lips thinned into a tight line. "Fine, but we'll need to talk at some point."

Tatyana must have sensed the tension in the air despite her age. She ran over and hugged her uncle's leg. Riko immediately dropped to her level and gave her a reassuring smile.

Heat rose to Elle's cheeks as she watched him with the

child, remembering the taste of his kisses on the balcony just a night ago. The way he'd looked at her with hunger flooding his eyes. How quickly things could change.

It had taken all her willpower last night to refrain from asking him to stay, to spend the night with her on the bed just a few feet away.

Thank the heavens above she hadn't done so. Imagining how much worse all this would feel if they'd actually been intimate had her shuddering inside.

Considering how shattering simply kissing him had been, she would never have recovered.

She probably never would anyway.

CHAPTER ELEVEN

THE WOMAN WAS everything Elle had imagined she would be. Elegant, graceful, charming and so very regal. A woman fit to marry a prince and serve as queen when he inherited the throne. Infanta Gina appeared to have been born and bred for just that purpose.

She had sparkling blue eyes and hair the color of spun gold. Exactly the way storybooks described so many fictional queens. She wore a smart navy blue suit and sensible matching pumps the exact same shade. Her shoes alone were probably worth more than the house Elle had grown up in.

Elle stood rod straight in the corner of the great hall, in a line with other staff members, as she was greeted by the royal family. She watched the scene unfold with a fake smile pasted on her face. She'd been careful to apply the correct mask and was doing her best to keep it in place.

Riko's glance kept darting in Elle's direction, but she made sure to keep her eyes averted. What was he expecting from her? A friendly smile? A flirtatious wink?

He'd called her repeatedly since this morning, but she hadn't had it in her to pick up, finally resorting to text messages.

You have to realize I didn't know.

Elle wasn't sure what she was supposed to do with that bit of information. It hardly made a difference to what she was experiencing right now, did it?

She scanned the room, glancing at anyone but Riko. When her gaze fell on Manny, she was surprised to find that he'd been watching her. He flashed her a kind smile. Elle paused, not sure how she felt about the sympathy. Did he know? Or was it because her mask wasn't working as well as she would like to think?

Not that it made any difference.

The last in line for introductions were Ramon and Tatyana. They each performed excellent curtsies until Tatyana took it too far and nearly toppled over. Elle would have to make sure to hug the little girl later for providing at least a sliver of lightheartedness to the otherwise miserable experience. Thank the spirits for the both of them. Ramon and Tatyana had kept her busy and distracted throughout the day leading up to this miserable moment. Well, as distracted as was possible.

Just when she thought the little discomfort was over and she could unclench her jaw, Riko and the infanta turned to the corner where Elle stood with the others. To her horror, they both approached.

"And this is our household staff you might be interacting with during your stay," Riko said, his gaze square on Elle's.

A brick dropped into her throat. She was going to be introduced to the infanta also? Why had no one told her? How in the world was she supposed to react?

How stupid of her not have figured it out. There had to be a reason she and the rest of the staff were here, after all.

As luck would have it, she was last in line. At least she

had some examples to follow. Each of the staffers before her bowed and welcomed the woman. She replied with a thanks and a smile to each.

When at last it came time for her turn, Elle managed the bow just fine. But when she went to speak the words of welcome, the brick had lodged itself fully at the base of her throat.

The words refused to come out. She'd completely lost her voice.

Riko was beginning to get tired of playing Prince Charming. Especially considering the way his mind kept wandering when he was supposed to be listening intently to Gina. Not very charming of him.

They were strolling through the Suarez gardens trailing the king and queen. His mother had decided to join them under the pretense of wanting fresh air, but Riko could guess her true motive. She was doing her best to strain and hear their conversation. So Riko kept falling farther and farther back.

"So both sides finally agreed to the terms of the intermediary and I was free to finally get on with my life. I was beginning to think I was going to age into an old lady by the time the issues were resolved."

"As you should," Riko said, absentmindedly. Where exactly was Elle now? He didn't dare risk checking his phone to see if she'd replied to any of his texts or voice mails.

He had to snort a laugh. When was the last time someone had dared ignore the messages of the crown prince himself?

Gina's step faltered. "I'm sorry? I'm not sure I quite caught your meaning."

He realized he must have misspoke then made things worse by chuckling afterward. He tried to rectify. "I mean, I'm glad all sides finally saw reason," he amended, figuring it should apply to the overall subject matter.

She seemed satisfied enough with his revision, and they continued their earlier pace. They'd fallen farther behind his parents.

"I'm sorry that I missed the first couple days of the National Spirit Festival. I do hope I get to attend many others." The innuendo in that statement wasn't lost on him.

"You can still attend this one. We've had a rain delay and will be picking up where we left off tomorrow. We still have several field races and tons of sport competitions coming up."

Gina rubbed her fingers along her throat. "I'm afraid I must come clean and admit that I'm not a terribly big fan of outdoor activities. It was the part of the trip I was least looking forward to, in fact."

She couldn't possibly mean all outdoor activities. What a dull way to go through life. "Really? You wouldn't even be enticed to participate or watch a kayak race along the river?"

"Sounds lovely," she said in a tone that was the audio equivalent of an eye roll. There was no mistaking the sarcasm in her voice.

A thought drifted into his mind. Whenever he'd encountered Gina in the past and so far into this trip, he'd always felt there was something off about the conversation. Something odd he couldn't quite put his finger on and hadn't really given much thought to. But he realized now what it was. He'd never actually seen or heard Gina laugh. The woman did have a rather pleasant smile and wore it often and well. But she never laughed. Not that he'd witnessed anyway.

He thought of Elle's lyrical laughter that first night she'd been performing the silly skit with Ramon and Tatyana. Or at Ramon's antics when she'd been dancing with him.

Just stop.

He had to stop comparing the two women. That's not what this visit was about. It wasn't what any of it was about. The simple fact was that he'd developed true feelings for Elle since meeting her.

This wasn't some sort of a competition.

Still, the realization was now clearer to him than the cloudless sky above: he was more likely to travel to the moon than spend a fulfilling lifetime with Infanta Gina Mariana DeLeon. The woman he saw by his side at next year's spirit festival was Elle. Not Gina. Not anyone else.

He'd let Gina settle for the night, but first thing tomorrow morning he would have to find his father and let him know once and for all that there would be no marriage proposal or offers of engagement being made as his parents planned for and desired.

He knew without hesitation it was the only decision that made sense. Royalty or not, mutually advantageous trade agreements or not. He was in love with someone else.

He was in love with Elle.

His mind made up, he began moving quicker than their earlier leisurely stroll. Gina didn't comment on the faster pace but kept up, and soon they were rounding the corner near the line of red leaf bushes.

His parents were several feet ahead, but they were no longer walking. His father sat perched on a nearby stone while his mother stood fanning him and mopping his brow. Concern and alarm pulsed through Riko at the sight.

"Excuse me."

He rushed to his parents.

"What's happened? Father? Are you all right?"

The king waved his hand in dismissal. "I'm fine, son. Don't go getting panicky. I just get winded sometimes these days."

These days? Did that mean this had happened before? Why was this the first Riko was hearing of it?

"Let's get the doctor down here." He reached into his pocket for his cell phone but his mother placed a hand on his arm to stop him.

"He's already seen the doctor this morning. He just needs a minute." At Riko's hesitation, she nodded once to drive the point home.

Gina had reached them by this point.

"Is everything all right?" she asked the queen.

His mother took Gina by the arm. "Everything is fine dear. Here, why don't we continue our walk and give the king a minute to catch his breath with Riko."

Riko waited for the two women to leave before addressing his father. "What just happened?"

His dad shrugged. "Nothing in particular. Your mother was telling the truth. I'm not young anymore, son. My heart isn't what it used to be and neither are my lungs. And as privileged as we are, the life of a leader comes with many responsibilities. It takes a toll."

Riko remained silent, letting his father speak when he was ready. The king took several more deep breaths before continuing.

"I'm a tired old man, son. I just want to be able to rest

and spend time with your mother before... Well, while I can."

There was a look in his father's eyes that Riko had never seen before. Fear.

The truth hit him like a ton of bricks then. His father wasn't being obstinate about marrying Riko off. He was scared. He was trying to prepare for when he was no longer able to perform his duties. He needed Riko to be ready.

To his traditional Versuvian parents, that meant he also needed to have a queen by his side when the time came. One with experience as a leader who was known and familiar to the kingdom.

Looking at his father now, noting the utter exhaustion on the king's face, Riko realized he'd been fancifully delusional about having any real choice in the matter of his own future.

His earlier resolve about the infanta began to deflate like a pricked balloon.

She needed some air. Elle descended the circular marble staircase and walked past the kitchens to the doors that led to the back veranda.

The infanta's visit so far was going swimmingly. That's what Elle kept hearing throughout the day. She'd been witness to it herself on more than one occasion. Whenever she caught sight of Riko over the past twenty-four hours, Infanta Gina was always on his arm.

The entire palace was abuzz with speculation about how well the two of them were getting along. Elle couldn't turn down a hallway or step into a room without overhearing the gossip.

To make matters worse, Isabel had an aunt visiting

today from Madrid who insisted on spending quality time alone with the children, so Elle didn't even have the benefit of the distractions they usually provided.

And every time she saw Riko and the infanta together, she died a little inside. She'd always thought that saying was so cliché. But now she knew exactly why it was worded so. Each encounter was a small stab to her heart.

She'd been wandering aimlessly but realized that she'd ended up near the maze.

Elle found the entrance and walked in. Her subconscious must have led her here. It was perfect, really. Quiet, private, away from all the talk about the prince and his potential new princess.

Still, probably better not to walk too far in. It would be all too easy to get lost. She hadn't even thought to bring her cell phone in her haste to get away from everything and everyone.

"Elle?"

She froze in her tracks, the all too familiar voice washing over her like a cold waterfall. Had Riko been behind her all this time?

Instead of answering, she rushed farther down the pathway then took a left down another. There was nothing to say to each other. And she really didn't have it in her to discuss anything with Riko right now.

Right. As if she could fool herself into thinking that was the only reason she was avoiding him. The truth was she didn't want to look foolish by launching herself into his arms first and asking questions later.

He called out her name again, his voice coming from a parallel path. She turned the opposite direction down another opening.

"Are you still in here?" he asked softly over the wall

of greenery between them. "I happened to be on the balcony and watched you enter."

It was no use. She couldn't avoid him forever. Plus there was no denying now that she was good and lost in here. She had no idea where the center or the opening was. "What do you want, Riko?"

"You've been avoiding me."

"That should have been your first clue that I wanted to be alone in here."

His soft chuckle sounded over the shrub. "Are you sure that's still what you want? I'm pretty certain you've lost your way."

He was right, damn it. There was no use denying it. But it wasn't her fault. The blame lay with him.

"Stay where you are. I'll come find you," he said, and she heard the rustling of feet moving. Within seconds he'd rounded a corner and paused when he saw her.

She hated herself for the way her heart tugged inside her chest at the sight of him. The moon provided enough light to see him clearly. He wore dark pants and a collared shirt with the top buttons undone and sleeves rolled up to his elbows. His hair was tousled, as if he'd been ramming his fingers through it. A five o'clock shadow darkened his chin. Her fingers itched to go fix his hair then run her hand lower along his strong jawline over the stubble there. She planted her feet firmly into the ground to keep from flinging herself at him like a lovestruck fool.

"Why did you follow me, Riko? Shouldn't you be tending to your duties as a prospective groom?"

He took a hesitant step closer, like she might be a skittish doe ready to take off at the slightest fright.

She crossed her arms in front of her chest. "They're

saying tonight will be the night. Actual bets are being placed."

"About?"

"When you'll propose."

He flinched, and she felt the slightest amount of satisfaction in his discomfort but it was short-lived. Nothing about this was satisfying in any way.

"Anyone who takes that bet is about to lose."

His words gave her no comfort. "Maybe. But it's just a matter of time. You can't deny it."

He tilted his head to the side. "I can't. And I won't. All I can do is ask you to understand."

He was asking too much.

"Do you remember what you were doing on your ninth birthday?" he asked suddenly, a question so random she wasn't sure if she'd heard him correctly.

"Vaguely," she answered. "Why?"

"I remember mine clearly."

"What happened?"

"Versuvia takes great pride in our national football team. That was the year we qualified for the European cup."

Soccer? How in the world were they suddenly talking about soccer?

Riko continued. "It was completely unexpected. Our team defied all odds, it was downright historical. We'd never gotten that far before. Of course, the royal family was invited to attend the tournament. It was held outside of Glasgow that year."

"I'm afraid I've never followed soccer. Or football, as you call it. And especially not when I was a child."

"Oh, I did. Manny and I were big fans. Have been our

entire lives. Kicked a ball around the courtyard every chance we got."

"So you went to the tournament."

Riko shook his head. "Well, only one of us did. I was scheduled to tour a hospital with my father. My schedule was determined months in advance. Even as a child. With very little leeway to change."

Elle's heart sank for the little boy who'd had so much responsibility thrust on his shoulders at such a young age, but she wasn't grasping the reason Riko was sharing this story now. "I'm sorry, did you just compare what's happening here to a missed soccer tournament?"

He shook his head, a sad smile forming over his lips. "No, *cariña*."

There was that word again.

"The point is, Manny got to go and I didn't. Manny got to marry the woman he loves, whereas I..." He let the sentence trail off.

Love? Had he really just uttered that loaded word in a context that included her?

It took her a moment before she could speak. "Whereas you what?"

He rammed his fingers through the hair at his crown. "Damn it, Elle. I have certain responsibilities, expectations that come with the title I was born into. About my very identity. I can't just turn my back on those responsibilities. Nor can I turn my back on the family I was born into on some kind of whim such as traveling Europe in pursuit of some dream."

His arrow hit exactly where it was supposed to. "Is that how you see me? As someone who turned her back on their family in a selfish pursuit?"

He bit out a sharp curse. "No. Of course not. That wasn't what I intended to imply."

She drew in a steadying breath. "It certainly sounded that way."

"I simply meant that duty to family has to come first to someone like me. I don't expect you to understand."

Yet another arrow. How many did he expect her to be able to deflect? How strong or uncaring did he think she was? His next words only served to amplify the question.

"It hardly matters the words I use to explain, does it? It is my truth and I must live it."

Elle sucked in a gasp at the insensitivity of the comment. Of course it mattered. It mattered deeply. To her at least. "What exactly is it that you're trying to say, Riko? Maybe you should just come out and say it."

He nodded. "Fair enough. I should have known my place, but I let my attraction for you take over. I should have never allowed myself to be alone with you. I should have never followed you up to your balcony. And I certainly should not have ever kissed you. It was all so reckless of me and I apologize."

He left unspoken the part that was shattering her soul. That he would make sure it never happened again.

Princess Isabel was looking exceptionally well when Elle checked in for their regular morning meeting five days later. Better than yesterday even and yesterday she'd looked better than the day before. Despite her inner turmoil, Elle's spirits rose ever so slightly when she entered to see her employer, who she now considered a friend, was slowly but surely on her way to a full recovery.

Elle settled into her usual chair next to the princess's

bed and clicked open the app on her phone she'd been using during their daily morning meetings to take notes.

The doctor was scheduled to see her later this afternoon to give an official opinion. The family and Isabel were cautiously optimistic that she'd be given the go-ahead to resume some light activities.

There was no denying that a pressing question presented itself given Isabel's improvement. How much longer would the Suarez family even need Elle?

"I think that's it for now," Isabel said, sitting up and propping another pillow behind her back. Her next words had Elle wondering if the woman had somehow read her earlier thoughts. "Elle, I've been thinking about what a godsend you've been these past few weeks."

Elle felt a slight flutter in her chest at the compliment. With the way she was brought up, she wasn't used to people commending her performance, the only exception being her singing ability. "I'm glad I was able to help when you needed it, Isabel. And the children have become quite dear to me."

Isabel's lips spread into a wide smile. "They adore you, you know. Like a dear auntie."

The feeling was quite mutual. A lump formed at the base of Elle's throat. When her time at Palacio Suarez came to an end, she was going to miss the children the most.

Except for Riko himself, but that was a thought best left averted.

"Which is why I wanted to make sure you knew that we're all unanimous in what I'm about to tell you."

Where was she going with this? "We've all grown quite fond of you, Elle. The Suarezes all sing your praises whenever your name comes up. Including the king and queen."

That was surprising. Riko's parents thought her praise-worthy? Right. As their nanny only. Certainly not as a potential daughter-in-law.

Whoa. She couldn't even let herself go there.

"I've become very fond of all of you as well," Elle said, recovering enough from her surprise to finally answer.

"I know your time here was meant to be temporary," Isabel said. "But we'd all like you to stay on in your role indefinitely. Again, that includes the king and queen."

Either Isabel was exaggerating the level of involvement the king and queen had in the matter or it just went to show just how little a threat the senior royal couple saw in Elle. Now that Riko's impending engagement was se-cure, his parents saw no reason to be concerned. If they ever were. She was probably giving herself too much credit as any kind of thorn in the royal couple's respec-tive regal hides.

"I'm deeply honored," she replied. And she really was. But there was no way she could remain here more than a few days after Isabel was given the all-clear by her team of doctors.

It would crush her soul to imagine Riko as he proposed to the infanta, seeing his ring on her finger. Picturing the two of them say their vows. Her heart felt tight in her chest as the visions swam in her mind.

"You and your family have all been so kind. Working for you has truly been a dream job."

"I'm sensing a 'but.'"

"It's just that I've started to miss home and Chicago. And my family." That was the absolute truth. Elle was particularly missing her sisters. She'd almost called Lizzie yesterday in tears to just purge all that was happening. But her sister was in the middle of a very complicated and sensational legal case. She didn't need to worry about the baby of the family on top of all her professional responsibilities.

"That's understandable. Maybe we could arrange for a quick visit for you."

Elle's heart swelled with gratitude at the suggestion. If only things were different. If only she somehow had the ability to shut off all her emotions and simply move on. If only she hadn't fallen in love with the heir in the first place.

"Thank you, Isabel. Truly. I'll think about it."

"That's all I can ask for," Isabel answered with a gentle smile. "Thank you."

Elle left the room before the tears could begin and made her way back to her own room. The children were to read with their mother for an hour or so, leaving Elle with some time to kill.

To get some air and collect her thoughts, she stepped out onto the balcony, trying to regroup. She hadn't been out here since that night with Riko. The memory of it assaulted her and she had to wrap her arms around her middle.

For several minutes, she simply stared at the horizon, the waves in the distance, the color of the sky. Versuvia was an absolutely beautiful island. She was fortunate really to be here at all. And in due time, her heart would heal and she'd find a way to move on with just the memories of her time here. What other choice did she have?

Enough of the wallowing and self-pity. She had to shake it off.

She could at the least do something productive before

it was time to go get the children. She owed several people responses to various messages so she might as well start with her texts and emails.

A note at the top of her inbox immediately caught her attention. She clicked to read the body of the email and had trouble believing what she was seeing.

...came across a video of your performance...compelling vocal range...audition at convenient time...please contact as soon as possible...

A major record label was actually seeking her out for a potential opportunity to sign with them. Completely unexpected and out of the blue.

Elle had to wonder if it was the universe giving her a sign about how to move forward.

The sign that appeared next was a lot less affable and much more jarring to her psyche. Elle stepped out of the shower and wrapped herself in the thick terry robe hanging on the back of the door, the offer from the record company still prominent in her mind.

An opportunity of a lifetime.

A knock on the door of her suite sounded just as she wrapped a thick Turkish towel around her wet hair.

Her heart pounded in her chest. Sebastian was on evening kitchen duty. The children were in bed. She wasn't expecting anyone else.

Riko.

Had he made his way back early? Had their heated conversation in the maze been weighing on him as heavily as it had been weighing on her? Her mouth went dry as she went to answer, anticipation pounding through her veins.

But it wasn't Riko who stood on the other side when she'd flung the door open.

It was the king himself.

Elle reeled in shock. Then she cursed herself for impulsively answering the knock without so much as inquiring who it might be.

"Your Highness, my apologies," she said, absentmindedly tightening her robe belt. "I wasn't expecting anyone."

"I must be the one to apologize, young lady. I have no right to drop by so unexpectedly." True as that was, the king made no move to leave. "It was rather an impulsive decision," he added after a beat.

At a loss for anything else to do, Elle stepped aside. "Please, come in. Just give me a minute to get dressed."

The king held a hand up before she could turn to do so. "No need. This won't take long."

Something about his tone and his demeanor, added to the wholly unexpected nature of the visit, rang alarm bells through her skull. She knew without a doubt that she was wholly unprepared for anything the king might have to say to her.

"Again, I apologize for being so informal," he began, taking a step into the room and leaving the door open behind him. "But I felt it important that we spoke."

Right. Elle had no doubt that he would be doing all the speaking.

He continued. "Please understand that the extent of my family's gratitude toward you is immeasurable and eternal. I should have thanked you long before now for pulling my son out of those waters."

She could sense a colossal "but" about to follow.

"And I'd like to personally extend an invitation to you remain in our employ." As congenial as those words were, his next ones felt like a dagger to her heart. "After all, I imagine both my sons will be in need of a nanny in the following years."

Everything else that followed was completely drowned out by the roaring in her ears and the herculean effort to keep the tears stinging behind her eyes from falling. Elle could only nod, at a complete loss for any other kind of reaction.

Several minutes after he'd excused himself and left, Elle was still reeling from the king's words. So, that was to be her lot in life then if she were to remain here in Versuvia. As a nanny potentially working for the man she'd fallen in love with.

The choice before her was crystal clear.

CHAPTER TWELVE

One week later

THE SIGNS KEPT COMING.

Elle slammed the cover of her tablet shut and tossed it across the mattress. She should have known better than to go onto one of the royalty focused websites. All of Europe and many countries of the Americas couldn't get enough about the gossip regarding the Versuvian crown prince and his potential princess. Speculation was rampant on when the prince would propose to his love and how he would do it. Would it be at his castle in Versuvia, using a glass of champagne with a ring at the bottom? Or would he meet her in Barcelona, or maybe Paris, and hand her a velvet box over an elegant dinner table atop a rooftop restaurant? Maybe what the prince had in mind was much more intimate. Elle had had to stop reading the article at that point.

Where did people get all this creativity anyway?

Elle hadn't seen Riko in several days, and Isabel had hinted that he was off the island on some business or other.

Ha! That business probably involved a striking golden blonde woman of Spanish noble blood who was probably hanging on his arm at this very moment.

She desperately needed to talk to a familiar and understanding voice. With shaky fingers, she reached for her phone and dialed her sister.

Lizzie picked up immediately, alarm ringing in her voice. "Elle? What's wrong? You're never the one to call."

She sniffled. "I know. I'm so sorry about that, Lizzie. I should try and be a better sister." She should try and be a better person.

"Uh-oh. Now I'm really alarmed. Tell me."

Elle couldn't contain herself any longer. She found herself pouring out everything that had happened since the day the infanta had arrived. Starting with the heart-shattering kiss the night of the concert, the news that Isabel had gotten the medical all-clear yesterday, the things the king had said to her, to the offer of an audition from a record company and finally ending with Riko's admission of love in the maze.

At last, when Elle had finally exhausted herself and stood there panting into the phone, she heard nothing but the sound of Lizzie's breathing on the other end. Quite an accomplishment to render an attorney speechless.

"Uh, you probably should have led with that last part," her sister said at last. "You know, about how he said he's fallen in love with you." Her voice rose several octaves on the last three words.

"Oh, Lizzie. I've fallen in love with him too."

"Well, yeah," Lizzie said in a tone that had Elle envisioning exactly how she must be rolling her eyes as she spoke. "I mean, I figured that out, Elle. Let's just say one wouldn't have needed any of the private investigators the attorney's office employs to come to that conclusion."

At the mention of her sister's job, Elle immediately felt a twinge of guilt. Lizzie really had more important matters to attend to than figuratively holding her sister's hand during an emotional meltdown while over an ocean's distance away.

"Lizzie, I have to go," she said, fibbing. Her sister would never accept ending the call if she thought Elle was doing so on Lizzie's account.

What time was it even in the Midwest United States? The chances that she'd interrupted Lizzie in the middle of something important were high.

Elle wasn't in the right frame of mind to figure out time zones or do the math. It was well past midnight where she was.

"Are you sure, Elle? We can keep talking until you feel better," her sister said, further upping the homesickness she felt down to her core.

"I already do, Liz. And I love you for getting me there."

"Love you too, sis. And that prince is a fool for letting you go. You should tell him so," she added before disconnecting the call.

That wasn't going to happen. No use telling Riko any such thing at this point.

As late as it was, Elle knew the chances of her getting any sleep after such an emotional purge were slim to none. She left her room and made her way downstairs as quietly as possible so as to avoid disturbing any of the other sleeping staffers. She had to find some of the horchata Riko had offered her when he'd found out she couldn't sleep. Back when they'd been on friendly terms and were only just discovering each other.

A lifetime ago.

The kitchen was dark when she entered, covered in shadows.

One of them shifted toward the center of the room,

tearing a gasp from her throat and making her jump. She wasn't alone. Her eyes finally focused enough to see Riko leaning his back against the counter with a steaming cup in his hand.

"Couldn't sleep either, huh?"

Elle had half a mind to turn around and walk back to her room. But the scent of vanilla and almond tickled her nose and ignited her taste buds.

What would be the harm in grabbing a cup and then leaving?

"I thought you were away," she said, stepping farther into the room. Even now, having him just a few feet away was wreaking havoc on her equilibrium.

She'd missed him. Achingly so.

"Returned earlier this afternoon."

She resisted the urge to ask where he'd been and with who. Or if he'd returned alone.

He reached his cup out to her. "Here, have mine. I'm not as thirsty as I thought."

If he was trying to soften her up by giving up his drink, she had to begrudgingly admit it was working. "I can't take all of it. Let's share."

"Fine. You go first."

The thought of sharing the same cup sent a jolt of desire through her center. She ignored the taunting suggestion and retrieved her own mug from the wall cabinet behind him.

He took it from her and poured in half the contents of his.

Elle took a small sip, her hands shaking at his unexpected nearness. She could only hope he didn't notice or guess the cause.

"I hear Isabel's been given the all-clear by her doctors."

She nodded. "Just this afternoon. They said she's out of the woods and can resume her old activities once more. Within reason for a pregnant woman," she added.

Riko put his cup down, turned to face her. "I also hear she would like you to stay on."

What about you? Do you want me to stay too?

Questions she desperately wanted answers to but didn't dare ask. "Yes, well, I haven't made my mind up yet. I'm still considering what I'd like to do."

"I know at least two small people who'll be sad to see you go."

He was referring to the children. A surge of anger shot through her and she slammed the cup hard enough on the counter that several drops spilled onto her hand and the surface.

"Don't, Riko. Don't try to use those kids as leverage. I've come to love and care for them deeply. My heart is going to break when I do say goodbye to them."

And it would completely shatter when she bid her final goodbye to him.

"You have to know that," she added. "And it's grossly unfair of you to try and use that knowledge in such a way."

He held both hands up as if in surrender. "That wasn't my intention. I apologize if that's how I sounded."

She didn't speak, afraid of what might leave her mouth. Equally afraid that she might just fling herself into his arms and beg him to hold her just for a few moments so that she could pretend he was hers, the way she did the night of the concert.

He rubbed a hand down his face. "I can't seem to say the right thing around you. Just like that night in the maze. Every word that comes out of my mouth seems wrong."

This had been a mistake. She should have turned right back around when she'd found him in the kitchen. At the least she should have thanked him for sharing his drink then taken it back to her room.

A mistake she could easily rectify by simply walking away.

"Good night, Riko. I hope you get some sleep."

She herself certainly wouldn't be able to.

Riko was halfway across the kitchen to chase Elle down before he stopped himself. She'd made clear twice already that she didn't want his company. Once in the maze and again when she'd come in here tonight.

It didn't help that he kept saying the wrong thing. Because he didn't know exactly what to say at all.

From what Elle knew, he'd made his choice. And he hadn't chosen her. She had no idea how much the choice had cost him. He had no way of finding the words that might help to explain. Maybe in due time, perhaps years from now, she would deign to forgive him. Until then, he should probably just leave her alone.

The door swung open again and his heart leapt with hope that she might be returning. Even if it was just to rant at him and curse him out in anger.

But it was Manny who walked into the kitchen.

"Oh, it's just you."

"Nice to see you too, big bro. How was your trip to Madrid? Did you secure the gambling licenses?"

"Fine. It went fine. What are you doing here so late?"

"Getting Isabel something to eat. That woman's appetite for food is fast approaching mine. Didn't want to bother the staff."

Riko realized he hadn't known that Manny was so familiar with their kitchens. Whereas Elle had been the one to show Riko where the damn refrigerator was.

"Well, she is eating for two," Riko said, refocusing on the conversation.

Manny executed a dramatic flinch. "Ouch. Must have been one grueling trip. You've resorted to unoriginal cliché responses. Isabel is fine, by the way. The doctors were very pleased with her recovery. Thank you for asking."

Riko pinched the bridge of his nose. "Sorry. I'm just rather distracted at the moment."

"Does it have anything to do with the way Elle nearly barreled into me on the way out of here just now?"

"You know it does."

"Wanna talk about it?"

"No. I do not." What he wanted was to find Elle and pull her into his arms.

Manny stepped to the counter and crossed his arms in front of his chest. "Well, I think we need to."

The sudden intensity in Manny's voice caught Riko off guard. Any hint of teasing or lightheartedness was completely gone. A rarity for his brother. He walked over to the wall and switched the lights on before returning to where Riko stood.

Okay.

"I just want to ask you a couple of questions. First, are you in love with Elle?"

"I think you know the answer to that," Riko said without any preamble. "I fell in love with her sometime between overturning my boat and watching her perform a silly skit in the nursery for a king and queen she'd barely been introduced to."

Manny nodded once. "Of course I know. I just needed you to hear yourself say it out loud."

"Why is that exactly?"

Manny held up a finger. "I have one more question before you can ask any of yours."

"All right," Riko said, resigned though admittedly curious about where his brother was leading them with all this. "What's the question?"

"Are you in love with the woman you're about to propose to?"

"No." Such a simple and direct word, it had left his mouth without any thought or hesitation.

Manny spread his arms out wide. "Then what are we doing here, man? What are *you* doing?"

Was he really serious? "You know it's not that simple. Mother and Father have expectations. I can't just marry anyone I please. Unless..."

Manny dropped his arms. "Unless what?"

Riko found himself verbalizing out loud the silent thoughts that had been rumbling through his mind for a while now. Maybe even years. Thoughts that had grown louder and louder over the past few weeks since he'd met Elle. "Well, maybe we can convince the king and queen to think differently about the accession to the throne. Offer them a novel way to approach the rule of the kingdom."

Manny quirked an eyebrow. "Come again?"

"I'm to inherit the throne and I need someone by my side. Someone who can step into the role and take over Mother's duties with the experience borne of years of living a royal life."

"That's well established, big brother. So what are you getting at?"

"What if someone who isn't queen takes over Mother's duties? Someone who's had years of experience living the life of a royal. Another prince to be exact."

It took Manny a minute to process his words. Riko knew what his brother had to be thinking—that this was either the most preposterous idea in the history of the Versuvian monarchy. Or it actually had a great deal of merit.

"Are you trying to suggest that I rule by your side?"

Riko nodded. "I'm not suggesting. I'm actually saying so. I mean, come on, man. I only beat you out of the womb by a couple minutes."

"Well, when you put it that way…"

"And don't even think about attempting some sort of power grab."

Manny rolled his eyes. "Hardly. You think I want to give up this life of leisure and actually do real work on the daily?"

He was being facetious. Manny did plenty for the kingdom. He monitored the casinos and made sure the buildings were up to code, among many other tasks that involved the main national industry. But under the surface, it was a valid question.

His brother's expression suddenly grew serious. "But I'd do it for your happiness, big brother. And I know you'd do the same for me."

That was the truth. Nevertheless, Riko had to be certain. "Are you sure, Manny? This isn't something you can change your mind about later."

Manny tilted his head. "Perhaps the better question is are *you* sure? You'd be giving up the status as sole heir, if I'm hearing you correctly."

"You are," Riko said with zero hesitation.

"Have you thought this through fully?"

Riko was surprised at just how much clarity he had about the proposal now that he'd actually spoken it out loud. "I've given it a lot of thought, in fact. We'd make sure to balance your duties as a father, of course. Especially with the arrival of the new baby."

Manny rubbed his jaw then shrugged. "Then, yes. I'm sure too. Besides, prince or not, you deserve to be with the woman you're in love with."

CHAPTER THIRTEEN

ELLE WATCHED THE blinking cursor on her screen and let her finger hover over the "enter" tab before pulling her hand back and curling it on the desk. If she clicked, she would be accepting the invitation. Once she did, there'd be no turning back.

Clicking *yes* would mean that by this time next week she'd be in New York in a recording studio in front of a group of music executives to sing an original song she'd had to compose herself. All in the hopes that it might lead to a second audition. Which in turn could mean the opportunity of a lifetime. An opportunity she'd been dreaming of since she was a little girl.

How ironic it was that she was even hesitating. If someone had told her a month or so ago that she would agonize over the decision for even a second, she would have offered to sell them the title to the Skyway Bridge.

Riko thought she had no sense of family responsibility. Well, maybe he was partially right. Maybe her father had been right all along. If she signed up for this audition, at least she'd be back in the States with her parents and sisters. But she'd be doing it on her own terms.

Without giving herself a chance to agonize any longer, she put her finger onto the key and pressed it. A confirmation box appeared on her screen almost immediately.

An odd sense of calm came over her now that she'd taken the plunge and accepted the offer. It was settled. She'd made her decision.

Riko was moving on and so would she. It had been silly and impulsive of her to be cross with him about Gina's visit. She realized that now. He was a man who'd been born into a life that came with responsibilities and expectations.

A life that couldn't and wouldn't include her.

It was time. Riko was done procrastinating. No more putting off the conversation he needed to have with his parents. He'd made his decision, and he wouldn't be turning back regardless of their displeasure.

And their displeasure would be considerable once they heard that he wouldn't be proposing to Infanta Gina, after all. Well, at least he'd be prepared to present them with something of a counteroffer, thanks to his and Manny's agreement.

Funny how a concept could linger in one's mind for decades before solidifying into a concrete idea. Incentive was all that it took apparently. Riko could think of no better incentive than the way he felt about Elle.

The idea that he and Manny could be equal partners in the ruling of the kingdom had lingered in the back of his mind for years. His feelings for Elle had finally pushed those thoughts to the surface. He had the utmost confidence that his brother would perform the royal duties equally as well as he could. No doubt there were some tasks Manny might even be better suited for. The more he thought about it, the more sense it all made.

Now, he just had to convince their parents to see reason.

He found them in their beachside cabana enjoying afternoon tea.

"What a pleasant surprise," his mother said when she saw him approach. "How lovely that you'll be joining us, son."

"To what do we owe this pleasure?" his father asked, his tone weary and suspicious. He'd obviously read Riko's expression better than the queen had.

"There's a matter I'd like to discuss with both of you," Riko began, taking an empty seat at the the teal wicker table.

The smile faded from his mother's face as she studied him. "What would that be?"

"I'd like to make an official announcement to the people of the kingdom within the coming days."

"An announcement to say what exactly?" his father demanded to know. "It had better be to declare that they may expect to hear of your engagement to the infanta."

Riko shook his head, his resolve not faltering even a little despite his father's ominous tone. "No, Father. That is not what I intend to say because it is not what I intend to do."

Their reactions were immediate. The king swore and rubbed a hand down his face. His mother's gasp was loud enough to warrant a glance from the butler several feet away.

"Riko, what is this about?" his mother asked.

Something in his chest snapped. Riko slammed both fists on the table hard enough to rattle the china and glasses. "It's about choosing how I spend the rest of my life and with whom. It's about not committing myself to a woman for eternity and hoping that I might grow fond of her."

His mother leaned back against her chair, her hand at the base of her throat. He'd shocked her. No surprise. Riko had never so much as raised his voice to either of them let alone physically acted out in their presence. Not even as a child.

The king made a noise akin to a growl and began to stand before his mother stopped him with a hand to his forearm. "Let's hear him out, dear."

Riko inhaled deeply and counted to three before attempting to begin. "As lovely as she is, I have no desire to marry Gina. And her reasons for wanting to marry me have nothing to do with affection or attraction. And certainly nothing to do with love."

His father bit out another, harsher curse before the queen patted his arm once more. "I take it you believe yourself in love with someone else," she said.

Riko could only nod. The answer had to be obvious.

The king grunted. "Love? Is that what you're after? When you have the responsibility of an entire kingdom waiting for you. Or have you forgotten?"

Riko shook his head. "No, sir. I haven't forgotten. And as far as the responsibility that awaits me, Manny and I would like to present the two of you with an idea."

Riko strode down the dock and jumped onto the hull of the new boat that had recently been delivered to replace the one the storm had wrecked all those weeks ago.

The conversation with his parents was finally behind him. And it could have gone much worse. Now he just had to find Elle and finally confess how he really felt about her.

It shocked him to learn that he was more nervous about

her potential reaction than he'd been about speaking to the king and queen.

He could hardly be faulted for wanting a quick sail around the bay to clear his mind and pull his thoughts together before he searched for Elle and poured his heart to her.

An odd sense of déjà vu struck Riko as he admired the new boat. It was a beautiful, sunny and clear day. Not a cloud in the sky. Should be smooth sailing. But that's what he'd thought last time—when a singing mermaid had to come to pull him out of the stormy waves.

"Isabel told me I could find you here," a soft feminine voice sounded from behind. He turned to find Elle standing on the dock, her hand shading her eyes from the bright sun.

A sliver of alarm ran up his spine. He couldn't imagine why Elle might have sought him out after avoiding him for so long. "Is everything all right? The children—"

She cut him off with a wave of her hand. "Everything's fine."

If everything was fine, why were her eyes clouded with sadness, her shoulders rigidly tense, her breathing so shallow? He had his answer a moment later when she spoke. An answer he was loath to hear.

"I've just come to say goodbye. I've asked Seb to take me to the ferry to Majorca later this afternoon."

Riko had to take a moment to let the words sink in.

She was leaving. After everything, he was too late. And he wasn't prepared to do anything about it. He shouldn't have waited to tell Elle his plan. Now it might be too late.

Riko walked portside to where she stood, then he

leaned over the railing. "What's this about, Elle? I thought you were still deciding your future plans."

She bit her lip and inhaled deeply. "I have decided due to an unexpected incentive."

"What kind of incentive?"

She wasn't making eye contact, her gaze trained off to the side toward the horizon. "I have an audition in the States. I'd like to head back and begin rehearsing. Isabel is fine now and her aunt is visiting more often. I think it's time I moved on."

Riko was stunned speechless. A barrage of questions assaulted his mind. He couldn't even choose where to start.

"An audition?"

"With a record label. An executive came across some videos of me performing and wants me to try out for them. It sort of landed in my lap, and I don't want to pass it up."

Elle's words rushed out like water through a fire hose. They sounded rehearsed, as if she was doing her best to just get them out and get this over with. "It really is an opportunity of a lifetime," she added. "One I have to take."

"I see," was all Riko could come up with to say.

"I've already said my goodbyes to Isabel, Manny and the children. I think drawing out such partings only makes them more painful. So I'll be leaving on the next ferry to Majorca and then flying home."

Nothing about what he was feeling right now was at all painless. "An audition. That sounds like quite an opportunity. Break an arm."

She blinked up at him in confusion, then seemed to put together what he'd been trying to say. "You mean break a leg."

He didn't know what he meant. He was having trouble getting his mind to work well enough to communicate with his mouth. Elle was leaving. For good.

He'd been a fool, and he was losing the only woman he'd ever loved because he'd been too afraid to defy tradition in order to fight for that love.

"But I can take you to Majorca—" he gestured around him to indicate the boat "—whenever you'd like, *cariña*."

She seemed to flinch at the last word. "I've already purchased the ferry ticket. And I've asked Seb to take me to the harbor. But thank you anyway."

What happened next shocked Riko into near paralysis. She boarded the boat then leaned toward him and planted the slightest peck of a kiss on his cheek, before turning on her heel and walking back toward the beach.

Riko yearned to call out to her and ask her to stay, to tell her that he'd been a fool to even entertain engaging himself to another woman when he'd fallen so completely for her.

But he stopped himself. He had no right to be that selfish. Elle said this was the opportunity of a lifetime for her.

Who was he to ask her to give it up? Especially given the way he'd messed things up so badly.

The sun had long set and the night had grown cool by the time Riko pulled back onto the dock and anchored. He'd lost track of time out on the water.

The castle was dark and quiet as he approached the front doors, the sky above it dark and moonless. Even from the outside, it appeared as if something was missing inside.

Elle was gone. When he woke up tomorrow, she wouldn't be there. She'd be well on her way to the States.

Unless she'd changed her mind. Highly unlikely. He was grasping at hope when he knew it was pointless. Still, he had to make sure.

So he bypassed his own wing and strode toward the staff quarters instead. Sure enough, her door was wide open, the room unoccupied. The bed was stripped and the closet emptied.

Riko strode inside, trailing a finger around the bureau that had once held her clothes. All the drawers were laid bare.

He could still smell her scent. Like a pathetic lovestruck character in some kind of rom-com, he inhaled deeply to savor it before it was gone for good.

A musical composition book sat in the wastebasket, otherwise empty. Riko reached in and pulled it out, flipping open to a random page in the middle. The top line said *Audition Piece*.

In between her duties with Ramon and Tatyana, Elle must have been composing an original song to use for her audition. The lyrics she'd penned immediately caught his attention.

About a woman who had fallen in love with a man she couldn't have, a man who she would never get over.

She'd entitled it "My Dear Prince."

Elle would have thought she'd be more nervous the day before an audition. But the butterflies fluttering in her stomach had nothing to do with her make-or-break performance scheduled in the city in under twenty-four hours.

No, they had everything to do with the way her mind insisted on replaying the moments that day on the dock when she'd said goodbye to Riko.

Now, sitting cross-legged on the bed in the guest room of her oldest sister's Long Island home, she tried to run through her vocal exercises one last time. But her throat felt raw and inflamed from all the effort of resisting the urge to cry.

He hadn't even tried to dissuade her from leaving. On the contrary, he'd even offered her a ride on his boat to the mainland. The memory felt like a lance through her chest.

The sobs threatened once more, and Elle knew it was no use trying to rehearse or practice. She was probably going to blow this audition, and all because she couldn't stop thinking about a man who was perhaps engaged to another woman by now.

She flopped backward onto the bed and draped an arm over her eyes. She couldn't be sure how much time had passed before her sister's voice drifted up from the first floor.

"Elle, you might want to come down here. Like now."

Elle bolted upright. That sounded rather urgent.

Shuffling down the stairs, she found her sister at the open front door, her arms crossed and her shoulders stiff.

"There. I've called her down, but I'm definitely not letting you in," Maysie was saying. "Your Highness," she added in an emphasized and accusatory tone.

The last two words had Elle's heart leaping to her throat.

"Fair enough," an all-too-familiar masculine voice answered from outside.

She rushed to the door and did a double take at the scene that greeted her.

Riko's gaze shifted from her sister to where she stood, his eyes softening when he saw her. "Elle," he said simply, the smile he gave her melting her insides.

She had no idea how, but somehow she got her mind and mouth to work enough to speak. "It's okay, Maysie."

Her sister never tore her eyes away from Riko when she answered. "You sure?"

"Yes. It will be fine."

Her sister blew out a deep breath. "Fine. But you should remind your prince here that I happen to be very adept with sharp instruments. You know, like scalpels and such."

Elle gave her sister a one-armed hug then stepped around her to the front stoop. "I'll be okay," she assured her, though not quite certain about the truth of that statement. Her limbs had gone numb and her pulse beat like a jackhammer through her veins.

"Riko, why are you here?"

He stepped forward just enough to reach the bottom of the stone steps. Their height difference brought them eye to eye.

He was so close, the scent of him threatened to overwhelm her senses.

"I had to find you. I realized that I'd forgotten to give you something before you left. A charm you're meant to have."

What in heaven's name was he talking about? "What kind of charm?"

"For good luck. During your audition."

Elle closed her eyes and released a long sigh. Why was he really here? To toy with her by giving her some kind of trinket? He couldn't be that cruel. Could he?

"Here, I'll show you," he said, climbing the steps as he reached into the inside breast pocket of his tailored suit jacket and pulling out a delicate gold chain. She took it from him, her fingers shaking, hating that he had to have noticed. On the chain was a small gold charm. A mermaid.

Despite herself, she couldn't help but feel touched. But she knew he couldn't have traveled all this way simply to hand her jewelry, as lovely a piece as it was. Riko had to be in New York on business or something, making a detour to ensure they ultimately left each other on friendly terms.

"It's beautiful, Riko. Thank you."

"You're welcome."

She thought about inviting him in. But she just couldn't do it. It had been soul wrenching enough to say goodbye to him once. Her heart wouldn't be able to survive going through it again.

"I'll be sure to wear it when I sing tomorrow."

He simply nodded, that charming smile of his tempting every cell in her body to fling herself into his arms and ask him to hold her and never let go.

"Oh, I almost forgot," he said, and reached into his pocket once more. "I have one more good luck token that I'd like you to have."

Elle would have laughed if the situation weren't so surreal. She'd had no indication the man was so superstitious all this time. But then she saw the object in his hand and felt her jaw drop.

A black velvet box with gold trim. It couldn't...

"Arielle Stanton, I know I already owe you a world of debt considering I might not even be here if you hadn't swum into my life one fateful day. But I'd like to ask you for yet one more favor." He held the box toward her and flipped it open to reveal a glittering diamond ring. "Will you marry me?"

Elle clasped her hands to her face, doing her best to

pull air into her lungs and remain upright. She just barely managed both. His name was the only word she had the ability to utter.

"I've missed you every moment since you left," he said, his voice tight and strained.

"I missed you too. So much I ached."

"I should have stopped you. I should have told you sooner, my love." The words landed like poetry to her ears. They'd wasted all this time, but he was here now.

"And I remember, Elle. I remember you reaching for me in the water, pulling me to shore. I remember every second of it."

"You do?"

"Yes. I remember every moment we've ever been together. And I know I'll never forget."

A sliver of worry crept into her mind, threatening to mar the spirit-soaring moment. But she had to ask, had to know. "What about the infanta? What about your parents?"

"She took it well, and they've both seen reason so have given their blessing. Respectively, and in that order. Not that any of that would have made one bit of difference. I love you, Elle. And I'd be honored to call you my wife."

She believed every word. Because she felt the same. Nothing and no one would ever change how she felt about this man. How much she loved him. "I love you too. With all I have and every fiber of my being."

He reached for her then, taking her in his arms and swinging her around in a circle. "Please tell me that's a 'yes,'" he whispered in her ear, his breath hot against her cheek.

She told him without the use of any words.

EPILOGUE

The reclusive recording artist known only as Mermaid remains at the top of our charts with her debut breakout hit. "My Dear Prince" has been shattering record sales, is dominating social media, and is on track to become one of the top downloaded songs of the summer.

Reports are that all proceeds from the song are donated to various charities throughout Europe and the rest of the world. Many rumors are circulating about the identity of the artist, though none have been confirmed. For now, Mermaid remains anonymous, and there is no clue as to who she might be. Maybe one day, she'll reveal herself.

ELLE HAD NO intention of doing any such thing. She scanned the article on her tablet screen with a smile, hardly able to believe those words were actually about her. It was a true marvel just how much her life had changed since she'd first arrived on the Spanish coast two years ago.

There was no reason to divulge to the world that she was the voice behind this summer's top hit. Her life as it was happened to be more than she could have ever hoped for.

The man mostly responsible for that idyllic perfection strode onto the veranda just then and dropped a kiss on her cheek before pulling out a chair to sit down next to her.

"We might have a problem," he announced, handing her a fresh cup of *horchata*. His teasing tone indicated the "problem" wasn't all that serious.

"We do?"

He nodded. "Yes. Ramon and Tatyana are begging me to use all my royal connections and clout to find out who Mermaid is and invite her to perform at this year's National Spirit Festival."

"Hmm, that is a problem."

The children were simply too young to be trusted with the truth. In due time, she would tell them that their former nanny and current aunt had written the song they both sang along to and hummed incessantly during the day. But right now, she couldn't risk her secret getting out.

"Speaking of the festival, we've received a few more RSVPs," Elle informed him. "Infanta Gina will be attending."

Not only had the infanta graciously accepted the fact that she would not become the next Princess Suarez, the infanta had actually admitted to feeling relief that the nuptials had fallen through so that she may focus on pursuing a career in politics.

Riko didn't get a chance to respond to Elle. Suddenly, without any warning, the sky above turned dark as night and spiderwebs of lightning lit the air. A roar of thunder echoed around them.

"Where'd that come from?" Riko asked, moving to help her up so that they could run inside out of the storm.

Elle shook her head, taking his hand and pulling him down for a long lingering kiss.

"I'd like to stay out here," she said, breathless after reluctantly pulling away.

Riko didn't argue, gave her a knowing smile instead. He had to have guessed where her thoughts had gone.

She didn't mind the rain, thunder and lightning in the least. In fact, it was a good omen of what was to come as far as Elle was concerned.

After all, if it hadn't been for an unexpected storm one otherwise bright and sunny day, Elle would have never found the man who'd become the most cherished part of her world.

* * * * *

COMING SOON!

We really hope you enjoyed reading this book.
If you're looking for more romance
be sure to head to the shops when
new books are available on

Thursday 1st February

To see which titles are coming soon, please visit
millsandboon.co.uk/nextmonth

MILLS & BOON

MILLS & BOON®

Coming next month

CINDERELLA IN THE SPOTLIGHT
Sophie Pembroke

He tried not to let his mouth fall open at the sight of her, but he honestly wasn't sure if he'd succeeded or not.

If he'd been blown away by the dresses she'd worn on previous nights, nothing had prepared him for tonight's gown.

It was black and white, fell all the way to the floor, and—crucially—was strapless. In fact, Eli assumed the thing was only staying up from sheer force of will. Or perhaps because it fitted so closely to her torso, before flaring out into a wide skirt with a slit that ran... oh, God. It ran all the way up to her mid-thigh.

She looked stunning - a point that was lost on none of the people she walked past.

She looked... she looked like she always did in the photos in magazines. The ones where she was on Ben's arm, going to some flashy event or another.

That thought brought him back down to the ground, fast. And when she reached him, he struggled to return her smile.

"Everything okay?" she asked, looking concerned.

"Everything's fine." *Except I've fallen for my brother's ex, who he probably expects to get back together with any moment. And she's so far out of my reach I shouldn't even be able to see her.*

But he could. And that fact was doing things to him.

"Is it the dress?" Willow looked down at herself, dismayed. "I was worried it was too much. But when I sent Kelly a photo, she said it was perfect."

"It is perfect." His voice sounded gravelly, even to his own ears. "You look perfect."

Perfect for Ben. Not for him.

"Okay. Good." Willow was still eyeing him sideways, like she was trying to figure out what was wrong with him.

But it wasn't like he could tell her, was it?

Kelly came to his rescue, thankfully, although she shot him an accusatory look as she did it. "Willow, you're here!"

The two women appreciated each other's dresses, and then Kelly whisked her off to chat to some of the kids she'd met at the Castaway Cafe the other week. But not before she paused to whisper at him, "That was lame, boss. Very, very lame."

And the worst part was, Eli knew she was right.

Continue reading
CINDERELLA IN THE SPOTLIGHT
Sophie Pembroke

Available next month
millsandboon.co.uk

afterglow BOOKS

Introducing our newest series, Afterglow.

From showing up to glowing up, Afterglow characters are on the path to leading their best lives and finding romance along the way – with plenty of sizzling spice!

OUT NOW

Two stories published every month, find them at:

millsandboon.co.uk

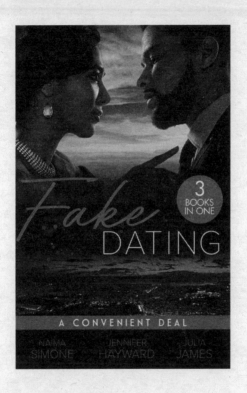

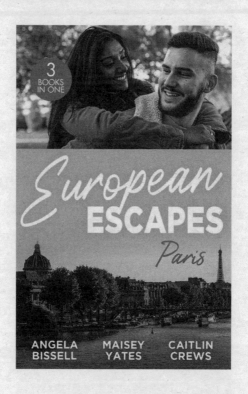

LET'S TALK

Romance

For exclusive extracts, competitions and special offers, find us online:

- f MillsandBoon
- 𝕏 @MillsandBoon
- ⬡ @MillsandBoonUK
- ♪ @MillsandBoonUK

Get in touch on 01413 063 232